THE CARE OF THE GOLF COURSE

EDITED BY:
J.PERRIS, B.Sc.
HEAD OF ADVISORY AND
CONSULTANCY DIVISION

R.D.C. EVANS, B.Sc.
TURFGRASS AGRONOMIST

PUBLISHED BY:
THE SPORTS TURF RESEARCH INSTITUTE.
BINGLEY, WEST YORKSHIRE,
ENGLAND, BD16 1AU.

COVER PHOTOGRAPH:

10th Hole, Hawkstone Course

COURTESY:

Hawkstone Park Leisure Ltd, Shropshire.

FIRST EDITION EDITED BY P. HAYES, R.D.C. EVANS & S.P. ISAAC AND PUBLISHED JUNE 1992 BY THE SPORTS TURF RESEARCH INSTITUTE, BINGLEY, WEST YORKSHIRE, BD16 1AU, ENGLAND. ISBN 1-873431-02-3

THIS FULLY REVISED AND UPDATED 2ND EDITION EDITED BY J. PERRIS AND R.D.C. EVANS PUBLISHED 1996 BY THE SPORTS TURF RESEARCH INSTITUTE

2ND EDITION: ISBN 1-873431-19-8

NOTE 1:   The fact that particular items of equipment or machinery are mentioned in this text should not be taken to imply that the STRI endorses one firm's products over another. When purchasing equipment for a golf club it is always wise to obtain details of all rival products and to make a choice based on full on-course demonstrations and on the exact requirements of the particular club, bearing in mind the supply of spare parts, local servicing facilities, etc.

NOTE 2:   The application rates given in the following text for pesticides should be regarded as being for guidance only, although every effort has been made to ensure that quoted rates are appropriate. It should be understood that pesticide users are under an obligation to comply with legal requirements governing the usage of such materials and that the instructions included with each product are mandatory, including instructions regarding application rates. Users should be familiar with the Food and Environment Protection Act of 1985 and the Control of Pesticides Regulations 1986. At a time of changing criteria for Pesticide approval and availability some of the chemicals mentioned in the text may become unavailable. Always check the current Pesticide Guide before usage.

NOTE 3:   The information presented in this book is of a general nature and is intended only to provide a basic guide. Such information is not intended to constitute a specification or comprehensive guidance in relation to any particular project or activity at an individual Golf Club which should only be undertaken after consultation with those holding appropriate qualifications. The STRI accept no responsibility or liability for any claims arising from work carried out pursuant to this book.

If you would like further information, please contact the Head of Advisory and Consultancy Division at the STRI.

ACKNOWLEDGEMENTS

The original articles which form the basis for the present text were written by the following members (and ex-members) of the STRI staff:-

S.W. Baker, BSc, PhD
N.A. Baldwin, BSc, PhD
D.F. Boocock, NDA
P.M. Canaway, BSc, CBiol, MIBiol
T.W. Colclough, BSc
A.R. Cole, BSc
P. Hayes, PhD, NDA, CBiol, MIBiol, FIHort
S.P. Isaac, BSc
D.M. Lawson, BSc, PhD
T.A. Lodge, BSc
G.C. Macadam, SDH
A.J. Newell, BSc, PhD

S.J. Ormondroyd, BSc
J. Perris, BSc
S.T. Pool, NDH, MIHort
J.P. Shildrick, BA, CBiol, MIBiol
D.M. Stansfield, BSc
R.S. Taylor, BSc
S.L. Thornton, BSc
J.W. Tucker, BSc
J.R. Westwood, BSc
D.D. Wishart, BSc
A.R. Woolhouse, BSc

The Editors most gratefully acknowledge their contribution to the present volume.

FURTHER ACKNOWLEDGEMENTS : SECOND EDITION

Additional articles included in the 2nd Edition and which were not a part of the original Edition were contributed by the following STRI staff members:-

S.W. Baker, BSc, PhD
N.A. Baldwin, BSc, PhD (ex staff member)
A.J. Beggs, BSc
D.F. Boocock, NDA
A.R. Cole, BSc
R.D.C. Evans, BSc
R. Everett, BTech
S.P. Isaac, BSc
E.C. Kirby, BSc (ex staff member)
D.M. Lawson, BSc, PhD
S.L. Mawdsley, BSc (ex staff member)

I. McClements, BSc, PhD
S.J. Ormondroyd, BSc
J. Perris, BSc
S.T. Pool, NDH, MIHort
N.R.W. Squires, BSc
R.S. Taylor, BSc
J.W. Tucker, BSc
J.R. Westwood, BSc
P.C. Winter, BSc
D.D. Wishart, BSc (now retired)
C.A. York, BSc, PhD

It would not have proved possible to produce this revised edition without their enthusiasm and expertise. The Institute's Chief Executive, P.M. Canaway, must be thanked for his support of this venture, and for checking a number of Sections of the text. To the STRI's External Affairs Manager, Anne Wilson, go thanks for help with the mechanics of printing and publication. The lengthy tasks of putting both the 1st and 2nd Editions of this book into the STRI Desk-top Publishing System were in the competent hands of Ann Bentley. The STRI is grateful to the United States Golf Association for allowing us to reproduce the drawing of the Stimpmeter, and to Steve Rankin, Editor of *Golf Club Management* for permission to reprint an article on Golf Course Ecology which first appeared in his magazine. The co-operation of Mrs. L.J. Hilton of SISIS Equipment (Macclesfield) Ltd. in supplying a number of photographs is very much appreciated.

CONTENTS

———————————————————❖❖❖———————————————————

LIST OF FIGURES

———————————————————❖❖❖———————————————————

LIST OF PLATES

INTRODUCTION TO THE FIRST EDITION

There has long been a need for a comprehensive manual on the maintenance of the British golf course. Golf is now after all one of the most popular participant games in the U.K., and ever-increasing numbers of players are demanding higher and higher standards of course presentation from their greenkeepers and Green Committees. In recent years scientific research, combined with practical experience, has provided a much clearer understanding of the underlying factors which contribute towards good golfing surfaces and a considerable body of knowledge has been accumulated.

Much has appeared in print, but scattered through various books, greenkeeping magazines, scientific journals and conference proceedings. The greenkeeper or Chairman of Green seeking a comprehensive source of background information on golf course management has therefore so far been deprived of an obvious single publication. This present volume seeks to correct that deficiency and provide a ready reference which can hopefully be relied upon to provide answers to the innumerable questions which arise during the day to day care of the golf course.

The above paragraph should not be taken as implying that no useful book on modern greenkeeping currently exists. A number of invaluable works have indeed been published and to give a comprehensive picture of available literature, an extensive Bibliography covering all aspects of golf course design, construction and management has been included at the end of the present volume. As an outstanding work on the subject, one might cite as an example Professor James B. Beard's "*Turf Management for Golf Courses*", published by the U.S. Golf Association in 1982. From a British point of view however, the value of this definitive textbook is limited by the climatic, environmental and managerial differences which exist between the U.S. and U.K. golf course scenarios, and a specifically British contribution to the literature is therefore an obvious requirement. Booklets such as the Royal & Ancient's "*Way Forward*" and Nicholas Park's "*The Management of British Golf Courses*" have recently played a part in focusing attention on the subject, but the Editors remain confident that there is still room for another volume on the book-shelf.

The body of accumulated international knowledge on golf greenkeeping, in both its practical aspects and in terms of background scientific research, is indeed now so vast that many volumes would be required to provide a fully comprehensive coverage of the subject. The Editors of the current work, however, feel that a general (and not too technical) book giving reasonably detailed information on the range of greenkeeping problems which arise in British golf course management will be of value to all individuals involved in this exacting and demanding task.

Over recent decades, one consistently popular and well-received periodical covering both turf maintenance and the construction of new sports facilities has been the quarterly Bulletin of the Sports Turf Research Institute. Appearing four times each year since 1951, and written largely by experienced members of the STRI staff (both research scientists and advisory agronomists), its accumulated articles are a rich source of information on all aspects of the subject. Many of the articles which have appeared over the years refer specifically to golf course management, and it is these which form the basis for the text of this book. To ensure their relevance to the modern up-to-date situation, the vast majority of articles selected are those which have appeared in the Bulletin issues of the past five years. Where appropriate to provide a comprehensive treatment of the subject, additional articles have also been gathered from other STRI publications.

As a compendium of articles by various authors, the present volume is perhaps not primarily intended to be read through from cover to cover - although it is hoped that at least some readers would find such an approach an interesting and rewarding exercise. In most circumstances however, it might be more appropriate for the reader to consult the Contents page, and then select a section or sections most appropriate as a source of information on any question which might be foremost in the mind at the time. Most sub-sections of the book can stand alone as sources of information on a particular subject, although they are inevitably inter-related to a certain degree, and the consultation of one section or article might logically lead to the need to consult another relevant topic.

Aimed primarily at Head Greenkeepers and their assistants, and at Chairmen or Members of Green Committees, it is hoped that the appeal of the book will extend to all those concerned in any way with the care of the British golf course. Indeed, it is hoped that the average club golfer himself will find something of interest within these pages, as an appreciation of some of the problems of course management can give the golfer a deeper insight into the characteristics of his course, and hopefully heighten his enjoyment of his game.

The Editors
STRI, Bingley, W.Yorks.
1992

INTRODUCTION TO THE REVISED SECOND EDITION

In the four years since the First Edition of *The Care of the Golf Course* first appeared, the confidence of its Editors in its usefulness as a guide for Green Committees and Greenkeepers has been amply justified. Feedback from readers has been pleasingly complimentary, and the volume has proved a best-seller among the Institute's published titles. With the original edition rapidly going out of print early in 1996, it was decided that a second, and hopefully improved, edition should be prepared.

The format of a series of essays or articles gathered from the STRI's periodicals and other published material has been retained for this new Edition. Material which has become somewhat outdated over the last four years has been eliminated or rewritten, whilst many completely new articles have been added, so updating and expanding the Contents very considerably. This new fully-revised Edition should therefore provide those concerned with the management of our golf courses with a modern and comprehensive guide to current techniques. The Editors trust that it will prove a useful reference for all readers, and aid the achievement of another small step towards that almost impossible theoretical goal ~ a perfectly presented golf course.

The Editors
STRI, Bingley, W.Yorks.
1996

SECTION 1
THE BACKGROUND KNOWLEDGE

--- ❖❖❖ ---

Grasses for the Golf Course

Plant Nutrition and Fertilisers

Soil Science

Water and Irrigation

Golf Course Agronomy & Research

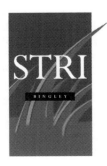

*The Care of
the Golf Course*

A BRIEF HISTORY OF THE STRI

The organisation now known as the STRI (or Sports Turf Research Institute) can trace its origins back to the early 1920's. Two Yorkshiremen, Percy Clough and Norman Hackett, were instrumental in persuading golf's ruling body, the Royal & Ancient Golf Club of St. Andrews, that a research and advisory foundation aimed at helping upgrade the standard of British golf courses would be of enormous advantage to the future of the game. In 1924 a general meeting of representatives of British golf clubs gave enthusiastic backing to the proposal, but a further five years elapsed before the plan came to fruition. In 1929, under the aegis of the British Golf Unions Joint Advisory Committee, the Board of Greenkeeping Research came into being and an ex-member of staff of the agricultural Rothamsted Experimental Station was chosen to be its first Director. That Director, Robert B. Dawson, brought much enthusiasm and expertise to the infant organisation sited at Bingley in West Yorkshire and subsequently did a great deal to ensure its high scientific reputation and long term success. Early experimental work included methods of leatherjacket and earthworm control (the latter involving highly toxic lead arsenate), improvements in grass seed purity, control of fusarium patch disease, investigations of New Zealand browntop bentgrass, and the development of an improved strain of fescue (Dawson red fescue). Educational courses for golf greenkeepers were organised (21 greenkeepers attended the first in October 1937) and up-to-date machinery was displayed in a Permanent Implement Exhibition. A greenkeeper's lending library was also established. Advisory work grew apace – the original staff of five visited 157 golf clubs in 1931 and by 1937 the staff had expanded to 23 and 395 clubs were visited and advised in that year.

The outbreak of War in 1939 obviously interfered seriously with the research station's development, but a reduced staff during the war years continued to operate the advisory service and maintained long term experimental grass plots, besides making contributions to emergency food production. In 1945 work commenced to bring the station into full operation once again, still under the able direction of R.B. Dawson who did not retire until 1963. His reputation was enhanced by the publication of 'Practical Lawn Craft', a book first published in 1939 but which became the bible for greenkeepers, groundsmen and gardeners alike in the post-war period.

Although founded by the authorities of golf, from the earliest years the Research Station had also interested itself in other sports and games played on grass, and bowling clubs, cricket clubs and winter games organisations had been amongst its early supporters. In order to recognise the interests of these other sports more fully, a decision was made in 1951 to reorganise the station as a limited company with the new title of The Sports Turf Research Institute. It gained a Royal Patron in the person of HRH The Duke of Edinburgh in 1961. The STRI's second Director, John R. Escritt was appointed in 1963 and the early years of his period of office saw a significant increase in its involvement in playing field construction projects, the STRI taking over responsibility for such works as Consultants in Charge or Consultants to an Architect. Much experience was gained in the problems of practical playing field drainage and construction techniques. For a non-profit making organisation, research funding had always been a problem and the situation was alleviated by grants in 1974 from the National Environmental Research Council (to investigate improved grass cultivars and seed mixtures). In 1978 further welcome grant aid was forthcoming from the Sports Council, although the backbone of the Institute's finance continued to be subscriptions from subscribing clubs and other interested organisations.

By this time, the educational side of the STRI's activities included regionalised seminars, week long courses at Bingley for groundsmen and greenkeepers, and a series of publications on relevant subjects. From the early years the staff had produced an annual scientific journal, reporting on the results of research work, and a more easily accessible quarterly Bulletin filled with more practical advice and articles. This continued, and books were also produced on Turf Diseases, Specifications for Playing Field Construction and J.R. Escritt's own ABC of Turf Culture.

The retirement of John Escritt in 1981 saw the appointment of the STRI's third Director, Dr. Peter Hayes, from a background in agricultural botany at Queen's University, Belfast and the Department of Agriculture in Northern Ireland. In recent years the STRI has been governed by a Board of Management which includes representatives from the R&A, the National Golf Unions, the F.A. and Football League, the R.F.U. & R.F.L, the E.B.A, the Hockey & Women's Hockey Associations, the Cricket Council, the PGA European Tour, the Association of Golf Course Architects, BIGGA and the Association of Golf Secretaries. The staff at that time included two Assistant Directors – J. Perris (Advisory Services) and P.M. Canaway (Research) – 18 agronomists, 15 research and technical staff, who with office and grounds staff make 55 in all. Agronomists, still largely based in Bingley but with regionalised colleagues in the South West, Wales, the Midlands, Scotland and Northern Ireland, still cover the entire country and parts of Europe, giving occasional advice even further afield. Research can be subdivided into: a) Research directly for sport; b) commercial research into fungicides, fertilisers and other new products and; c) grass cultivar testing. Educational work also continues, with courses, seminars, conferences and an increasing volume of publications.

1995 saw the retirement of Dr. Peter Hayes whose period as Director has seen a significant increase in the involvement of the STRI in golf advisory work and research in particular, but also much useful work for Association Football, Lawn Tennis, Bowls and the Sports Council. Who knows what fresh challenges and further progress the appointment of Dr. P.M. Canaway as Chief Executive of the STRI may bring in future years.

(RDCE : B.189)

FESCUES, BENTS AND *POA ANNUA*

The origins of golf stretch back into antiquity and no-one can say with certainty just when or how the game started. We can be sure, however, that the Scots played a big part in popularising the game. King James VI of Scotland took up golf on the North Inch at Perth and in 1658 re-affirmed the golfing rights of the people of Earl's Ferry and Elie. It is fairly certain that in those days golf flourished initially on the upland downs and heaths and seaside links – areas that were of limited use agriculturally and devoted mainly to sheep grazing which 'maintained' a playable turf before the advent of mowers. Such ground would be inherently infertile, very often free draining and drought prone, only capable of supporting the dwarf growing, hardy bent and fescue grasses that are so well adapted to that harsh environment.

The first recorded experiments with grasses for turf were carried out by J.B. Olcott between 1885 and 1910 at Connecticut in the United States. He came to the conclusion that the best types of grasses for turf in that region were to be found in the genera *Agrostis* and *Festuca*. Subsequent work over the years both by the Sports Turf Research Institute at Bingley and elsewhere has confirmed this. Characteristics which enable these grasses to perform well as turf maintained for golf are summarised below.

Bents (*Agrostis* Species)

There are 5 species of bents which may be considered for turfgrass purposes but in the UK only 3 of them are normally used – browntop bent (*A. tenuis*), creeping bent (*A. stolonifera*) and velvet bent (*A. canina*).

For fine turf, the virtues of the best bents are high shoot density which, on close mown golf greens, can reach 120,000 shoots per m². Their leaves are small, relatively broad and flat, giving good ground cover and, with satisfactory growing conditions, they can maintain a reasonably green appearance the year round. All of them are capable of vegetative spread, 'Highland' browntop bent quite vigorously by rhizomes, whilst other cultivars of browntop spread more moderately by both stolons and rhizomes. Creeping bent widely used for putting greens in the United States and Mediterranean countries spreads vigorously by stolons, is tolerant of greater extremes of heat and cold than 'Highland' and probably other browntop bents as well. However, it has never been popular in the UK, despite having been used on a number of courses and included in trials here at Bingley. It is possible that our mild, wet climate allows 'weed' grasses such as annual meadow-grass and, indeed, other turf species a greater competitive advantage, especially in spring following winter wear and tear. American experience suggests that for optimum growth this grass requires summer temperature regimes of the order of 15–20°C at night and 18–24°C during the day – rarely achieved for more than a few days at a time in our typical summers. Thus grasses better adapted to our cooler summer weather do better. Clearly, American selections of creeping bent have a handicap from the start – we need perhaps to be looking at creeping bents of UK provenance. Nonetheless, this grass has a lot to offer and although its stoloniferous habit has disadvantages – a tendency to form nap and thatch rapidly unless regularly verticut – its vigorous growth and ability to recover from damage are such that further trials with it will undoubtedly be carried out.

Velvet bent is even finer-leaved than browntop bent and the cultivar 'Kingstown' is dense and attractive in appearance during the summer and outstanding in drought, though with much poorer winter appearance. For this reason, as well as a tendency for its stolons to form a nap, it is rarely used, and then only in mixtures.

Close mown bentgrass turf with high shoot density and only limited thatch formation is quite wear tolerant given good management, especially plenty of aeration and avoidance of over-feeding and watering.

Fescues (*Festuca* species)

There are also 5 species of fescue on the market but only 3 of these – Chewings fescue (*F. rubra* ssp. *commutata*), slender creeping red (*F. rubra* ssp. *litoralis*) and strong creeping red (*F. rubra* ssp. *rubra*) – are used to any extent for golf turf.

Useful characteristics of fescues include quite high shoot numbers – up to 90,000 per m² – a fine-bladed leaf that blends well with bentgrass and differences in surface texture and seasonal colour which complement those of bent. They are particularly well adapted to drier, infertile soils. Since germination and early growth is rapid, they help provide a quick ground cover whilst the slower-growing bents establish – the two are frequently sown together.

Chewings fescue has neither rhizomes nor stolons so is very slow to colonise bare places but it is fine-leaved, of low growth habit, very tolerant of close mowing, fairly resistant to two common diseases, red thread and dollar spot. Once this grass is established and has developed a little surface thatch, it supports abrasive and golf spike wear during the summer quite well.

Slender creeping red fescue spreads moderately by rhizomes, is fine-leaved, low growing and can survive close mowing well. It is, however, susceptible to red thread disease and the sea-marsh varieties of this grass are also susceptible to dollar spot, though these types are most tolerant of salt. When established, it is quite capable of withstanding abrasive and golf spike wear during the summer and recovers from such wear moderately well.

Strong creeping red fescue has more numerous, longer rhizomes but a rather coarser

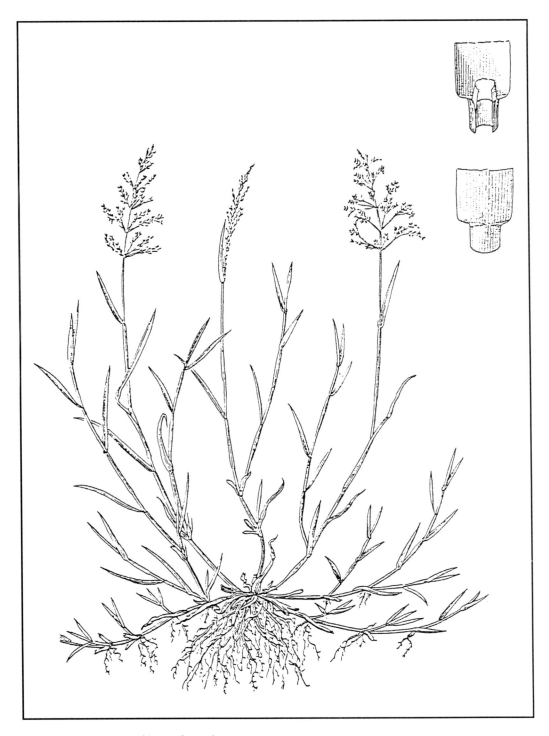

FIGURE 1: Bentgrass (*Agrostis* spp.)

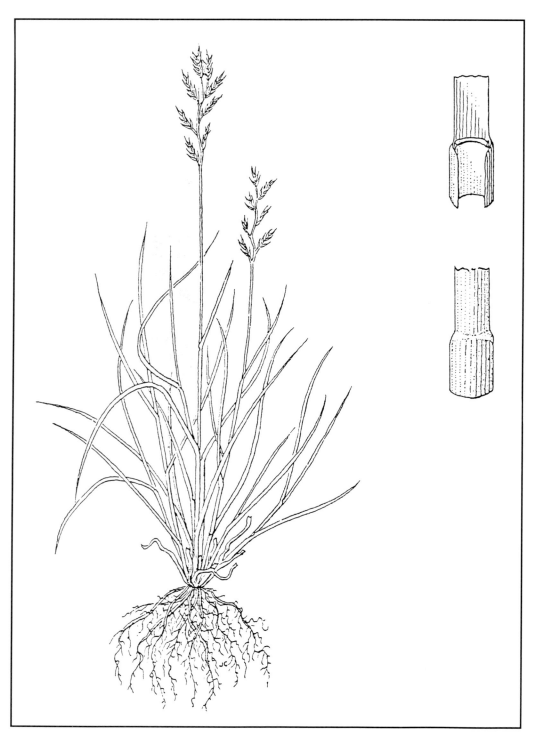

FIGURE 2: Fescue (*Festuca* spp.)

leaf and thus produces a much more open sward. It is non-persistent under close mowing, but satisfactory at fairway heights of cut. It is susceptible to red thread but quite resistant to dollar spot, although its tolerance of heavy wear is poor.

Annual Meadow-Grass (*Poa annua*)

Almost universally derided as a poor species for fine turf, and that includes all three main playing areas on a golf course, annual meadow-grass is still a very ecologically successful weedgrass. The single species name covers a wide range of plant types, those most commonly found in turf being biennials or short-lived perennials. In fine turf, annual meadow-grass often occurs as tufts or in isolated patches which look unsightly and, by their variable growth rate, affect the smoothness of the playing surface, especially in spring and autumn. The grass is capable of producing seed heads below the normal cutting height on greens and this is the main way by which it spreads – this characteristic too affects appearance and smoothness of the playing surface at times.

There is no doubt that this grass is extremely tolerant of heavy wear and even when completely worn away it has the capacity to regenerate quite rapidly from seed shed in previous years lying dormant in the soil – seed can remain viable in the soil for up to 10 years. Although criticised as shallow-rooting, it will in fact develop an extensive and deep-rooted turf in open, well aerated soil conditions; like any other grass, it becomes shallower-rooting in compact soils but in such conditions has a competitive edge over other grasses and tends to survive better. Thus annual meadow-grass is often seen as practically the only species present through central areas of golf greens that are most used for pin positions.

Other disadvantages include its susceptibility to fusarium patch disease, poor colour in drought and during the winter. It is less tolerant of extended periods of ice and snow cover than the finer grasses and, particularly relevant in the UK, is readily killed in low lying areas where standing water develops in extended freezing and thawing cycles over winter. When these effects, loosely termed 'winter kill', are added to the natural annual die-back of some plants in a population of biennials and short-lived perennials, there is small wonder that putting greens colonised extensively by annual meadow-grass can be weak, thin and open through the spring and early summer.

Management Factors

We have seen that annual meadow-grass has many disadvantages – far too many for it ever to provide the reasonable putting surfaces for 12 months of the year that today's golfer demands. One object of management therefore must be to reduce the proportion of annual meadow-grass throughout the golf course – not just on putting greens – to insignificant proportions. This goal will not be achieved quickly or easily and all aspects of management must strive towards this end. It is not simply a question of using nil phosphate fertilisers and forgetting everything else. Annual meadow-grass becomes dominant in fine turf areas because it is better adapted to the prevailing conditions than anything else and it will not be possible to reduce it, never mind eliminate it, unless those conditions are changed.

The most important aspect in control is to ensure that growing conditions and all inputs will favour the browntop bent and fescue grasses. These finer grasses, particularly the fescues, are naturally adapted to drier, infertile soils which is one reason they do so well on seaside links, and they clearly have a wide tolerance of pH from acid heath to alkaline links and downland. Bents are equally at home on heavier, more moisture retentive soils of heath and moor, also characterised by low soil fertility. Neither of these grasses likes poorly drained, compact soil or excessive use of fertiliser and water. First, ensure that soils and drainage are good enough and make improvements where they are not. The main thrust of maintenance must be aimed at regular spiking appropriate to season to relieve compaction, keeping the soil open, well aerated and free draining. Compaction, and all the ills that follow, is the main enemy on intensively used areas of the golf course.

Fertiliser use must be correct, with the main emphasis on nitrogen – though without creating lush conditions from excessive applications. In particular, avoid excess phosphate since this element assists seedling establishment, rooting and seed production, all three essential stages to eventual dominance of annual meadow-grass. Many golf green soils are so over-supplied with phosphate that it will take years to deplete these reserves. Maintain inland fescue/bent turf at a low pH and ensure top dressing materials are not alkaline (including bunker sand) and also that they have the right physical characteristics to maintain or improve existing soils on greens.

Irrigate sensibly to keep the grass alive but avoid over-watering, especially on low lying and central areas which take most play. Never apply water simply to produce a soft, holding putting surface. Verticutting must be a light and regular operation throughout the summer to control thatch formation and remove flattened, straggly growths as well as seed heads. Avoid late season severe verticutting which will leave the turf surface open and thus more vulnerable to invasion by annual meadow-grass seed. Avoid cutting the greens at 4 mm or less as this will scalp the grasses and the better ones will die out and the ingress of annual meadow-grass will take place.

Only through adopting an integrated management plan with each component designed to favour the right types of grass will it be possible to look forward to a gradual reduction in annual meadow-grass.

(CGC 1 : 1)

BENTGRASSES FOR FINE TURF

There are three species of bentgrass currently available in the UK. These are: *Agrostis castellana* (Oregon browntop bent also called dryland bent), *A. tenuis* (Dutch browntop bent) and *A. stolonifera* (creeping bent). There are a number of different cultivars of Dutch browntop and creeping bents. These are listed in "Turfgrass Seed 1992", which also gives merit ratings for the different bentgrass types and cultivars. Only one cultivar of Oregon browntop bent is available and this is 'Highland'. Historically, 'Highland' was classified as *A. tenuis* but was found to be so distinct from the others in this group that it was re-classified as *A. castellana*. This cultivar has generally been more readily available and cheaper than other bentgrass cultivars. As a result, it has in the past made up the majority of the bentgrass proportion of seed mixtures containing bentgrasses.

The cultivars of Dutch browntop bent which are available and listed in "Turfgrass Seed 1996" are 'Egmont', 'Sefton', 'Lance', 'Bardot', 'Duchess', 'Tracenta', 'Heriot' 'Denso' and 'Litenta'. The common name, used here, for these bents may be a little misleading as not all of them originated in Holland. Indeed, 'Egmont' and 'Sefton' were selected in New Zealand.

In the UK, 4 cultivars of creeping bentgrass are currently listed in "Turfgrass Seed 1996". These are 'Carmen', 'Prominent' 'Penncross; and 'Penneagle'. There has been much debate over the years regarding the use of creeping bents for fine turf in the British Isles. Much of this discussion has revolved around observations of creeping bentgrass performance in the USA. In America, the creeping bents ('Penncross', 'Penneagle', etc.) are regarded as the best grass for golf greens. However, what needs to be stated very strongly is that good performance in the USA does not necessarily mean good performance in the British Isles. There is a marked difference in climate between Britain and America, as a result we would expect grasses to perform differently in these two areas. In the regions of America where creeping bents are used, the summers are generally warmer and the winters colder. Creeping bentgrasses grow aggressively in warm temperatures, but become dormant under cool temperatures. A problem occurs if play is continued on dormant grass, as would happen in Britain. In America, this does not tend to occur as bentgrass greens are snow-bound for the winter months or in the Southern States of the USA the temperatures are high enough in the winter for active growth of Penn cultivars to take place. That creeping bents do not grow aggressively in the British summers and that they have a particularly short growing season, in comparison to browntop bents, was noted as long ago as the early 1960s in trial work at the STRI.

In contrast to the creeping bents, 'Highland' tends to maintain some growth during normal British winters, it also has a longer growing season than the Dutch browntop bents. 'Highland' is also more drought tolerant than the other available bentgrasses. However, in close mown turf trials at Bingley, many of the other characteristics of 'Highland' have been more comparable with the creeping bentgrasses than the other browntop bentgrasses. 'Highland' has therefore been consistently out-performed by other browntop bentgrasses. It is now STRI policy to encourage the greater use of Dutch browntop bents (A. tenuis) at the expense of 'Highland' in seed mixtures and purpose-grown turf for golf greens. 'Highland' is still strongly recommended for other fine turf uses, such as golf fairways, golf tees and golf roughs. In these situations the cheaper 'Highland' is probably the best bentgrass, especially when irrigation is not feasible.

(CGC 1 : 2)

CHOICE OF GRASSES FOR THE GOLF COURSE

Sometimes our American colleagues can be a little insensitive about the British way of golf and how grasses grow under our climatic conditions. I am speaking here about the blanket use of 'Penncross' and its near relatives especially in the northern part of the British Isles. In the early part of the 20th Century pioneering work on golf course agronomy was done by two American agronomists C.V. Piper and R.A. Oakley, culminating in their book 'Turf for Golf Courses' in 1917. Piper and Oakley were keenly aware of the influence of climate and stated in the introduction to their book: "good grass turf is conditioned by two great factors, climate and soil. The latter can be modified but the former must be accepted as it is." As a consequence they adapted their agronomic practices to the climatic conditions of North America. The lack of sensitivity on the part of our American friends is in trying to tell us what type of grass to grow and how to grow it as if the situation was exactly the same as in the USA. The main climatic differences between Britain and North America are well known, but these are worth reiterating through the words of an American writer. The following is an extract from an article entitled "British and United States golf courses, how different?" by Professor William Dest of the University of Connecticut, who spent a period of sabbatical leave at Bingley.

"A comparison between golf courses of the United States where cool season grasses are grown and Great Britain cannot begin without a discussion of the weather. Britain's winters and summers are milder than in the northern states where seasons are governed by extremes in temperature. Snow cover often lasts the winter in these areas with frosts greater than 2 feet in depth. Grasses go dormant in December and do not green-up until the end of March/early April. Most golf courses stay closed, whilst in Britain the often mild winters allow golf to be played the year-round. Summer temperatures in the States are hotter than in Great Britain with the daytime temperatures in the mid-eighties and on occasion within the 90°F range. The differences in winter and summer between the two countries result in the time difference that the major stress periods occur. British turf is under stress during a mild winter as play conditions. Wear is often excessive due to little or no growth and soil compaction is inevitable on soils that say wet for prolonged periods of time, particularly in places where drainage is inadequate. The opposite occurs in the United States. Cool season grasses are under great stress during the summer months when temperatures are high. Root systems are generally less extensive as roots are lost during this period compared to the extensive root growth observed in the spring and fall."

"Rainfall in the United States if of longer duration but less frequent than in Great Britain and is often followed by prolonged dry spells between rainfall events. This compares with Great Britain in which rainfall usually is of shorter duration but occurs with greater frequency. The warmer summer temperatures in the United States result in greater water consumption by the grass plant than is found in Britain. The differences in weather conditions between the two countries have a large impact on the selection of cool season grasses for golf course use and their management."

I could not have expressed it more cogently than Professor Dest and it is precisely for these reasons that Penncross and its relatives do not thrive under our conditions. Penncross is a cultivar which enjoys the heat and grows aggressively under hot summer conditions, competing well with annual meadow-grass which is stressed by the same conditions. British summers (a few years excepting, and notably part of, 1995) are simply not hot enough to get the best from Penncross. In Madrid it is excellent but in Manchester it is miserable, let alone in the Highlands of Scotland. Our winters though are the final nail in the coffin, Penncross goes semi-dormant in late autumn, we then subject it to winter play as a consequence of which it soon degenerates to annual meadow-grass. There are a few privileged courses which might, with a combination of a low number of rounds per year and high budgets for maintenance, be able to keep their Penncross greens going for some time longer. Then there is the vexed question of take-all patch disease for which there is no approved chemical treatment available and which can destroy whole greens comprised of pure bentgrass, especially on newly constructed and expensive sand-based greens. Fescue on the other hand is immune.

All of this leads us to the conclusion that we should stick with what works in Britain. Namely, for greens we should use a mixture of 80% Chewings or slender creeping red fescue and 20% browntop bent, choosing cultivars which score highly for shoot density and tolerance of close mowing in the STRI "Turfgrass Seed" booklet. For tees the same species would be used but reinforced with smooth-stalked meadow-grass to confer improved wear tolerance. An example of a tees mixture would be: 35% smooth-stalked meadow-grass, 25% Chewings fescue, 30% slender creeping red fescue and 10% browntop bent. Occasionally it is necessary to use a turf-type ryegrass on small, narrow tees where there is limited scope for tee enlargement. In this case the choice of cultivar needs to compromise between wear tolerance and tolerance of close mowing and therefore both tables of ryegrass cultivars in the "Turfgrass Seed" booklet should be consulted and an appropriate short list of possible cultivars selected. For fairways and roughs the demands placed on the turf are less exacting and because of the large areas involved price becomes a more important consideration. Disease resistance and the aesthetic considerations such as colour are also important for large areas, especially fairways. For these, however, we would still aim to use a mixture of bent and fescues, not ryegrasses and smooth-stalked meadow-grass as in cool season parts of the USA. For roughs, strong creeping red fescue may also be included, not on its merits *per se* but merely as a means of reducing costs, the "commodity" cultivar 'Boreal' often being used in mixtures with Chewings and slender creeping red fescues and browntop bent. Roughs may present the need for special mixtures if the site has any ecological significance. This may entail the inclusion of wild flowers or the use of special mixtures based on the locally occurring flora. In such cases the STRI Ecologist should be consulted with a view to specialist advice.

In conclusion, I am not against course managers and head greenkeepers experimenting with different grasses and methods of management – such is the path of innovation. However, they also have a duty to provide the best playing conditions for members and this duty is not served by architects from foreign shores imposing their ideas of what is golf, and what are suitable grasses for golf, on British courses without proper consideration of climatic differences and their effects on grass selection as outlined by Piper and Oakley and reiterated by Professor Dest. However in mitigation, if you spare no expense then Penncross will grow well in Southern England, but this is not a choice for most private member clubs who should stick with what works in Britain.

(PMC : B.187)

POA ANNUA ON THE GOLF COURSE

Ask a number of greenkeepers, golf course green convenors or turfgrass advisors about *Poa annua* (annual meadow-grass) and they will tell you about its disadvantages. No other grass species has generated so much folklore about its attributes and control from both greenkeepers and research workers. The majority consider it to be an inferior weed grass, but is it really a weed and can it be successfully eliminated from fine turf, or is it a question of minimising its presence? If it is inferior why is it so successful?

Before attempting to eradicate, reduce or control *Poa annua* it is worth considering the reasons for its success and in doing so identify possible weaknesses and a strategy for attack.

Annual Meadow-grass Success

(a) *Diversity*

One key factor attributed to the success of annual meadow-grass is the existence of a large diversity of ecotypes or forms and the plant's ability to adapt morphologically to its environment. On the golf green, the height and frequency of cutting, amount of trampling and wear, fertiliser applications and the community which it invades can each affect morphology. In intensively managed turf there will exist populations of *P. annua* which vary from short-lived upright annuals, common at the start of the season though to prostrate vigorous forms which are commonly biennial or perennial. Thus, the annual meadow-grass found in golf greens will be distinct from the annual meadow-grass of the fairway or rough. This has important consequences for a *P. annua* management programme as new seedlings arising from seed out of the rough may be only short lived and not persistent, whereas seed arriving from an intensively managed surround or approach will be better adapted to colonising bare areas on the green.

(b) *Seed production*

Annual meadow-grass has the potential to produce large quantities of seed, given its ability to produce a large number of flowers and set seed for most of the year. Upon dispersal the seed will either die, be transported on mowers and footwear to new areas or more probably enter the soil seed bank and act as a source of future outbreaks in years to come. This is a major source of re-infestation and figures as high as 200,000 seeds per m^2 of the turf surface have been reported in Australia and America, but in the British Isles this is considered to be nearer 70,000 seeds per m^2.

(c) *Meadow-grass ingress*

When the sward cover is lost or weakened whether due to disease, vandalism or wear, voids left in the sward can either be filled with new growth via stolons and rhizomes of the bent and fescue grasses if present, or by the germination and establishment of bent/fescue seed if introduced. Annual meadow-grass, on the other hand, has also the opportunity to infill by lateral growth, but in addition by germinating from seed in the vast soil reservoir. The outcome of the battle between the species will depend largely upon the management regime.

Reducing Annual Meadow-grass Levels

Tackling annual meadow-grass is not for the faint hearted and many greenkeepers and committee members all too easily concede early defeat just at a time when their efforts are beginning to bear fruit. Undoubtedly, settling for annual meadow-grass dominant greens is perhaps the easiest management path to follow, requiring little thought – after all this species is so successful it will grow practically anywhere with little interference from man. In the longer-term, however, such greens are more expensive to maintain requiring a higher level of fertiliser, water and pesticide inputs, not to mention a more intensive aeration programme to counteract thatch production.

In the same way as bad breath is better than no breath at all, it is true that a cover of annual meadow-grass is better than no grass at all and we must never lose sight of the fact that putting surfaces must be produced to satisfy golfers' demands, but why give them second best when a superior surface dominated by bent and fescue may be attainable?

Creating the Right Environment to Tip the Scales

As this is likely to be a long-term strategy it is useful to determine the starting point, by making a note of the proportions of each species in a number of greens on the course. Well-established greens are likely to be at an ecological equilibrium, whereby each species has reached its peak level of infestation given the current levels of play, environmental conditions and management programme. Adjusting the management programme to create environmental conditions which favour the bent and fescue grass or which place the annual meadow-grass at a competitive disadvantage, will help to increase the finer grass component of the sward. Factors which affect *Poa annua* are:–

(a) *Drainage*

Good drainage is fundamental to the germination, establishment and growth of the bent and fescue grasses. Annual meadow-grass is more common on moist, wet soils and dry surfaces will in fact inhibit germination. A sound aeration programme, which commences early in the autumn and continues for as long as possible in the spring, will help reduce ingress during spring and autumn germination peaks.

All too often, clubs wait until the end of the competition season in October to implement the autumn renovation programme. Yet this is the worst time to undertake such work. Growth and recovery is slow and the tine holes offer an ideal environment, free from competition, for the germination of recently-shed annual meadow-grass seed. The same work, undertaken earlier in the season, gives the finer grasses a competitive advantage as they will be growing more strongly at a time when most of the nutrient resources of the annual meadow-grass will be involved in seed production.

Soils with a high fines content (silty/clay soils) not only have lower infiltration rates but also a tendency to consolidation and compaction. *P. annua* is often wrongly assumed to be a shallow rooting grass because it is frequently found growing under compacted soil conditions where no other grass species will survive. However, it does not follow that annual meadow-grass will automatically disappear if consolidation is relieved.

A free-draining growing medium is a major advantage, but the ecological adaptability of annual meadow-grass means that new forms soon arrive which are suited to these conditions, shifting the emphasis onto other management factors which will now play a greater role in its persistence. Nevertheless, an initial step has been made in favouring the bents and fescues.

(b) *Fertility and pH*

It is well documented that the bent and fescue grasses can tolerate a lower pH than annual meadow-grass, but in addition a low pH will also restrict phosphate availability. This is important because *P. annua* does have a higher phosphate requirement than either bent or fescue, due to its rapid growth rate and greater turnover of leaf tissue. Unfortunately, withdrawing phosphate fertiliser applications from turf will not immediately reduce annual meadow-grass levels, due to the phosphate reserves in many greens and the grass's ability to extract its phosphorous requirements even from soils with a low phosphate concentration. Therefore, needless phosphate applications are unnecessary and do little to give the finer grasses a competitive edge over annual meadow-grass.

Nitrogen is the single most important controllable element which can determine the sward's species composition. The judicious use of nitrogen and the proper timing of applications can favour bent and fescue over annual meadow-grass. This latter species is better adapted to utilising applied fertiliser and high levels of nutrient only favour increased flowering and seed production, storing up potential problems for the future. Conversely, lower rates of nitrogen favour the bent grasses by denying annual meadow-grass a supply of energy needed to compete with the slower-growing grasses. Early, heavy applications of fertiliser, particularly on heavy soils which are slow to warm up, will again favour annual meadow-grass germination and its colonisation of any bare areas left after winter play.

(c) *Irrigation*

Annual meadow-grass dominated greens on heavy clay soils can have higher irrigation requirements than fescue/bent swards on sandy soils, due principally to greater compaction and shallower rooting in the former. In normal circumstances shallow root systems prove adequate until the surface dries, at which point *P. annua* dies. The tendency is to apply more water to sustain a sward cover, which in turn only encourages more shallow rooting. Under such conditions, the finer grasses have little chance of out-competing the annual meadow-grass and applications of water at a time of high seed production and dispersal only favours their subsequent germination and establishment. Tackling the underlying compaction and reducing water application is the only way to break the vicious circle of events.

Conclusions

Annual meadow-grass forms a significant proportion of the sward in many golf greens in the British Isles yet there exists the potential to increase the proportion of finer grasses in a large number of cases. Having greens dominated by the finer bent and fescues is not a reason for complacency as annual meadow-grass is ready to exploit every opportunity to invade if given the chance.

Annual meadow-grass reduction can only be a long-term strategy as there are no quick fixes. Even if these were available they would only leave many greens devoid of a grass cover, together with a large number of frustrated golfers and unemployed greenkeepers.

At the end of the day the greenkeeper must produce a satisfactory putting surface for the average club golfer, yet the type of surface required has still to be clarified.

We do know that meadow-grass dominated greens are softer, slower and spongier and produce poorer winter playing conditions. Research funded by the R&A has given some indication as to which playing quality characteristics are important to most golfers.

Annual meadow-grass can be dismissed as an unbridled nuisance, but one can also admire its versatility and adaptability which make it one of the most successful grasses of the golf course in the British Isles.

(IMcC : B.185)

CHOICE OF CULTIVARS FOR GOLF COURSES

There are two main grass species which should be used on golf courses in Britain. They are as follows: fescues and bents.

The following merit lists are taken from the STRI publication "Turfgrass Seed 1996".

Chewings, Slender Creeping and Strong Creeping Red Fescues (Tables 1, 2 and 3)

Cultivars of chewings fescue and slender creeping red fescue are shown in order of their suitability for use in close mown turf (mown at 5-10 mm). This order was determined from the mean of each cultivar's tolerance of close mowing and shoot density found in close mown trials. Strong creeping red fescues are shown in order of their suitability for use in low maintenance amenity turf. This ranking was derived from the mean ratings for cover, compactness and short growth in low maintenance trials. The new cultivar section of each table contains cultivars which have recently become available but have only been assessed in the latest STRI trials. Information for cultivars in this category should be treated with less certainty than that given for the more established cultivars in the main body of each table.

Cultivars of strong creeping red fescue are not generally suitable for use in close mown turf (cutting height less than 13 mm). Whereas, the better cultivars of Chewings and slender creeping red fescues are suitable for use in close mown turf and will tolerate mowing at 5 mm, for use in golf greens. Cultivars of slender creeping and Chewings fescues also tend to produce finer and denser turf at other heights of cut. In low maintenance situations where wild flowers are to be encouraged the less dense cultivars of fescue may be more appropriate than the high density (A or B for compactness) turf-type cultivars. However, the high density cultivars would be more desirable if ground cover and soil stabilisation was the primary objective of the low maintenance mixture.

Cultivars at the top of each list may not be the best cultivars for every use. Users should identify which characteristics are most important for their intended use and then select cultivars accordingly. Short growth will be important where the frequency of cutting is low, such as low maintenance areas. Resistance to disease will be important where the incidence of disease is likely to be high or if disease is unlikely to be controlled.

The merit ratings for each characteristic are comparable between tables. Therefore, seed specifications may be prepared which contain a mixture of the different types of fescue, using the range of desirable characteristics found in different cultivars and types of fescue. For instance, in close mown turf a mixture of chewings and slender creeping red fescues may be advantageous. This would combine the greater drought tolerance and ability to spread from rhizomes of the slender creeping red fescues with the greater disease resistance of the chewings fescues. It should be noted that there are often several cultivars of equal merit for any particular use. In such cases, the final selection of cultivars can be made according to price or other commercial factors.

TABLE 1
CHEWINGS FESCUE (*Festuca rubra* ssp. *commutata*)

Cultivar	Tolerance of close mowing	Shoot density	Mean	Short growth	Freedom from red thread	Freedom from dollar spot	Summer greenness	Winter greenness
Center	7.4	7.4	7.4	6.8	7.1	7.0	MG	MG
Lobi	7.3	7.5	7.4	6.1	7.,0	6.9	DG	MG
Nimrod	7.3	7.3	7.3	5.9	6.1	7.2	MG	MG
Frida	7.2	7.4	7.3	6.4	7.4	7.1	MG	MG
Enjoy	7.1	7.3	7.2	6.7	6.8	6.8	MG	MG
Olivia	7.1	7.3	7.2	7.3	6.6	6.7	DG	MG
Bargreen	7.2	7.2	7.2	7.7	7.3	6.7	DG	MG
Baruba	7.0	7.1	7.0	6.7	7.1	7.2	MG	DG
Waldorf	6.9	7.0	7.0	6.0	7.5	7.4	MG	MG
Baroxi	6.5	7.4	6.9	7.3	7.6	7.2	LG	DG
Trophy	7.0	6.8	6.9	6.6	7.3	7.1	DG	MG
Atlanta	6.9	6.9	6.9	6.6	6.3	5.2	MG	DG
Rainbow	6.8	6.9	6.8	6.9	6.9	7.1	MG	MG
Roulette	6.8	6.8	6.8	7.3	7.5	7.7	MG	DG
Bingo	6.8	6.8	6.8	6.5	6.3	6.8	LG	DG
Simone	6.6	6.9	6.8	6.5	7.5	6.5	MG	MG
Alltop	6.6	6.8	6.7	6.2	7.4	7.0	MG	DG
Mary	6.7	6.7	6.7	6.5	6.6	6.3	MG	MG
Wilma	6.8	6.5	6.6	6.6	5.8	6.4	LG	MG
Agram	6.4	6.5	6.5	6.9	7.1	6.6	LG	MG
Tamara	6.5	6.3	6.4	5.8	7.1	7.1	MG	DG
Raymond	6.4	6.3	6.4	6.6	6.4	6.3	MG	MG
Weekend	6.4	6.2	6.3	7.2	6.1	6.6	MG	DG
Capitol	6.4	6.2	6.3	6.5	6.3	7.0	MG	MG
Lifalla	6.1	6.0	6.0	6.5	7.5	6.9	MG	DG
Lustre	6.2	5.8	6.0	5.9	7.0	7.3	MG	MG
Banner	5.9	5.6	5.7	5.5	6.1	6.0	MG	MG
Barnica	5.7	5.5	5.6	5.2	6.6	6.1	MG	DG
Ivalo	5.5	5.3	5.4	5.0	7.0	6.2	MG	DG
Koket	5.5	5.3	5.4	5.7	6.8	5.6	MG	MG
Tatjana	5.3	5.3	5.3	5.1	6.3	6.6	MG	DG
New cultivars								
Darwin	7.0	7.3	7.1	8.0	5.9	6.4	–	LG
Melody	6.8	7.1	7.0	6.9	7.0	6.2	–	MG
Licato	6.6	6.3	6.4	7.4	6.4	6.6	–	MG
Angela	6.3	5.8	6.1	8.1	6.0	6.1	–	MG

TABLE 2
SLENDER CREEPING RED FESCUE (*Festuca rubra* ssp. *litoralis* etc.)

Cultivar	Tolerance of close mowing	Shoot density	Mean	Short growth	Freedom from red thread	Freedom from dollar spot	Summer greenness	Winter greenness
Barcrown	8.5	8.9	8.7	7.4	8.0	7.1	MG	DG
Smirna	7.2	7.3	7.3	6.7	6.1	6.0	MG	MG
Logro	6.9	7.3	7.1	6.4	6.9	6.2	MG	MG
Oriflamme	7.1	7.0	7.1	6.4	6.0	5.4	DG	DG
Jupiter	7.0	7.1	7.1	6.5	6.0	6.0	DG	DG
Estica	7.0	7.1	7.0	6.9	5.5	5.5	MG	DG
Recent	7.1	7.0	7.0	6.3	4.6	5.5	DG	DG
Barlander	6.7	6.9	6.8	7.7	6.9	7.2	MG	MG
Cinderella	6.8	6.9	6.8	6.5	5.4	5.8	MG	DG
Symphony	6.7	6.8	6.8	6.2	6.7	7.3	DG	DG
Liprosa	6.7	6.8	6.8	6.3	6.0	6.2	MG	DG
Horizon	6.6	6.8	6.7	5.8	6.1	5.7	DG	DG
Dawson	6.6	6.6	6.6	5.2	5.5	5.5	DG	DG
Lovisa	6.6	6.4	6.5	5.6	5.3	6.1	MG	MG
Rufilla	6.3	6.4	6.3	5.4	6.3	7.0	DG	MG
Samanta	6.5	5.9	6.2	5.6	5.7	6.3	MG	DG
Rondo	6.1	6.2	6.2	5.5	5.4	5.3	DG	MG
Suzette	6.2	6.1	6.1	5.1	5.0	6.1	DG	DG
Merlin	6.1	5.6	5.9	5.8	6.0	6.7	MG	DG
Virtus	5.7	5.5	5.6	6.5	5.3	5.0	DG	DG
New cultivars								
Mocassin	7.8	8.2	8.0	5.9	8.5	7.7	–	DG
Helena	7.0	7.9	7.4	6.7	5.8	6.4	–	DG
Barskol	7.3	7.2	7.2	6.0	5.3	–	DG	DG

TABLE 3
STRONG CREEPING RED FESCUE (*Festuca rubra* ssp. *rubra*)

Cultivar	Tolerance of close mowing	Shoot density	Short growth	Mean	Freedom from red thread	Freedom from dollar spot	Summer greenness	Winter greenness
Diego	5.8	5.7	6.6	6.1	4.4	5.9	MG	MG
Cindy	5.3	5.3	6.4	5.7	5.7	5.1	DG	MG
Hollywood	5.7	5.8	5.6	5.7	5.3	5.6	MG	MG
Herald	5.4	5.2	5.7	5.4	4.5	5.0	DG	DG
Ensylva	5.1	5.2	5.7	5.3	5.1	5.1	DG	DG
Elanor	5.2	5.2	5.2	5.2	5.5	5.3	MG	MG
Jasper	4.7	4.7	6.1	5.2	4.3	3.9	MG	DG
Pernille	5.2	5.1	5.1	5.1	5.1	5.2	DG	DG
Sunset	4.7	5.1	5.4	5.1	5.8	5.0	LG	MG
Flyer	4.5	4.8	4.9	4.7	5.0	4.6	LG	MG
Victor	4.7	4.7	4.7	4.7	4.4	4.1	MG	MG
Laxton	4.5	4.6	5.1	4.7	4.9	4.8	MG	MG
Franklin	4.5	4.7	4.7	4.7	5.0	5.2	LG	MG
Boreal	4.8	4.5	4.3	4.5	4.7	3.9	MG	MG
Ceres	4.5	4.8	4.1	4.5	5.3	4.4	MG	MG
Commodore	4.0	4.3	3.6	4.0	5.6	4.8	MG	MG
New cultivars								
Aniset	5.1	5.3	6.0	5.5	4.9	4.3	–	MG
Picnic	5.4	5.3	5.2	5.3	4.9	5.0	–	MG
Sylvia	4.6	4.6	5.0	4.7	4.6	5.4	MG	MG

TABLE 4
BROWNTOP AND CREEPING BENTS (*Agrostis* ssp.)

Cultivar	Shoot density	Fineness of leaf	Short growth	Freedom from red thread	Summer greenness	Winter greenness
A. tenuis						
Heriot	7.7	7.5	7.1	5.7	MG	DG
Lance	7.5	7.5	6.6	6.3	MG	MG
Sefton	7.5	7.6	5.8	4.6	MG	DG
Egmont	7.0	5.8	5.9	6.3	MG	DG
Bardot	6.7	7.2	6.8	5.8	MG	MG
Duchess	6.5	7.0	6.7	5.5	MG	MG
Tracenta	5.9	7.0	7.1	4.1	MG	MG
New cultivars						
Denso	7.4	7.1	6.6	6.4	MG	MG
Litenta	5.4	6.4	5.0	5.5	MG	MG
A. castellana						
Highland	4.9	5.3	3.4	3.6	LG	DG
A. stolonifera						
Penneagle	6.0	5.3	6.0	6.8	MG	MG
Carmen	5.9	5.8	5.6	6.6	LG	MG
Penncross	5.7	5.5	6.3	6.6	MG	MG
Prominent	5.2	5.6	5.2	7.1	MG	DG
New Cultivar						
Providence	6.9	6.0	6.5	6.1	LG	MG

Browntop and Creeping Bents (Table 4)

Cultivars of browntop bent (*Agrostis tenuis*) and creeping bent (*A. stolonifera*), with the exception of new cultivars, are listed in order of their suitability for use in close mown turf. The new cultivar section for browntop bents includes cultivars which have recently become available but have only been tested in the latest STRI trials. Although the data for the new cultivar category should be treated with less certainty than that for cultivars in the main body of the table, the new cultivars listed have so far been found to be comparable with the very best of the established cultivars and should therefore be considered for use on golf greens. 'Highland' browntop bent is generally acceptable for most UK situations, especially golf fairways, in which bent is sown and seed of this species is usually more readily available than that of other cultivars of bent. However, for very fine turf such as golf greens the STRI now advises that finer and denser cultivars of *A. tenuis* are used in preference to 'Highland'. In other situations the compactness, summer appearance and disease resistance of bentgrass turf can be improved by replacing some of its 'Highland' content with a finer browntop bent, to the extent of 30–50% of the bentgrass fraction of a bent/fescue seeds mixture.

Golf Greens

For turf mown at 5 mm or less the traditional mixture is approximately 80% Chewings fescue and 20% browntop bent by weight. (NB The difference in seed size means that proportions of 80% fescue and 20% bent by weight are reversed when expressed by seed number, i.e. for every 2 fescue seedlings there are 8 of the smaller, weaker bent seedlings.)

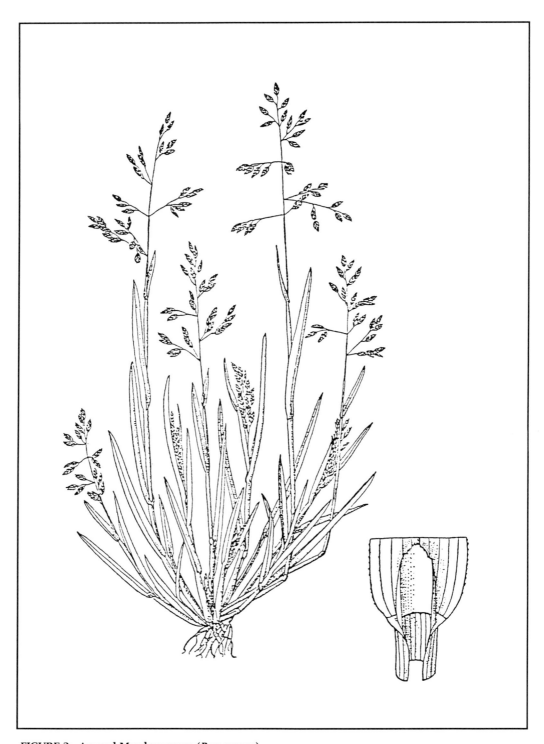

FIGURE 3: Annual Meadow-grass (*Poa annua*)

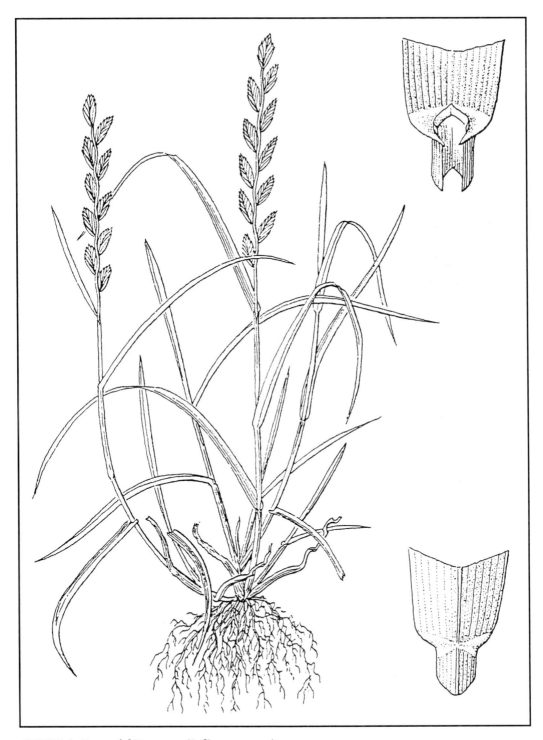

FIGURE 4: Perennial Ryegrass (*Lolium perenne*)

The two species will not remain evenly balanced. High fertility and adequate water will favour the bent, low fertility and dry conditions the fescue. Disease, management and weed competition will help to tip the balance. Two variations on the basic mixture can be considered – a combination of two or more cultivars or species of bent, and partial replacement of the Chewings fescue by other fescues. A monoculture of bent may also be considered.

Fairways

The most natural and appropriate grasses for UK fairways are the bents and fescues (70 or 80% fescue). There is, however, less need for the best and most compact cultivars, and therefore some possibility of financial saving. Strong creeping red fescue, which is quite unsuitable for greens, can nevertheless be used on fairways, which are mown more leniently, and the seed of acceptable cultivars will generally be cheaper than that of acceptable Chewings fescue or slender creeping red fescues.

Fairways should receive enough seed bed fertiliser to ensure vigorous establishment of the sown grasses, but thereafter they are unlikely to receive much fertiliser, if any, and they will tend to become increasingly like the mown or grazed areas of natural grassland in the locality. It may therefore be sensible to help this process by introducing other species into the fairway mixture if they are clearly well adapted to the soil and climate. Smooth-stalked meadow-grass and fine-leaved sheep's fescue are two species of which seed could be obtained, to add to the fairway mixture if appropriate.

(AJN : *Turfgrass Seed 1996*)

PLANT NUTRITION

The growth of a fully developed mature plant from a tiny, apparently lifeless seed has forever fascinated mankind. In this process the mysterious forces of life become manifest. Thus, when man began to cultivate plants for his own needs he felt it his duty to entreat the co-operation of Nature's forces in his work. However, scientific investigation has shed much light on the factors required by plants from their environment. Early European scientists put forward many interesting ideas as to which substances plants used to form their structures; indeed it was once proposed that plants were formed solely from water. It was only when chemistry became a more precise science that the composition of plants could be ascertained and hence the elements needed by plants from their surroundings could be determined.

In the early 19th century a great step forward in our understanding was made when Théodore de Saussure showed that the carbon in plants was obtained from carbon dioxide in the atmosphere. He also showed that the air supplied plants with oxygen and that water from the soil was used to construct plant tissue. De Saussure's pioneering discoveries were later bolstered by the work of the German chemist Justus von Liebig. He proposed also that nitrogen was taken in by the plant as ammonia and that other elements found in plant ash, such as potassium and phosphorus, were taken up from the soil. At Rothamsted, England, J.B. Lawes and J.H. Gilbert took up Liebig's work by setting up field experiments in the 1840's to show the elemental requirements of crop plants. Some of these experiments are in progress to this day.

Basic research into plant nutrition has become so sophisticated that now scientists investigate, in minute detail, the mechanisms used by plants to absorb chemical elements from the soil into their roots. However, the plant kingdom has not yet yielded all of its secrets.

In strict terms nutrition is the function by which plants use glucose to obtain energy. The plant itself manufactures the glucose using carbon dioxide from the air, water from the soil and sunlight by the process of photosynthesis. Although this is a highly complex and extremely important subject, it need not be gone into in any further detail here. The intention in this section is to describe the individual mineral elements which plants need to take up from the soil in order to grow healthily. It will show what these mineral nutrients are needed for, the forms in which they are absorbed and symptoms observed when a particular nutrient is deficient. The nutritional requirements of grasses are in general similar to those of all plants, but where interesting differences do exist these will be pointed out.

Nitrogen

Nitrogen (N) is the mineral element required in greatest abundance by plants. Leaves commonly contain between 2 and 5 per cent N in their tissue. It is present in proteins; in the DNA which carries genetic information, in chlorophyll (the green pigment which absorbs sunlight for photosynthesis) and within other chemicals which are needed for energy production in the plant. Thus, nitrogen has a vital role to play in the plant's well being. There are numerous other nitrogen-containing compounds, many of whose functions are not known.

The plant absorbs nitrogen from the soil solution mainly in the form of the nitrate molecule (NO_3) which, being the most soluble form found in the soil, is the most freely available to the plant root. The ammonium molecule (NH_4) can also be absorbed, along with other molecules of larger size such as urea and amino acids.

Some experiments with perennial ryegrass have shown that when the roots are grown in solutions containing both nitrate and ammonium forms of N, a greater proportion of its N is taken up as ammonium at lower temperatures. As the temperature at the root surface increases up to 25°C, a greater proportion of nitrogen is taken up as nitrate. (See Grassland Research Institute, Annual Report, 1981, pp. 19-20.)

Plants taking up their nitrogen in the ammonium form release acidity into the soil. This leads to a lowering of soil pH in the area immediately surrounding the root surface (the rhizosphere). On the other hand, if the plant is supplied with nitrate–N, the decrease in pH is not so pronounced and in some plant species an increase in rhizosphere pH has been observed. This latter phenomenon has been observed with certain grass species.

Once inside the plant, nitrate–N is converted to ammonium which in turn is used to produce glutamate, an amino acid. This can then be converted to other amino acids, for protein formation, and to other nitrogen-containing compounds. It is important for the plant that the concentration of ammonium does not become excessive as this could lead to toxicity.

The amounts of nitrate and ammonium available in the soil for the plant root vary enormously during the growing season and depend largely on the release of ammonium from soil organic matter by soil microorganisms. The ammonium is subsequently converted to nitrate by soil bacteria. In addition, the rate at which soluble forms of nitrogen are leached out of the soil has important consequences for the amounts of plant-available N. The cultivation of plants by man has led to supplementary nitrogen being added to soils through fertilizing. The materials used may be organic compounds such as dried blood or mineral fertilisers such as ammonium sulphate. Some plant species have developed additional systems for obtaining nitrogen. Here, gaseous nitrogen present in the earth's atmosphere is 'fixed' by bacteria which live in conjunction with the plant roots. (Clover and other leguminous plants can, for example, perform this feat.)

The air contains 78 per cent nitrogen but it is in such an inert form that only relatively small amounts can be converted to nitrates which the plant can use. The conversion occurs during lightning discharges in the earth's atmosphere. The fertiliser industry has to expend a vast amount of energy in order to convert the atmospheric nitrogen into natural fertiliser. However, leguminous plants have nodules on their roots containing nitrogen fixing bacteria which convert the gaseous nitrogen to organic nitrogen compounds. These are released into the plant root. The bacteria tend to be rather choosy about the conditions under which they will function and they generally require a soil of neutral pH with a sufficient supply of phosphate, a low nitrogen content and with adequate amounts of trace elements such as molybdenum. Through the techniques of genetic engineering, scientists are trying to introduce the faculty of atmospheric nitrogen fixation into crop plants such as wheat.

Because nitrogen-containing compounds are required for so many different biological processes within plants, its deficiency leads to an overall decrease in leaf growth. In grasses, the amount of tillering is suppressed. However, root growth may be enhanced by conditions of nitrogen starvation. The amount of chlorophyll (green colouration) in the plant decreases markedly, leading to a fading of the green colouration and yellowing of the leaves. Because nitrogen compounds move from the older into younger leaves during growth, it is the older leaves which first show nitrogen deficiency symptoms. In addition, as nitrogen becomes deficient leaves become more fibrous and contain less water. On the other hand, if the nitrogen supply is excessive then leaves become extremely succulent and cell walls thin. These 'softer' leaves are more susceptible to fungal and insect attack as well as being less wear tolerant and frost hardy. Excess nitrogen and soft grass growth lead to slow pace on golf greens.

Phosphorus

In nature, phosphorus is not found as a free element as it prefers to combine with other elements to form a large variety of compounds. One such combination is with oxygen to form phosphate which is the compound found in rocks, soils, animal bones and in teeth. Man has manufactured many phosphorus-containing chemicals such as the highly poisonous phosphine gas, which is phosphorus in combination with hydrogen.

Plants commonly contain from 0.3 to 0.8 per cent of their dry weight as phosphorus within various compounds. Although this is less than one eighth of the nitrogen concentration, the phosphorus-containing materials are just as vital to the plant as those of nitrogen. A group of the phosphorus compounds carry out the job of storing and transporting energy within the plant; the most important of this group being adenosine triphosphate (ATP). This stores energy in its three phosphate groups and releases it by losing one of them to form adenosine diphosphate. In order to produce adenosine triphosphate in the first place, energy is obtained from sunlight by the process of photosynthesis.

Another vital role for phosphorus in both plants and animals is for the formation of the nucleic acids DNA and RNA which hold the organism's genetic code. The growth and proper development of a plant depends intrinsically on these molecules. DNA and RNA are needed particularly where plant cell division is taking place, that is within actively growing plant tissue. It is for this reason that when plants are chemically analysed phosphorus is found at higher concentrations in young plant tissue than in the older, less active parts. The same reason explains the fact that during the young seedling stage plants have a higher requirement for phosphorus than in the older established stages. In perennial ryegrass, the greater absorption of phosphorus by the plant has been shown to promote the tillering process.

The combination of phosphate with glucose and other sugars within the plant causes them to become 'activated', allowing them to form long chains of carbohydrate. These carbohydrate chains are required to produce strong cell walls and to manufacture energy reserves for dormant periods. It has been shown that where the phosphorus content of grass plants is low, they are less cold tolerant during the winter months as a result of their weak cell walls and poor reserves of energy.

In the soil, phosphorus is present in a variety of forms, both organic and inorganic. Soils of an alkaline nature have phosphorus present mainly as calcium phosphates, whereas if the soil is acidic it is generally in the form of iron and aluminium phosphates. All of these phosphates are rather insoluble in the soil. Some phosphorus is also held within the soil's organic matter and, although it is thought that it is not normally important for plant nutrition, if the content of inorganic phosphate is low, then the organic fraction may be useful in releasing phosphate to the plant root. As with the other plant nutrients, it is the phosphate in the soil solution which is the immediate source for the root. Because the inorganic forms of phosphate mentioned above are so insoluble, the amount of phosphate released into the soil solution is extremely low at any one time and would be inadequate to maintain plant growth for any period. Thus, as the root absorbs phosphate from the soil solution, it has to be replenished from phosphate in the solid compounds of iron, aluminium and calcium. The phosphate diffuses very slowly from these solid sources, through the soil solution, to the root surface. In order to make best use of this phosphate, the plant roots have to penetrate and explore a large volume of soil. Also, by increasing the surface area of the root, the quantity of soil phosphate which can be exploited becomes greater. Plants do this by the production of tiny hairs on the root surface which may only be one millimetre in length, but can potentially allow the plant to take four to five times the amount of phosphate absorbed without root hairs. Many plants also have fungi (mycorrhiza) attached to their roots. These mycorrhizal fungi obtain carbohydrate from the plant root, but in return may help the root to withdraw phosphate from the soil. This aid is of particular importance where the soil is low in the total amounts of phosphate held.

Even when the plant has used these various tactics to increase the amount of phosphate at the root surface, it still has an uphill task to move this phosphate inside the root for despatch to the leaves. This is because the concentration of phosphate at the exterior of the root is still considerably lower than the interior. The plant thus has to expend metabolic energy in order to pull phosphate into the root; this process being commonly known as active transport. It is for this reason that the uptake of phosphate from soil is dependent on soil temperature. At low soil temperatures the root's metabolism is sluggish and it is less able to actively pull in phosphate. During cold springs when the soil is slow to warm up, the growth of leaves may be restricted by the inability of the root system to supply them with adequate quantities of phosphate. Indeed, in crop species visual signs of deficiency have been observed under these conditions.

In some species of plant it has been observed that the root system appears to react to an inadequate phosphorus state within the plant. It does this by secreting mineral or organic acids, such as citric acid, into the soil causing the normally insoluble inorganic phosphate compounds in the immediate vicinity of the root to dissolve.

Plants differ in the amounts of phosphate which they need to take up for growth. Even within the limited number of grass species used for turf, differences are evident. For example, perennial ryegrass has a much greater requirement for phosphate than browntop bent or fine-leaved fescues and it is possible that even between different cultivars of the same grass species the requirements may vary.

Although the visual symptoms of phosphorus deficiency change from plant species to species, it has been seen to cause a general pattern of colour change in the leaves of turfgrasses in the rare instances where it occurs. Initially, the older leaves turn a darker green and then the leaf edges become red-purple. Eventually the whole leaf turns dull red in colour. If the supply of phosphate to the plant continues to be deficient, then ultimately it will die.

Potassium

The word 'potash' refers to the alkaline substances obtained when the washings of burnt vegetable matter were dried in pots. The name was Latinised to 'potassium' which refers to the pure element. In plants the amounts of potassium can vary considerably, but it commonly makes up from one to 8% of the plant's dry weight. In fine turfgrasses the potassium content has been measured at 1.2% of the dry weight of the leaf blade. Its concentration tends to decrease as the plant matures.

Although potassium is the plant nutrient required in greatest quantity after nitrogen, there is still some mystery as to why plants need such large amounts. It does not form any part of the solid structures, but tends to stay soluble in the plant sap. One of its roles may be to neutralise the negative charge on organic acids produced in the plant and on the nitrate, sulphate and chloride absorbed by the root. However, other elements such as sodium could also carry out this role. Potassium's association with the functioning of plant enzymes has been well documented. Many enzymes use the element in order to fulfil their function in promoting biochemical reactions and in this function potassium is termed as an enzyme activator or cofactor. Synthesis of proteins from amino acids is particularly dependent on potassium activated enzymes at many stages of the process.

Another function in which it appears to be specifically required is for the control of the stomata on the leaf surface. These stomata are the openings through which the plant loses water vapour and transfers gases to and from the external atmosphere. The chloroplasts, where photosynthesis takes place within leaf cells, contain relatively large amounts of potassium and so it is assumed to be required for the photosynthetic process whereby plant carbohydrate is manufactured from carbon dioxide and water.

The rate at which potassium is taken up by a plant depends primarily on its concentration just outside the root surface. It is absorbed in solution within the water which the plant withdraws from the soil. In a soil with a high potassium status, this will be the prevalent method for the movement of the element in soil solution towards the root. However, where the total potassium concentration of the soil is very low, then diffusion to the root surface assumes greater importance. This is the process by which soil phosphate moves to the root. Potassium in the soil solution is normally quickly replenished from the fraction held by the negative electrical charge on the surfaces of clay and organic matter particles; known as the exchangeable fraction. It in turn is replenished from potassium bound within the mineral structure of the clay particles and from decomposing organic matter.

If there are extremely high concentrations of soil potassium available to the root, then its uptake becomes excessive to the quantity actually required by the plant. This is known as "luxury consumption". Although high levels of potassium within the plant may not be harmful, the absorption of magnesium may be reduced, eventually leading to magnesium deficiency.

Potassium deficiency rarely occurs in turfgrasses but signs are normally seen first in the older leaves. In grasses, the leaves begin to droop, the areas between the leaf veins turn yellow and the tips wither. Eventually the yellow colour extends to the whole leaf apart from the mid-vein. Because of its association with so many plant enzymes, when the potassium concentration is low the plant may be physiologically impaired without showing any of the visual symptoms mentioned. For instance, because potassium is needed for the manufacture of carbohydrate, low potassium levels will cause insufficient quantities of carbohydrate to be produced. This leads to the formation of thin and weak cell walls which cause turfgrasses to be more prone to frost damage and fungal infection. The proneness to disease infection is enhanced by impaired protein synthesis in the plant leading to an accumulation of soluble nitrogen compounds. This produces extremely favourable conditions for the spread of fungal pathogens. A plant's tolerance to drought conditions is also reduced under conditions of low potassium. This results from its role in controlling the opening and closing of leaf stomata.

Calcium

Plants normally contain 1 to 3% of their dry weight as calcium. It is of extreme importance for the physical structure of the plant, particularly in the root. The formation of membranes within the plant cells requires calcium for their integrity and if these membranes disintegrate, then all the metabolic functions cease and the cell dies. High levels of calcium are also contained in the plant cell wall and here it forms chemical compounds with pectin substances which are required for cell wall stability. It is also found within plant cells as calcium carbonate or calcium oxalate. Calcium is present on the negatively charged sites on the surfaces of clay minerals, but in calcareous soils most of it is present as calcium carbonate. Normally, it is one of the predominant elements in soil solution and is only likely to be deficient in acid sandy soils.

The signs of deficiency are first observed in young leaves. In grasses, a reddish-brown discolouration occurs along the leaf margins which develops to a lighter red. Root tips are damaged by calcium deficiency and root growth may cease altogether when deficiency is severe.

Sulphur

The dry matter of plants contains around 0.1 to 0.2% of elemental sulphur. It is found within two essential amino acids: methionine and cysteine, both of which are components of most proteins. It is taken up by the plant from the soil solution as the sulphate molecule, but the principal reservoir of soil sulphur is the organic matter which, as it decomposes by microbial action, releases sulphate. As well as being present in the soil solution, it also becomes chemically bound to iron and aluminium oxides. The soil also obtains sulphur from the atmosphere as sulphur dioxide in gaseous form or dissolved in rainwater. This is particularly significant in industrial areas. Plants are able to absorb sulphur directly into their leaves from these atmospheric sources.

Deficiency of sulphur in turfgrasses is practically unknown in Britain as many fertilisers used on golf courses contain sulphate, but its visible symptoms are similar to those of nitrogen deficiency; i.e. the leaf blades turn pale green and then yellow.

Magnesium

Magnesium is best known in plant nutrition for its part within the chlorophyll molecule which absorbs incident sunlight and gives the leaf its green colour. About 10% of the plant's magnesium is taken up in chlorophyll; the whole plant normally containing between 0.2 to 1.2% of its dry weight as magnesium. It is essential also as an enzyme activator, particularly in the enzymes associated with photosynthesis. However, most plant magnesium is associated with ribosomes in the plant cell which are required for the synthesis of plant protein. The soil solution receives magnesium from the negatively charged sites on clay particles and organic matter. Uptake of magnesium by plant roots is adversely affected by the presence of high potassium concentrations. Absorption of phosphate by the root appears to be enhanced by high magnesium levels.

Deficiency of magnesium, which is most likely to occur on acid sandy soils, produces visual symptoms associated with the loss of chlorophyll from leaves. In addition, the leaf margins turn reddish-brown in the same way as for calcium deficiency.

Micronutrients

The micronutrients are those elements which are essential for plants, but only in minute quantities ranging from 0.1 to 200 parts per million of dry weight. In many cases if their concentration is too high above normal, then they become toxic. The elements iron, manganese, copper, zinc, boron, molybdenum and chlorine are all known to be required by plants.

Iron in soils is present in large quantities, but the amounts needed by plants are only small (100 to 200 parts per million of dry matter). It is needed as an activator for several plant enzymes and is required for the synthesis of chlorophyll. In soil, iron is present principally as iron oxide. Because these oxides are relatively soluble at low soil pH, there is generally sufficient iron available in acid or neutral soils. However, at high pH iron deficiency may be encountered, resulting from the insolubility of the oxide. This is most commonly observed in soils derived from chalk and limestone. The plant takes up most of its iron in the ferrous form. Deficiency symptoms appear as a yellowing between the leaf veins with the whole leaf becoming almost white in advanced stages. Iron is commonly used in greenkeeping, not as a plant nutrient, but to give swards an attractive dark colour, to scorch moss and to give some protection against fusarium patch disease.

Manganese acts as an activator for some plant enzymes, especially within the photo-synthesis system. In the soil it is present in solution; is held on the clay and organic matter by electrical attraction; and forms insoluble manganese oxides. Like most micronutrients, there is much less present in soil solution at high pH and so less is available to the plant root. At low pH the amount of available manganese may be so high as to become toxic to the plant. The deficiency symptoms of manganese are at first similar to those of iron, but there follows the development of small distinct lesions on the leaf and the leaves droop.

Boron appears to have a role in the metabolism of carbohydrate within plants. Soil boron is derived from weatherable rocks, particularly those laid down in the sea. It enters the soil solution as boric acid and this is the form taken up by plants, but in alkaline soils the boric acid becomes attached to aluminium and iron oxides, so becoming less available to the plant root. Grasses can grow in soils of low available boron content without showing any harmful effects. Where deficiency symptoms do occur, there is stunting of the growth point and the leaves become shortened. Discolouration of the leaf interveinal regions then takes place. Toxicity is normally seen as a blackening of the leaf margins and it often occurs where irrigation water contains high levels of boron.

Copper and Zinc are both needed by many plant enzymes as activating agents. In soils they are held by clay minerals, oxides and by the organic matter. Copper deficiency causes young leaves to become rolled or curled and often causes a bluish discolouration of the leaf tip in grasses. Deficiency in zinc results in the restriction of leaf development and causes them to become thin. There is also a darkening of leaf colour. Where either or both elements are present in toxic concentrations, then the uptake of iron becomes impaired and plants show symptoms of iron deficiency.

Molybdenum is required for the enzymatic conversion of nitrate–nitrogen in plants to ammonium before incorporation into amino acids. The element is also needed by leguminous plants such as clovers in order to fix nitrogen from the air through their root nodules. It is taken in by the plant root as molybdate from the soil solution, which in turn is replenished from molybdate bound to the iron oxides. It is interesting that at high soil pH more molybdate becomes detached from the oxides, so making it more available to the plant. Deficiency is more likely to occur in acid soils. Symptoms of deficiency are shown in most plant species by a bright yellow-green mottling before the leaf withers. This first shows in the older leaves.

Chlorine is required specifically for part of the photosynthesis pathway. It is taken up from the soil solution as the negatively charged chloride and, because plants normally take in more than is required for metabolic processes, deficiency is not normally a problem. Wilting damage may occur, however, to plants growing on soils with high chloride contents such as in coastal regions where there are high inputs of chloride from sea spray.

(CGC 1 : 5)

SOME PRINCIPLES FOR THE USE OF FERTILISERS ON GOLF COURSES

Introduction

A fertiliser programme for any turf area used for golf should be based upon a supply of nitrogen in sufficient quantity to gain optimum growth. Optimum growth means sufficient growth of both shoots and roots to produce the desired playing surface characteristics, without creating a need for more treatments than are absolutely necessary.

Supply of nitrogen by natural processes is very slow, so for most turf areas extra nitrogen is needed at intervals during the growing season to assist in producing a strong turf density and resistance to wear, amongst other factors. In comparison to the need for nitrogen, the requirement of turfgrasses for other nutrient elements is very small – often absent. Where there is a deficient level of these other elements, the purpose of applying them is to enable the grass plants to make best use of the nitrogen supplied. The need for nitrogen is best assessed visually while the need to supply minerals other than nitrogen should be determined by routine soil analysis at intervals (every 3 years for the average golf green) which take into account the likely rate of leaching on a particular site, in conjunction with an understanding of the type of turf required and its status as regards establishment.

Golf Greens and Tees

On golf greens and tees the fertiliser programme should be an integral part of the maintenance of a fine-textured sward of fescue and bent, the nutritional requirements of which are rather different to those of perennial ryegrass. There is the need for some nitrogen during the growing season to compensate for wear and clippings removed, and so to maintain a good turf texture. The frequency of application must, however, be strictly controlled. This strict control is just one aspect of maintenance which is necessary to avoid the development of the excess thatch and disease problems which result in a long term deterioration in turf quality and a dominance of annual meadow-grass *(Poa annua)*.

To obtain an even effect on fine turf, fertiliser is applied as a powder or as mini-granules. A basic fertiliser will supply nitrogen-only from both organic (usually dried blood and hoof and horn meal) and inorganic (usually ammonium sulphate) sources, with a view to controlling factors such as weed, moss and worm invasion and drought susceptibility, as well as the growth rate and the period of response to a single dressing.

Should the condition of the turf, the nature of the rootzone and soil analysis indicate that a wider range of nutrients are needed by the turf on a particular site for the grasses to make best use of the nitrogen supplied, then it is usually sufficient to incorporate sources of these into the spring fertiliser dressing and subsequently to supply nitrogen as necessary thereafter during the growing season.

As fescues and bents require only very limited supplies of elements other than nitrogen, it should not normally be necessary to apply other sources of nutrients as this may lead to accumulations, particularly of phosphate, in the rootzone. Over-supply of supplementary nutrients is at best a waste of money and at worst could reduce the competitive edge of the desired grasses within a sward in favour of less desirable turfgrass species.

The application rate of any one fertiliser dressing should be based on the nitrogen content, with a maximum of 40 kg/ha of nitrogen per dressing. The frequency of application during the growing season should be aligned to the minimum consistent with providing a dense but not lush turf which will give a smooth surface under mowing.

Golf Fairways

Routine fertiliser treatment of fairways is not normally recommended. The slow growth required from such areas is usually promoted by the natural processes supplying nitrogen.

(CGC 1 : 6)

FERTILISER – WHAT DOES THE ANALYSIS TELL YOU

The number of fertilisers which are on the market for use on sports turf has increased considerably in recent years and the range of nitrogen sources, analyses and presentations for solid and liquid application is now extensive. As such, not only is the choice more difficult to make but it is now more important to look at the information supplied with the product if you are to be sure the fertiliser is actually going to provide what you think it should.

Nutrient Requirements

It is very much easier when having to do any calculations relating to fertilisers to think and work in the actual amount of nutrient required or to be supplied. This is usually expressed as grams per square metre (g/m^2) for smaller areas or by multiplying by 10 to convert this to kilograms per hectare (kg/ha) for large areas. This makes for easier comparisons to be made between proposed applications and the total requirements of the turf and similarly comparisons between the nutrients supplied by products and their true costs. The recommended requirements of various types of turf for different sports on various constructions are given in the STRI publication "Fertiliser for Turf". These are and can only be guidelines and must be used with the combined knowledge of the chemical soil analysis and local knowledge of the environment and the demands on the turf. In general it should be possible to define the requirements for phosphate, potash and magnesium from the chemical soil analysis. The need for nitrogen can only be given in guideline terms for a particular situation since the effects of rainfall, irrigation, length of growing season, turf condition and soil type will amongst others influence the requirements. Hence within the guidelines the turf manager must decide when to apply nitrogen and how much of it according to conditions at the time. Clearly these guidelines are of little value unless there is knowledge of the amounts of nutrients which are being applied.

Regulation

A variety of legislation covers the manufacture, sale and marketing of fertilisers both here and in the E.E.C. The Agriculture Act of 1970 is the umbrella legislation which covers the marketing and sale of fertilisers whilst the Fertiliser Regulations 1977 and its amendment of 1984 cover the composition and labelling of fertilisers. As such these determine: how fertilisers must be named, how the major nutrient content should be declared, the minimum nutrient content, the permissible limits of variation on the declared analyses and the information which must be given on the labels. The regulations also cover the comparative description of liquid fertilisers and the fineness of grinding of materials for liming. Much information may be provided both in sales literature and on the labels with respect to the rate of use, timing of applications etc. Such information together with advice on any health risks associated with the product will be covered by the relevant consumer protection legislation. The more recent regulations are those concerning hazardous substances, namely the Control of Substances Hazardous to Health Regulations 1988 (COSHH). Whilst only products containing more than 45% by weight of ammonium nitrate (which require labelling with an "Oxidising" symbol) are directly covered by the COSSH regulations; a product which would offer a hazard because of its dust content would be covered under the general terms. Similarly to comply with COSHH regulations it is necessary to adhere to the manufacturers' advice on the storage and handling of their product.

The Analysis

The stated analysis is given as the percentage by weight of the nutrient as compared to the total weight of the product in the bag eg. the 20% of nitrogen (N) in a 20:10:10 analysis product will give 5.0 kg of nitrogen from a 25 kg bag ($^{20}/100$ x 25). This method is satisfactory for dry fertilisers whether powder, granular or soluble for liquid application. Fertilisers sold as liquids should show the analysis as weight for weight (w/w) allowing the above calculation. However a weight for volume (w/v) declaration may also be given which does not give the correct nutrient content although it is often used for practical purposes. For example, a liquid product 10:0:0 analysis on weight for weight basis sold in a 20 litre drum weighing 23 kg will contain 2.3 kg of nitrogen not 2.0 kg.

Similar calculations can be made for other nutrients but the phosphorus content is expressed as P_2O_5 (phosphorus pentoxide), the potassium content as K_2O (potassium oxide) and magnesium as MgO (magnesium oxide). These figures are usually used in considering fertiliser analyses and nutrient requirements of turf rather than the single elements P, K or Mg, although simple mathematical conversions can be made to the elements if required by dividing the P_2O_5 figure by 2.29, K_2O by 1.2 and MgO by 1.66.

It will be noted that the phosphorus content of proprietary fertilisers is expressed with solubilities in different solutions - commonly in water, ammonium citrate or citric acid. This gives an indication of the solubiltities of the phosphorus source used in different soil situations. The availability of phosphorus to the plant is complex and cannot be considered here, however as an example a product with a phosphate source which is high in water soluble phosphorus would be most appropriate for a pre-seeding dressing where the grass needs the phosphorus to be easily available in the short term; the residual amount reverting to insoluble reserves for the future.

For sports turf, particularly fine turf, the choice of raw materials used in a fertiliser mix is as important as the actual analysis. The continued use of some materials may adversely affect the quality of the turf and conversely the use of others may be beneficial. Similarly to avoid short term flushes of growth the release pattern of the nitrogen is important relative to the analysis and application rate. Also ease of accurate spreading is critical for fine turf products. Since the foregoing characteristics are not part of the statutory declaration the analysis only gives a skeleton of information. It is obvious therefore that two products can have identical analyses but be very different as regards their ingredients, performance and cost.

Other Information

How then can you know what types of fertiliser you are applying to your turf? The surest way, although much less popular now, is to mix the raw materials and a bulking agent or carrier, or to have them mixed for you. Appropriate mixtures of ingredients such as sulphate of ammonia, dried blood, sulphate of iron and, where needed, superphosphate and sulphate of potash perform well and have passed the test of many skilled groundsmen and greenkeepers over many years. However, the majority will choose a proprietary fertiliser for the ease of storage and application as well as a measure of quality control. In this situation it is necessary to gather up as much additional information to the statutory analysis as possible in order to choose the product most suited to the turf situation and its requirements. Sight of a bag or container label at your stockist, together with sales literature will provide as detailed information as the manufacturer is prepared to give, but obtaining a Health and Safety sheet will provide some extra information. Here may be found information on the fertilisers which are used in the product or product range, although not the proportions of each, together with a description of the formulation eg. powder or granule and any hazard such as dust.

The nutrient on which most will judge the performance of a fertiliser, in the short term at least, is the nitrogen. The source or sources of nitrogen used is critical in the short term regarding its release pattern and in the long term regarding its effect on soil pH and the quality of turf. For example sulphate of ammonia is strongly acidifying and very quickly available whereas urea and its more complex compounds such as IBDU (isobutylidene diurea) have little effect on soil pH and the nitrogen will become available quickly or over an extended period as with the more complex compounds. Although the analysis may show a breakdown of the total nitrogen into that supplied as ammoniacal, nitric or ureic nitrogen the user will largely have to rely on the manufacturer's voluntary information as regards the release pattern and longevity.

Nutrient Values and Costs

Working out the nutrient totals allows easier comparison of the true costs of equivalent products. However a word of caution is necessary. Do make sure that having calculated the cost of 1 gm or 1 kg of nitrogen to make the comparison, the other beneficial features of the products are noted down. These would relate to the ease of use of the product such as the quality of packaging, granulation, freedom from dust and whether the granules are all the same or a blend of different fertiliser granules. Similarly a product with organic nutrient sources and those with slow or phased release characteristics are likely to be more expensive.

Records

It is now essential to keep accurate records of work done and materials used. Not only should the fertiliser product be recorded but the date of application and the rate used with respect to named areas should be noted. It is then useful to record the actual nutrients supplied. For example an 8:0:6 + 1% MgO fertiliser applied at 35 g/m^2 supplies 8% of 35 gms as nitrogen and potash as 6% of 35 gms etc. Thus this application gives 2.8 g nitrogen, zero phosphate, 2.1 g potash (K_2O) and 0.35 g magnesium (MgO). All the nutrients applied can be totalled to allow comparisons to be made on an annual basis taking into account factors such as rainfall and irrigation, and the standard of turf and playing surface that was produced.

The calculation should be done for liquid fertiliser applications as well as in this case it is necessary to work back from the quantity of products applied per square metre to the nutrient using the analysis percentages. Liquids have the great advantage of flexibility in application rates by adjustment of the water volume in the tank mix or in the spraying rate to give the required quantity of nutrient. However, it is often not fully appreciated how low the actual amount of nutrient may be in liquid feeds particularly at the lower or tonic feed rates. So here again the true nutrient values will give the turf manager a far clearer picture of the quantities applied relative to the results which are obtained.

The Future

It is quite likely that regulations will appear to impose a responsibility on the user of fertilisers, particularly for nitrogen, as has been done with pesticides. Concerns centre around soluble nutrients such as nitrates passing into water courses and aquifers and, as the turf industry has experienced before, the activities of the vastly larger agricultural sector leads to the amenity horticultural industry being required to comply with the same regulations. No doubt time will reveal all. Hopefully the manager who knows the actual nutrients applied to the turf as g/m^2 or kg/ha will be one step ahead.

(PCW : B.188)

SLOW RELEASE FERTILISERS

The proper healthy growth of turfgrass requires a balanced uptake of mineral nutrients by the grass plant from the soil. Nitrogen (N), phosphorus (P) and potassium (K) are needed in greater quantities than other mineral nutrients and it is essential that ample supplies of these three elements are present in the soil. The grass root absorbs nutrients in a soluble form from the soil water and so when fertiliser is applied to turf the fertiliser components must dissolve in the soil solution before the plant can take them up. On the other hand, a surplus amount of mineral nutrient in the soil solution, above that required by the turf, can lead to large losses of nutrients into the drainage water. This is particularly true for freely drained, light, sandy soils.

A material which could release enough nutrients for grass growth without any losses by leaching would be highly desirable for turf cultivation. If nutrients were released only at the times of the year when grass was actively growing, this would be even more advantageous. Unfortunately, mineral fertilisers commonly used today do not have these properties. In fact, fertiliser application causes an immediate dramatic increase in the amounts of nitrogen and potassium in the soil solution. The turf takes up a proportion of these nutrients, causing a sudden flush in growth. The nitrogen is taken up mostly in the nitrate form although some ammonium-nitrogen is also absorbed. Excess ammonium is held at the surface of clay minerals or converted to nitrate by soil bacteria. Any surplus nitrate is easily leached out of the soil. Any potassium not absorbed by the grass roots may also be held by clay minerals or leached out.

Slow release fertilisers are materials which when applied to the soil can release plant nutrients slowly into the soil solution. This confers a more even pattern of grass growth, a reduction in leaching losses and a decrease in the frequency of fertiliser dressings. In fact, because the phosphate compounds in ordinary mineral fertilisers are rather insoluble, they release phosphate very slowly into the soil solution. Fertiliser potassium, on the other hand, tends to be very soluble in the soil. Nitrogen, which is the mineral element required in greatest abundance by plants, can form many compounds which are practically insoluble in soil solution and which slowly release plant-available nitrogen compounds. Because of this, there is a potential for the production of fertilisers containing slow release nitrogen.

Natural Organic Nitrogen Compounds

Greenkeepers have been using natural organic materials for many years. These include hoof and horn meal, dried blood and the compost in top dressings. In these materials the nitrogen forms compounds such as proteins which are gradually broken down by soil microorganisms to soluble ammonium and then to nitrate. Trials on turf have shown hoof and horn to have better slow release fertilizing properties than dried blood. However, both of these natural organic fertilisers have a rather unpredictable rate of ammonium release. They also tend to produce a turf which is more susceptible at certain times of the year to fusarium patch disease than fine turf treated with ammonium sulphate.

In response to the need for a fertiliser which will slowly release nutrients in a consistent and predictable fashion, fertiliser manufacturers have produced a variety of materials. These can be divided into three categories: synthetic organic nitrogen compounds; soluble fertiliser compounds treated to reduce their solubility and fertilisers containing chemicals which inhibit the conversion of ammonium-N to nitrate-N in the soil.

Synthetic Organic Nitrogen Compounds

Isobutylidene diurea (IBDU)

In the British Isles this is the synthetic organic compound most commonly used in slow release fertilisers. It contains 32% nitrogen. Its solubility in cold water is very low, but when added to the soil it is broken down by microorganisms to soluble urea-N which itself is further decomposed to ammonium and nitrate. The grass plant may absorb some urea and ammonium, but will take up most of its nitrogen as nitrate. Because soil microorganisms become more active at higher temperatures, the rate at which IBDU is broken down to urea increases as soil temperature rises. As the amounts of soil moisture increase, the amount of IBDU decomposition increases also. The size of fertiliser granule is important. The larger the granule, the better are the slow release properties obtained.

During the winter months when the soil temperature is below about 10°C, the microbial breakdown of IBDU virtually ceases. However, there is still a very small release of soluble nitrogen. This results from a slow, purely chemical breakdown of the compound. Trials at Bingley have shown that the small release of soluble nitrogen during the winter months leads to a better turf colour and earlier spring growth than with ammonium sulphate treatments. The use of IBDU leads to less acidification than where turf is treated with ammonium sulphate.

There is a range of compound fertiliser products containing IBDU. They contain varying proportions of IBDU along with more soluble fertilisers such as ammonium nitrate and urea.

Crotonylidene diurea (CDU)

Although used as a slow release fertiliser in Japan and some European countries, this material is not readily available in the British Isles. It contains 32.5% N and the rate at which it releases plant-available nitrogen is dependent on the same factors as those described for IBDU. As with IBDU, there is very little decomposition of CDU to urea below 10°C. Tests at Bingley have shown CDU to produce an excessively high flush of grass growth when applied in spring, although good early spring growth was obtained by a carry-over effect from the previous autumn's application.

Ureaform

This is the oldest of the synthetic organic compounds used for fertiliser. It is now manufactured in the USA and is commonly used on the golf courses of that country. Ureaform is not a single chemical compound. In fact, it contains a range of different compounds which are formed when urea and formaldehyde react together. These compounds vary in their solubility and their speed of nitrogen release to the turf. The total nitrogen content is about 40% in most commercial products.

Ureaform releases soluble urea into the soil solution, the factors controlling this release being similar to those for IBDU and CDU. However, trials at STRI have shown that the more soluble fraction of the Ureaform quickly releases plant-available nitrogen in the soil whereas the rest is released so slowly that it has little fertilizing property. This may be due to the fact that the breakdown of Ureaform to urea is much reduced below 15°C. Its application tended to make the playing surface soften and produced a turf which was more susceptible to disease and invasion by weeds. A carry-over effect from autumn application to the spring was observed.

Fertilisers with Restricted Solubility

Magnesium ammonium phosphate

The chemical nature of this compound causes the ammonium to be only slightly soluble in the soil. Any release of ammonium is due to a chemical reaction and is not so dependent on microbial activity as with the organic compounds described above. The solubility depends largely on the size of the fertiliser granule. Unfortunately, the high phosphate content of magnesium ammonium phosphate (8 N : 40 P_2O_5) makes it rather unsuitable for turf unless it is supplemented with other nitrogen fertiliser.

Trials with this compound on fine turf have shown the granular form to produce more even grass growth during the summer than does the powdered form. A carry-over effect during winter has also been noted.

Resin coated fertiliser

With this type of product the soluble fertiliser salts are coated with a plastic resin through which they can slowly diffuse out into the soil solution. There is a range of products available which contain various ratios of N, P and K. A major advantage of these materials over other slow release fertilisers is that all of the contained nutrients are released slowly to the turf, not just nitrogen. As soil temperature increases, greater amounts of plant nutrient diffuse out into the soil solution. Their slow release properties have been found to be particularly suitable for seed bed applications.

Sulphur coated urea

The sulphur coated urea product most commonly available in the British Isles contains about 32% N. By coating water soluble urea with elemental sulphur its solubility in the soil is much decreased. The urea-N gets into the soil solution by diffusing through the coating or by the decomposition of the sulphur. The rate of urea-N release increases as soil temperature and soil moisture content increase and is also dependent on the thickness and uniformity of the sulphur coating.

Trials at STRI have shown sulphur coated urea to have fairly good slow release properties on turf, but its main drawback is that the coating may be damaged by mower blades. Over a two year test period the soil pH decreased to a greater extent with ammonium sulphate than with sulphur coated urea. Over a longer period of time the sulphur is likely to cause significant acidification in the soil.

Nitrification Inhibitors

The biological process by which ammonium is converted to nitrate is known as nitrification. If this process could be slowed down in the soil, the leaching of nitrate could be diminished with a consequent decrease in fertiliser application requirements. Smaller amounts of nitrate would then be available for plant uptake over a longer period of time. A number of chemicals can inhibit nitrification. Two of the most commonly used are Dicyandiamide and Nitrapyrin. Fertilisers containing nitrification inhibitors have only recently become available in the British Isles.

Conclusions

The slow release fertilisers available on the market are by no means perfect at their job. However, they do have particular qualities which may make them useful in particular situations, even though the costs of these materials are higher than conventional soluble mineral fertilisers. The use of slow release fertilisers can lead to reductions in the quantity of fertiliser used and frequency of application. This is particularly the case on very sandy soils where there is a large leaching loss of soluble nitrogen compounds. Slow release compounds can also give a more even pattern of grass growth during the summer in comparison to the application of a fertiliser like ammonium sulphate. However, the degree of consistency of growth will depend on the type of soil and situation.

Probably the greatest advantage of many slow release products is their ability to release some plant-available nitrogen during the winter period. The grass is able to use this nitrogen when milder temperatures allow growth. In addition, the grass is able to get off to a quick start in the early spring.

Manufacturers will no doubt introduce more products with slow release fertilizing properties in the future. With the increase in promotion for individual commercial products the need for independent research into their value for amenity turf becomes more essential.

(CGC 1 : 7)

THE VALUE OF SOIL TESTING

The nature and health of a particular soil are fairly apparent to the experienced eye by the examination of a sample in the hand and by looking at the quality of the associated turf. However, often these observations are not enough. In many situations laboratory testing of soil for its physical and chemical properties can supply the turf grower with precise information which can be used as a firm basis for decision making. For instance, from laboratory tests the relative merits of topsoils to be used in the construction of a golf green can be judged accurately; or the possible need for application of phosphate and potassium fertilisers to a green can be ascertained.

The soil tests commonly carried out fall into two categories: physical and chemical. The physical analysis of soil reveals its texture, the amount of organic matter present, the rate at which water moves through the soil and the size of pores within the soil. Chemical analysis produces information on soil acidity or alkalinity, the amounts of mineral nutrients available for the grass plant to take up and the presence of toxic substances which may be harmful to the turf. Some of the tests carried out at STRI are described briefly below. They are based on methods used in soil analytical laboratories throughout the world.

Physical Analysis
Particle size analysis
In order to measure the texture of a soil (that is the proportions of sand, silt and clay present) a particle size analysis is carried out. The soil mineral material is first dispersed in water and the sand size particles separated out by passing the liquid through sieves of varying mesh size. The coarse, medium and fine sands caught on the sieves are then separately weighed. Silt and clay particles, which pass through the sieves, are mixed in a vertical cylinder of water and allowed to sediment by gravity. By finding the quantities of material which have descended to a particular depth after a set time the weights of silt and clay can be determined. The proportions of sand, silt and clay present allow the soil to be designated a textural class such as 'clay-loam', 'sandy-clay' or 'silt'.

Organic matter content
The organic matter content of a soil is determined by igniting a soil sample at 400°C in a furnace and measuring the loss in weight. Other methods of destroying the organic

matter employ oxidising chemicals.

Hydraulic conductivity

This is a measure of how potentially freely draining a soil is. It depends on the size of pores within the soil. Measurements are made by determining the rate at which water will descend through a sample of soil.

All of these physical tests are of particular value when samples of topsoil are being evaluated for their suitability in new constructions of golf greens or for top dressing mixes.

Chemical Analysis

Soil pH

The acidity or alkalinity of a soil is designated by its pH value. This is measured in a soil-water mixture using a pH meter equipped with a glass electrode. The actual conditions used vary slightly from laboratory to laboratory, so it is important that the specific method used is known when comparing results.

The obtained pH value is interpreted using the pH scale which runs from 0 to 14. As pH values decrease from 7.0 it indicates greater acidity and, as they increase above 7.0, greater alkalinity. In fact, mineral soils generally have pH values ranging from 4.0 to 8.0 with most being around 6.0 to 6.5.

The pH of soil supporting fine turf to be held at an acid pH value of around 4.5 to 5.0, while ryegrass turf should have a more neutral soil pH of 6.0 to 6.5. However, the actual values of soil pH are probably not as important as the rate at which the value increases or decreases over a number of years. When a fast rise or fall in pH is observed it is usually advisable to take remedial action.

It is worthwhile noting that although the numerical difference between a soil pH of 6.0 and 5.0 appears small, a soil at pH 5.0 is ten times more acidic than one at 6.0, which in turn is ten times more acidic than a soil with a pH value of 7.0.

Extractable nutrients

The amounts of phosphate and potassium held by a soil, which are potentially available for the grass to take up, are measured by the technique of soil extraction. This simply involves shaking a sample of soil in a chemical solution for a standard time. The soil is then filtered off leaving a clear extract in which the concentrations of phosphate and potassium are subsequently measured. The actual chemical solutions used for soil extraction vary amongst laboratories and so, as in pH measurements, it is important to know the exact method used when interpreting results.

When the concentrations of phosphate and potassium extracted from the soil are found to be extremely low or extremely high, then advice can be given indicating that fertilization is, or is not, required. When the concentrations are found to be between these extremes, the advice given on fertilizing will take into account the particular situation at which the soil was sampled.

It was stated above that the technique of soil extraction indicates the amounts of soil phosphate and potassium *potentially* available for the grass to use. This is of some importance. By looking at grass growing healthily at the beginning of the season it would probably be assumed that there is an ample supply of nutrients in the soil. However, the plant nutrient reserves may, in fact, be rather low and later on in the growing season the turf could suffer from nutrient deficiency. The laboratory tests will show if there are indeed sufficient supplies of phosphate and potassium present for the whole growing season.

At the present time there is no generally used routine method which can quantify the amounts of plant-available nitrogen in soils. Because nitrogen is the soil nutrient required in greatest amount by turf, it is assumed that it should be regularly applied.

SOIL PHYSICAL ANALYSIS

SOIL SAMPLE RE: Nowhere Golf Club   DATE: 1996

BRIEF DESCRIPTION: Soil-Sand Mix for New Green   SOIL REF.NO: 001

CATEGORY	DIAMETER mm	%	
Stones	>8	0	SOIL TEXTURE
Coarse gravel	8–4	0	Sandy
Fine gravel	4–2	0	

Particle size distribution of mineral matter smaller than 2 mm

V. coarse sand	2–1	0	
Coarse sand	1.0–0.5	22	
Medium sand	0.50–0.25	61	
Fine sand	0.250–0.125	8	
V. fine sand	0.125–0.050	3	
Silt	0.050–0.002	4	
Clay	<0.002	2	
Loss on ignition (% of oven-dry fine earth)		3	
Calcium carbonate (% of air-dry fine earth)		0	
PH		5.3	
Phosphorus (P_2O_5) (mg/litre)		20	
Potassium (K_2O) (mg/litre)		50	

FIGURE 5: Typical Physical Analysis Results from a Well-Constructed Golf Green.

SOIL CHEMICAL ANALYSIS

SAMPLES RECEIVED FROM: Nowhere Golf Club

DATE SAMPLES RECEIVED: 1996   ADVISER: —

SOURCE	pH	PHOSPHATE P_2O_5: mg/litre	POTASH K_2O: mg/litre
Green No.1	5.2	14	62
Green No.2	5.2	12	65
Green No.3	5.3	13	70
Green No.4	5.2	16	72
Green No.5	5.4	15	65
Green No.6	5.3	14	69
Green No.7	5.3	14	62
Green No.8	5.1	13	63
Green No.9	5.4	12	67
Green No.10	5.3	11	59
Green No.11	5.4	13	61
Green No.12	5.2	15	65
Green No.13	5.3	15	63
Green No.14	5.2	16	63
Green No.15	5.1	11	74
Green No.16	5.6	9	72
Green No.17	5.4	10	79
Green No.18	5.4	15	79
Putting Green	5.3	15	78

FIGURE 6: Typical Chemical Analysis Sheet from a Golf Course

Tests can be carried out for other nutrients in soils such as magnesium and copper. In addition, the possibility of toxicities arising from the high concentrations of metals such as copper, nickel and zinc can be confirmed or denied by laboratory analysis of soils.

Soil Sampling

When taking soil samples for physical or chemical analysis the following points should be borne in mind:

(1) The sample should be representative of the whole area under examination. Thus, if a sample is being taken from a heap of topsoil then materials should be obtained from depth within the heap as well as from the surface. If the sample is being taken from beneath established turf, then small sub-samples should be obtained from the whole area of interest, such as the golf green, and bulked together. The reason for this is that soil properties may vary quite markedly over even a small area, and so by taking a good representative sample these differences are evened out.

(2) The depth to which the soil is sampled should be similar to the rooting depth of turf. This will normally be around 150–200 mm depth.

An ideal way to fulfil the above two requirements is to use the soil cores obtained from hollow tining in order to obtain a sample.

(3) The time of year at which soil is sampled is important for chemical analysis. It should be obtained as late as possible after the previous fertiliser application, but early enough for analysis to be carried out and recommendations given prior to the next fertiliser application. This normally takes four to five weeks.

(4) For chemical analysis on established turf, samples need to be sent for analysis every four to five years. However, where turf has been only recently established, and particularly where the soil is of a very sandy texture, samples should be analysed every one to two years. This is due to the fact that there are likely to be rapid changes in the chemical properties of the soil during the initial establishment period.

(5) When sending samples for chemical analysis about 0.5 kg of soil is sufficient. This is also the case for physical analysis except that where a hydraulic conductivity measurement is requested, 5 kg is required.

If the sample of soil obtained is heavier than that required for analysis then the sample should be well mixed before a sub-sample of the appropriate weight is taken. This should then be wrapped securely in a strong polythene bag along with a label indicating the source of the soil. A covering letter should also be sent which outlines the analyses required.

(CGC 1 : 8)

THE UPS AND DOWNS OF SOIL pH

When we consider pH measurements from soils, we may define them as mildly acid, very acid, alkaline or neutral. But what do these terms mean; indeed what do we mean by the pH value? Although a simple number it is actually the result of many chemical and biological processes taking place in the soil, some natural and some from routine turf management techniques. Before looking at the more important of these processes we must first consider the concept of pH.

In a container of absolutely pure water a proportion of the water molecules (H–O–H) split apart to produce a positively charged hydrogen ion (H^+) and a negatively charged hydroxyl ion (OH^-). The term 'ion' refers to the fact that they are charged particles. The two ions immediately recombine to form a water molecule again, but at any one time approximately one in 560 million water molecules is split – a very small proportion. However, this means that there is always a certain number of hydrogen ions present in the water. This is defined in terms of 'molarity' and the hydrogen ion concentration is in fact 10^{-7} 'molar'. If hydrochloric acid (or any other acid) was added to the water the hydrogen ion concentration of the water would increase. A tenfold increase produces a concentration of 10^{-6} molar and a further tenfold increase produces a hydrogen ion concentration of 10^{-5} molar. In order to simplify matters the pH scale was introduced to describe the concentration of hydrogen ions so that, in the case above, the pure water had initially a pH of 7.0 which changed to pH 6.0 and then 5.0. Thus as more acid was added to water the hydrogen ion concentration increased and the pH value decreased.

If caustic soda (sodium hydroxide) had been added to the water, hydroxyl ions from the caustic soda would combine with the hydrogen ions already present to produce water molecules. Thus the hydrogen ion concentration decreases. A tenfold decrease would result in a concentration of 10^{-8} molar, i.e. a pH value of 8.0.

The pH scale extends outwards from 7.0 (or neutrality) in both directions, lower pH values indicating greater hydrogen ion concentration than 10^{-7} molar (ie. greater acidity); higher pH values indicating concentrations lower than 10^{-7} molar and as such termed alkaline.

However, a soil is vastly different from pure water as it contains mineral matter, organic matter, micro-organisms and a gaseous fraction as well as water. It is essentially the effect of these components on the hydrogen ion concentration of surrounding water which defines the soil pH value. Of particular importance in this is the role of the clay materials and soil organic matter. These components can hold the positively charged hydrogen ions by electrostatic attraction and so if an acidifying material is added to soil the clay and organic matter can absorb some of the added hydrogen ions and prevent them from being free in the soil water. Therefore, the soil pH would not decrease to the same extent as in water alone. If an alkaline material such as lime is added to an acid soil, hydroxyl ions are produced as the lime dissolves. However, the pH of the soil may not increase to the expected extent because the reserve of hydrogen ions on the clay and organic matter will be released into the soil water, in order to replace those being lost in combination with hydroxyl ions.

Soils which have an ability to avoid great fluctuations in pH value are said to have a large buffering capacity. Generally this depends on the clay and organic matter content. In high sand content rootzones the buffering capacity is very low and so pH values may change very rapidly indeed.

Normally the pH will not drop much below 4.0. This results from the fact that if any acidifying material is added to a soil which is already at a pH of 4.0, the clay material begins to decompose, using up hydrogen ions in the process. In soils of pH 7.0 and above the precise pH value is determined by the amount of calcium carbonate present (as limestone, chalk or ground shell) in the soil. The greater the amount and the more finely divided it is, the higher is the pH value due to the production of hydroxyl ions as it dissolves in the soil. However, calcium carbonate has only a limited solubility in soil and for this reason the pH value in alkaline soils is rarely much above 8.0.

A soil with pH value in the range 6.0 to about 7.0 is said to be neutral in reaction. Above this range they are alkaline and below, acidic.

Factors Influencing Soil pH

There are a number of factors which will influence the pH values of soils. First of all rain-fall.

Normally rainwater is slightly acidic with a pH value of around 5.5. As this percolates through the soil it will with time, reduce soil pH. The rate of pH decrease will depend on the buffering capacity of the soil. In many areas the rainwater is much more acidic due to sulphur dioxide pollution in the atmosphere. The sulphur dioxide dissolves in the rainwater to produce a dilute solution of sulphuric acid and so soil acid-ification takes place at a much greater rate. In some areas the rainwater may in fact be alkaline (greater than pH 7.0) due to the presence of ammonia in the atmosphere released from agricultural systems. At times these two atmospheric pollutants mix together so that it actually rains sulphate of ammonia!

On many golf courses the irrigation water is alkaline because the water source has percolated through limestone or chalk. In such situations a dilute solution of lime is being applied to the greens which with time may raise soil pH, particularly during hot, dry summers. In soils with a low buffering capacity (i.e. low clay and organic matter contents) the increase in pH may be fairly rapid.

However, the greatest effect on soil pH is likely to be from fertiliser use. Ammonium sulphate application is particularly effective in reducing soil pH due to its acidifying nature. This arises from bacteria in the soil which convert the fertiliser ammonium to nitrate. Every time this takes place two hydrogen ions are produced which lower overall soil pH. This process will not take place in nitrate-based nitrogen fertilisers. With urea-nitrogen fertiliser hydrogen ions are produced as the urea is decomposed in the soil. However, some carbonate is also produced which has the effect of neutralising a proportion of the hydrogen ions.

Organic sources of nitrogen, such as hoof and horn meal, are broken down in the soil by microorganisms by a series of chemical reactions. There is no significant net effect on hydrogen ion concentration from these reactions however. The same is true for synthetic slow release fertilisers such as IBDU and ureaform.

Compared to nitrogen fertiliser sources commonly used on turf, potassium and phosphate fertilisers have little or no effect on soil pH. In neither case do the materials used significantly increase or reduce the soil's hydrogen ion concentration.

Ferrous (or iron) sulphate, as well as having cosmetic and fungicidal properties, is well known as a soil acidifier. This is due to the fact that when the iron enters the soil water it becomes a very strongly positively charged ion. Indeed, the charge is so strong that it can split water molecules into hydrogen and hydroxyl ions. The hydroxyl ions attach themselves to the iron leaving the hydrogen ions free, causing a reduction in soil pH. However, when the amounts of material normally applied to turf are taken into account it is evident that ferrous sulphate is not nearly so acidifying as ammonium sulphate fertiliser.

Because acidifying materials are applied to the turf surface soil pH tends to be extremely low at the top of the rootzone soil and gradually increases with depth. Thus for a soil which has an overall pH of 5.0 in the top 10 cm, the surface 2 cm may show a pH value of only 4.0.

Obviously application of top dressing materials will have an influence on the rootzone pH. In general, maintenance of fine turf one of the functions of top dressing is to prevent the over-acidification which is likely to occur with constant, regular use of acidifying fertilisers such as ammonium sulphate. The materials used are therefore neutral or just slightly acid in pH value.

(DML : B.182)

WATER WORKS : SOIL WATER MANAGEMENT

Everyone breathes a sigh of relief when the rain eventually stops after a wet winter, but after a few weeks of continual hot, dry summer weather, we pray for rain again. How can we possibly cope with such extremes?

If there is plenty of money available for construction, we can select very free-draining materials for the wet winters and irrigate in summer when it is dry. For the majority of grass sports facilities, this simply is not feasible. The management of soil moisture conditions is a major factor in the maintenance of sports turf grown on any medium but it is particularly important when dealing with a natural soil which, in most cases, will be susceptible to poor surface drainage. It is essential to recognise the soil as a complex biological system in an air, water and mineral matrix. These constituents should generally be in the approximate proportions shown in Figure 7. These are very variable but a balance of air and water-filled pores is essential for good rooting and healthy turf.

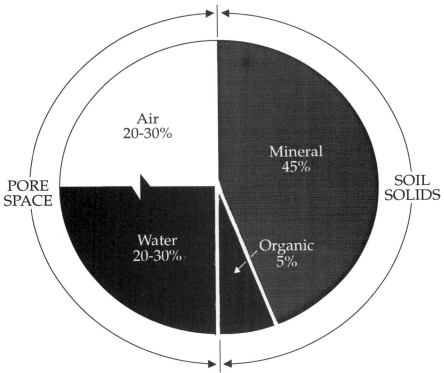

FIGURE 7: Volume composition of a typical loam soil.

The moisture stored in the soil is just one element of the hydrological cycle shown in Figure 8. Although I suspect we all know what happens when it rains (apart from getting wet), it is worth looking in more detail at the way in which the balance of these components can be modified to the benefit or detriment of the turf. It is evident that the balance between infiltration and surface run-off is a critical factor in determining the quality of a playing surface as this will influence the amount of moisture entering the soil and available to the turf during dry conditions, as well as the moisture content of the surface during wet periods.

Rainfall and evapotranspiration are outside our control, unless you have a particularly special relationship with the Almighty. We therefore tend to look to drainage and irrigation systems to redress the balance. Before investing a lot of money in such facilities, it is essential to ensure that the best possible soil conditions are achieved.

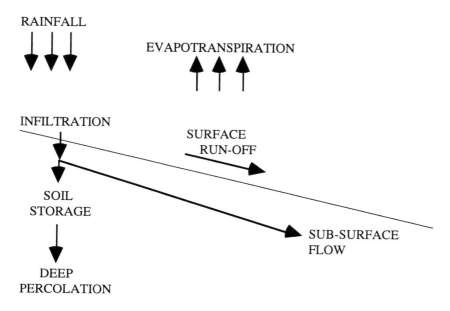

FIGURE 8: Hydrological cycle.

Soil compaction caused during construction is the most common problem encountered on new facilities. The turf suffers from poor drainage in winter and paradoxically from drought stress in summer when it should be growing vigorously to recover from winter use. There are a number of techniques to overcome these problems. Getting it right at the construction stage will avoid a lot of problems later.

Installing an intensive system of slit drainage will remove surface water by-passing the compacted soil. This will frequently be required for winter pitches and sometimes for golf fairways but it does not overcome the compacted conditions which restrict root development and the vigour of the sward. Relieving compaction will allow more moisture into the soil. Deeper, more vigorous rooting will increase the depth of soil from which the turf can obtain moisture, reducing the effects of a drought. It is worth bearing in mind that a fine textured soil will hold more water in total than a coarser grained soil but much of this water will not be available to the turf because it is held tightly within very fine pores and around soil particles.

An ideal rooting medium will have a range of pore sizes to allow good drainage and root penetration, as well as moisture retention during dry periods. It may not always be possible to import the materials for an ideal rootzone, but it is usually affordable to ameliorate the surface of the indigenous soil by working in a layer of suitable sand. This will improve infiltration rates and increase the bearing strength of the soil surface to maintain a better, firmer playing surface.

These techniques are particularly appropriate to winter pitches but they can be applied to golf fairways where drainage conditions are particularly poor. On fairways there is also potential for modifying the soil moisture regime by grading the surface to shed water away from critical areas such as a landing zone, green approach or other heavily used area. This is an extremely useful technique on 'heavy' soils but should be done sympathetically without massive adjustment to the landform and provision must be made to deal with the run-off in the low collecting areas.

Drainage and irrigation systems are fundamental tools for sports turf construction and maintenance but there is no point in spending money on such systems if the soil is not in good condition itself. It is essential to adopt an overall view of soil water management in order to achieve optimum conditions for a healthy sward and good playing surface. This approach is just as important, if not more so, during maintenance where, preventing problems in the first place can avoid the need for costly remedies.

Aeration work should achieve exactly what it says i.e., to improve aeration of the soil. It is not just a question of stirring the soil up a bit. The object is to increase the volume of larger pores and fissures in the soil, to improve movement of water through the soil profile. This should correct any imbalance in the air/water ratio in the soil pores and again improve the rooting depth of the sward. There are numerous machines available now which can be used to alleviate compaction at a range of depths without causing massive disruption and it is a question of selecting one appropriate to the situation. It is therefore important that any such work is carried out in the right conditions if the desired results are to be achieved. With the present day demands on sports facilities it is often difficult to fit these operations in but ideally the surface should be dry with just sufficient moisture to allow tines to pene-trate to the required depth.

Optimum soil conditions are fundamental to the main-tenance of a healthy vigorous sward. It can reduce the need for watering and costly drainage systems. Watering turf at the first sign of dry weather is not necessarily the best approach. If the soil has a range of pore sizes water will be released gradually to the roots and there will be a tendency to promote deeper rooting.

Do not think just of drainage and irrigation think <u>soil water management</u>.

(RE : B.191)

PLATE 1: The Dutch Verti-Drain sub-aerator first became available in the UK in 1982 and since that time has proved extremely effective for deep aeration on the golf course. Variants of the original design are now available from a number of competing manufacturers.

SECTION 2
GOLF COURSE MANAGEMENT: GENERAL CONSIDERATIONS

———— ✦✦✦ ————

Aspects of the Care of Links, Parkland, Heathland Courses, etc.

Dealing with Wear & Tear and Winter Conditions

Mechanical Equipment

Turf Nurseries : Compost-making, etc.

The Care of the Golf Course

PROBLEMS OF 9-HOLE COURSE MANAGEMENT

On the face of it, managing 9 holes should be no more difficult than looking after 18. However, there are factors, often inherent at the very concept of the golf course, which makes 9-hole course management more of a challenge. The decision to develop a site for 9-holes, as opposed to 18, usually relates either to a lack of space or finance. Generally, it is these basic constraints which follow through to produce management problems for the shorter course.

The Poor Relation

There are many excellent 9-hole courses around the country but many golfers consider them the poor relation to 18-hole facilities. This perception is grossly unfair as some have as good, if not superior, quality of layout when compared with individual sets of 9 on 18-hole courses. To emphasise this point, the renowned golf writer Bernard Darwin described the 9-hole course of the Royal Worlington and Newmarket Club in Cambridgeshire as "a revelation", although this description related as much to the quality of the turf as to the layout. Although other courses may not deserve this epithet, any suggestion that there is a correlation between courses with holes numbering less than 18 and inferior playing quality cannot be substantiated. Indeed, if a 9-hole course is developed on land insufficient to support 18 there may be more room to design a superior course in terms of its playing qualities, assuming that the architect fully appreciates and capitalises on the opportunity. There are many 18-hole courses ruined because two or three holes have been squeezed into the available area.

Having argued the case for the shorter course, there is no doubt that 9-hole courses do have difficulty attracting visitors due to the perception of a standard 18-holes being desirable. This belief may, in part, be due to televised tournament golf where 9-hole courses are conspicuous by their absence. The supposed tedium of playing the same hole twice in a round may be another reason for the negative attitude to 9-hole courses taken by golfers. This can be overcome to a degree by having two sets of tees per hole, sited well away from each other to provide a totally different tee shot to fairway on par 4 and 5 or direct to the green on a par 3. This is only feasible where there is the available spare ground, often a luxury not afforded to 9-hole courses.

Given the opportunity there are few 9-hole courses which would turn down the chance to expand to 18. This has happened to many clubs in recent years with the decline of agriculture and farmers removing the original land constraint making fields adjacent the course available, if often at inflated prices. For those courses comprising 2,500 to 3,000 yards and a Standard Scratch Score as low as 60, the option to go to 18 should perhaps be resisted if there is only the room to double the existing yardage, and it may make more sense to create a quality 9-hole layout with a better balance of par 3, 4 and 5 holes. There are some superb 9-hole layouts with a special character of their own which would be impossible to replicate through 18, it is not unknown for a good 9-hole to be ruined by adding on additional holes.

Practical Problems

Even if only 9-holes are available, a round of golf still constitutes 18 and the consequence of this is double the wear for each hole on the shorter course. If room was a constraint in the concept of the 9-hole course it is unlikely that much thought will have been given to producing large greens, tees of adequate size and number or wide, diverse traffic flow routes. With a "double pass" of golfers playing a full 18 there will be greater tracking and chance of erosion around the same navigational routes. Those 9-hole courses having the luxury of playing from separate tees for corresponding holes on front and back nine, can see a reduction in localised wear damage if the layout provides for a variation in fairway landing area and approach from tee to fairway or green. A tighter layout provides less opportunity for diverting winter play, making trolley bans and traffic regulation more important to preserve the 9-holer through the winter. This question of access around the course has implications for machinery as well as golfers, concentrating tracking and limiting options for navigating the course. If the layout takes up most of the available room then maintenance vehicles may encroach more onto the playing areas of the 9-holer. Less room through the site may necessitate having to mow everything, an additional maintenance burden which many 18-hole courses negate by promoting banded rough and conservation areas.

With half the number of holes it will not take long for the 9-hole course to become choked with golfers first thing in a morning, leaving a minimum of time for important maintenance, e.g. greens mowing. On 18-hole courses play is occasionally staggered, golfers teeing off on 1 and 10 simultaneously, a practice which can give the well organised course manager a little leeway in keeping in front of golfers. This prospect is not even afforded to the manager of a 9-hole course. Maintenance time for 9-holes is not half that of the 18-holer because the down-time, i.e. travelling around the course, manoeuvring around small greens and small tees, can take up a major proportion of management hours where there are fewer options for traffic movement. The manager of a 9-hole complex will also have more interruptions to his work through the day than will his 18-hole counterpart, the same number of golfers on each course will leave far more gaps for work when they are spread over the greater number of holes.

Golf courses developed on poor land or with poor quality materials will always perform badly in adverse weather and require constant attention, with drainage and aeration to provide playable conditions through all but the driest of months. Any such difficulties on an 18-hole course will be magnified on the shorter course as a consequence of traffic restrictions. If finance was a constraint in the original decision to build 9, then the problems of attracting visitors and charging a large fee may ensure that inadequate resources are available to carry out necessary improvements and to repair damaged ground properly.

Balancing the Budget

Essentially the same machinery range is required to look after 9-holes as for 18; a greens triple mower is still required to cut the greens however many there may be. At first glance it may be thought that hand cutting is more feasible on a 9-hole course, but the time factor, or lack of it, may make triple cutting essential. The only significant saving made in the maintenance budget will be for materials where half the top dressing, fertiliser and fungicide can make for a tidy saving, although the difference can be eaten up by increased costs for repairs. However, fertiliser and pesticide bills may not necessarily show a reduced level of expenditure, due to playing demands requiring a greater input to stimulate growth, compensating for the greater concentration of wear and possibly a greater level of disease control to weakened turf.

Equivalent costs with reduced income will not make the club's accountant a happy man and 9-hole courses will struggle when it comes to major out-lays, e.g. irrigation, construction projects, and the purchase of large machines such as a Verti-Drain. In terms of promoting the course towards fulfilling its potential these are items which the 9-hole course will benefit from as much as, if perhaps not more than, an 18-hole but they can be a long time coming if not neglected altogether. Teeing grounds are possibly the one area on 9-hole courses which suffer most from wear and a lack of maintenance input often due to financial restrictions. Irrigation to tees and enlargement may fall by the way when they are perhaps of greater necessity to courses where the same tees are played off twice in a round.

Let's not forget the men who actually do the spade-work on the golf course, the greenkeeping staff. More often than not two men are asked to do to 9-holes what five, and sometimes six cope with on 18. Bearing in mind the practical drawbacks of maintaining 9-holes, this mathematical imbalance is exaggerated. There is also the major problem of holidays and sickness, at least there is some back-up on the 18-hole facility.

The 9-Hole Dilemma

9-hole courses are handicapped from the outset by being subject to double the wear of their 18-hole counterparts. Charging lower fees to attract golfers, 9 hole courses must draw a greater number to bring similar revenue and the result can be a lack of resources to make up for heavier wear damage. The balance between desirable revenue and coping with a high level of play is a difficult one to achieve for any course, the restrictions of circumnavigating 9-holes twice with duplication of wear routes makes the equation even more difficult. The unfortunate image that 9-holers tend to be saddled with, i.e. being the intermediary between the park pitch and putt and a full blown 18, if you like a stepping stone up the golfing ladder, is unjustified as the demands involved in looking after the shorter course are as great as those imposed on any course manager. A quality playing surface comes through sensible greenkeeping practices and the basics of course management are universal however many multiples of 9 holes are being overseen. Resources are the key to having the opportunity to fulfil the potential of any course and in this respect, the 9-holer is severely disadvantaged.

(SPI : B.185)

MAINTENANCE OF SEASIDE LINKS: PARTICULAR PROBLEMS

Over-use of fertilizer has created many problems on links greens and hopefully this is a thing of the past now. It has given rise to the invasion of annual meadow-grass on many courses, especially on greens, and deterioration in playing conditions always results where this poor turf species is present in any quantity. It is not simply the poorer surfaces during early spring, late summer and winter, because of unevenness due to variable growth, but the year-round inferior playing qualities of this type of turf and surface. The natural growth of annual meadow-grass tends to be softer and more succulent, which alters the response of a ball hitting the green surface, which golfers have complained about for years and which ball bounce tests confirm. Its growth habit also affects pace and smoothness of the surface adversely. How can you achieve consistent pace day by day when faced with a 'spring flush' of seed heads that can continue intermittently the rest of the summer? Grooming can and does help in this situation but under links conditions it can rapidly lead to stress problems at the outer edges and on features. That brings pressure for more water and more fertilizer and so the cycle of annual meadow-grass spread can continue. The recent push for sales of golf green rollers – turf irons and the like – is more a sales gimmick and admission of defeat than anything else – where annual meadow-grass rules, their use may be necessary. What is absolutely certain is that the more rolling you do, the more aeration will be needed to counteract its ill effects – and any form of aeration in summer is an anathema to golfers.

The control of annual meadow-grass is never easy but on naturally free draining links soils you have far more chance of success than on heavier loams inland. The links may be alkaline as a result of shell content of sand and the shell may contain some phosphate, although this is likely to remain unavailable to plants and hence does not favour annual meadow-grass. Good soil structure, air-filled porosity and capacity for high drainage rates really favour the fine grass species. Plenty of aeration, then correct moderate use of nitrogen fertilizers, as well as strict control of irrigation will set things on the right path. If you supplement that with judicious late summer overseeding to physically introduce some of the better grasses into areas dominated by annual meadow-grass or patch in with hole cut plugs of better turf from the edges during the winter months, the process of improvement can be expedited.

Wrong Top Dressing

Top dressings form an essential part of good green management – how else in the face of spiked shoes, unlifted ball pitch marks and the never ending requirement for aeration do you maintain smooth surfaces? Choice of materials for the purpose is often not given the care it deserves, even today with our greatly improved knowledge of sands, their behaviour and role in maintaining a satisfactory growing medium for turf. In years gone by many dubious practices were followed, including use of peaty or organic compost mixtures or ones with a high component of heavier inland soils – with the misguided objective of improving fertility and/or water retention. What you could get away with 30 or 40 years ago when there were far fewer golfers, and even links courses were not played all that much during the winter, is giving rise to problems today. Layers of organic or incompatible material in the soil profile lead to rootbreaks and disrupt the soil pore system, or provide a physical barrier to free movement of air and water through the soil. That in turn leads to a weaker growing, more easily stressed and drought prone sward and lets inferior grasses gain a competitive edge. The rule for links has to be consistency in top dressings – very sandy mixtures with a fine to medium dune sand combined with no more than 20 to 30% light sandy soil.

Aeration

Of course, sandy soils compact and the same goes for pure sand constructions. As always, the main agent of compaction is a compression of players' feet, some 20 lb. per sq.in. at the heels. This consolidates and smears the topsoil closing up the pore spaces which permit rapid drainage and allow roots to breathe. The process is ongoing and far quicker under moist soil conditions, gradually leading to increased compaction at deeper levels from the top down. Clearly, the varying qualities of soil applied with top dressings which occur within the profile can and will add to problems.

Since links as a whole will usually permit far more regular play than inland soils, especially through late autumn and winter, simply because of their superior drainage and almost frost-free condition, the scope for vastly increased soil compaction is that much greater.

Regular attention then is essential and must include comprehensive treatment such as work with a Verti-Drain unit from time to time. Normally, early autumn is the best time for the latter since we need to maximise drainage potential over the winter and it also gives several months for the initial softening effect the work has on surfaces to settle down, so that firm, true playing conditions can be quickly restored in spring.

The work must be backed up by frequent slit tining. Having opened up the soil to depth using a Verti-Drain, it is necessary to maintain the link between the top and the uncompacted soil below as the effect of play is always to reconsolidate. In this respect, slit tining is ideal and can be completed on a fairly regular basis with depth of treatment altered to suit ground conditions and time of year.

It has to be said that summer aeration is frequently sadly neglected, mainly because of the adverse effect most spikers have on putting surfaces and howls of protest such work brings from golfers. The plain fact is that the more play there is on a course, the greater the need for aeration. That is especially so during a wet late summer period when the effects of play on moist soil will always be at their worst. This frequently leads to the classic situation where casual water is retained for longer and longer following heavy showers until the day of that important late summer meeting when a thunderstorm shuts the course down. Alternatively, and worse, the water is pushed off with squeegees time and again from those low lying hollows and since you cannot avoid taking some grass with it, the greens go into the winter with a thin, weakened turf cover. That is certainly bad news, for with much slower growth in autumn, and effects of winter play the surfaces are bound to be very much thinner by the spring and what better way of letting in free-seeding ubiquitous annual meadow-grass?

There is certainly a need for at least some aeration during the summer months, perhaps not as frequently as in winter, but averaging about once a month. Shallow slit tines and chisel tines have traditionally been used for the job, but do have their drawbacks. On the mounds and features which are always drier the slits tend to gape open badly. This could lead to excessive drying out in prolonged drought, although conversely an open slit lets both natural and applied water penetrate more easily. However, the main criticism is that in wet spells slits close up far too quickly to be of real benefit in maintaining drainage. The daily passage of the mower over the surface starts off the process and players' feet quickly finish it.

A small diameter solid tine or a pencil hollow coring tine are much better bets for summer aeration and maintenance of drainage. Such tines are now available with the punch-action type aerators and the operation can be completed quickly with virtually no surface disturbance. There is also the HydroJect which can, on occasion, be a useful treatment in summer, leaving no visible effect on surfaces.

Dry Patch

The development of localised and occasionally widespread harder, dry places on greens, and especially on links, has been a recognised problem for many years. Not only do they have an adverse effect on play, ball bounce being anything but predictable, but the condition also seriously weakens the turf, leaving a thinner sward prone to invasion by moss and free-seeding grass species and in severe cases can lead to death of the turf.

There are several basic causes of this problem, all of which tend to occur more readily on the free-draining and rapid drying conditions of links soil.

Higher features and mounds within putting surfaces are clearly vulnerable, they are often more exposed to drying winds or sand accumulation near bunkers and always subject to surface water run-off. Even minor differences in level across a surface will give rise to run-off. With gradual and natural drying processes from early spring on, such areas imperceptibly become drier until the organic material at the surface becomes virtually waterproof and deterioration can follow.

Corrective measures based on adequate aeration including hollow tine coring, use of wetting agent solutions and appropriate hand hose watering will all help. In the case of fungal-induced dry patch, particularly where no active fungus is present, regular treatment is vital and often needs to be continued well into the autumn and winter long after visible surface effects on the turf have disappeared – indeed until underlying soil is evenly moist once more.

Hand watering is frequently neglected of necessity in the spring with so many other urgent jobs demanding attention and this can result in problems developing later in summer, especially if weather conditions remain dry. Opening up the turf without unacceptable surface disturbance during the main golfing season is then the problem in order to allow effective use of wetting agents and hand watering once manpower is available for the job. The punch-action solid tines or pencil hollow coring tines are a great help, reducing the need for hand forking which often had to be resorted to in the past. This is also an area where the HydroJect has an invaluable role.

Fairway Damage

A good deal of the problems we see on fairways arise from past neglect. Any build-up of soil compaction inevitably results in restricted root development of the turfgrasses, as well as impeding water penetration into the soil. Not surprisingly, the routes followed by players and the almost inevitable caddie carts, as well as those used by maintenance vehicles which are often restricted by terrain, are the most vulnerable. Drought and a weakened shallow root system unable to cope with its ill effects means a rapid decline in those grasses that are best adapted to the sandy soils and often harsh environment. Fescues and bentgrasses simply do not thrive in a compacted, structureless and poorly aerated soil. Once lost, their place may be taken by annual weeds or ephemeral grasses, principally annual meadow-grass and early hairgrass. These grasses, however, can never provide the fine, dense turf cover and firm yet resilient fairway surfaces that are the true delight of links. Any hint of summer drought and these annual grass species die back completely. Once the surface becomes broken as a result of traffic over bare ground, the light soil is exposed to wind blow and its usually shallow depth is eroded to the underlying sand which does not readily support any plant growth at all.

Mowing

Over-close mowing, particularly with gang units skinning the tops of mounds in order to ensure hollows are not left too grassy, has long been a problem. Injudicious use of strong weedkillers (not necessarily over-dosing) when the sward is weak or when immediately followed by drought, as well as ill-advised use of fertilizer can all lead to steady and gradual deterioration over a succession of dry summers, ending in a coup de grace when a dry winter is thrown in for good measure. Remedies are a matter of common sense. Fairway mowing with lighter triple units whose floating heads cope far better with undulations is not necessary overall, although such measures have been adopted by a few Clubs. However, their use can be well justified on localised, more uneven parts of fairway and for the occasional topping that may only be required in grassy hollows in long continued drought.

Aeration

Recovery is always a long, slow business, often extending over years rather than months. Never was the adage 'prevention is better than cure' truer than when applied to links fairways. The first essential is to sort out an effective aeration programme and to start implementing this at a time when it can be expected to do most good. Since the main problem inevitably is a dry or waterproofed turf surface, this needs to be opened up **early**, ie. late September/early October, and shallow spoon tining or hollow coring is the first step. Repeat two or three times so that early autumn rains have a chance to penetrate and then with moisture at the root and still reasonably high soil temperatures, the remaining live turf has a chance to respond and recover. Neglect such work until November when there may be plenty of rain but soil temperatures are far lower, and the chances of a good response are virtually nil, especially in the North. This should be backed up with a regular programme of deep slit tining as frequently as every two or three weeks until the turn of the year. Supplement where necessary, especially on severely compacted traffic routes using the Verti-Drain or air injection via the Robin Dagger or Terralift as time permits over winter.

Fertilizer

The question of fertilizer treatment for weakened fairways is always raised by

Committees and may well be vigorously advocated by farmer members. The last thing we want is heavy dressings of so-called complete fertilizer which only promote soft, lush growth in spring and is promptly decimated by drought in June, serving to weaken the better turf species even more. Continue on such lines and deterioration to a sward dominated by annual meadow-grass and other agricultural grass species is assured, often with a build up of soft surface thatch thrown in for good measure. The correct approach, if fertilizer is required at all, is to use a very mild organic product based on farm slurry, seaweed extracts or a mixture of both and possibly fortified with a little extra nitrogen. The organic-based pelleted fertilizers which should be virtually free of phosphates will give similar results. Initial spray application during wet weather in spring can be followed up with another treatment in late summer. If spring weather is always consistently dry, these sprays or granular product may be better applied during late summer showers. Early autumn rain, allied with spiking treatment, can then help recovery during the open weather that frequently persists through to December.

Fairway irrigation is another emotive subject. On the drier east coast links after a succession of dry summers and often a dry winter or two which means that very little natural recovery can occur, particularly in the short northern growing season, the ability to irrigate during the main growth period can be a distinct advantage. Used with considerable care to keep the turf alive and only growing slowly and backed up with ample aeration, this approach has every chance of stemming the damage which results from non-stop play 12 months of the year and the ravages of drought.

Renovation

Turning to the problem of renovation, this is always far more difficult on the sandy thin soils and dry climate at the coast. There are two golden rules – get the seed buried just below the top, hopefully into moist soil, and do it early enough. Showery weather from August through to early September is ideal in Scotland, and a deadline of mid to late September should be the rule further south. Remember we are not simply wanting seedlings to establish – that is easy enough. What we require is a young grass plant sufficiently well established during the autumn to enable it to survive the winter, and with a good enough root system to cope with the almost inevitable dry weather in spring and early summer the following year.

Where larger areas have badly weakened and require major renovation, some preliminary aeration work may be required first to open up the top using either spoon or hollow tines to ensure that rain or artificially applied water has a chance to get in, though the job is often best started once the weather breaks. Follow this up when weather and ground conditions are suitable using a disc type seed drill, making at least two passes at an angle to each other and putting the seed anything from 3 to 12 mm below the top. The units normally have a rear roller which closes and firms the slits, leaving a neat finish and minimal interference with golf. Care is obviously required on more undulating ground. The more acute humps and later on possibly smaller localised areas will need tackling with hand work such as intensive hollow coring or using a pedestrian-operated seeder, rubbing grass seed and a prepared sandy top dressing into the opened surface.

With good establishment, a mild feed during September can be useful to exploit growth in a normally mild autumn to the full. A similar feed will almost certainly be required in spring to help young seedlings continue to make progress during indifferent growing conditions that are the 'norm' at that time of year.

It is also necessary to take steps to prevent even more damage occurring as a result of winter golf. Where damage has not been too severe, golfers might be requested to use tee pegs for shots off fairway. Where the sward has been badly weakened, the worst affected places should be roped off and all play and traffic diverted to the sides of the fairway and semi-rough, right through until April.

Conclusion

Seaside links will always support the fine, wiry turfgrasses that from time immemorial have provided the ideal surfaces on which to play golf. However, the basics which allowed colonisation by these grasses in the first place – the free-draining sandy infertile soils and the often harsh environment – mean that there is a fine dividing line between good and bad management. Greenkeepers must be ever vigilant for the often obscure indicators that signify the onset of dry patch or turf stress which can lead to a rapid deterioration in playing condition and ultimately turf quality.

(DFB : B.181)

SOME ASPECTS OF HEATHLAND COURSE MANAGEMENT

Preserving the natural heathland characteristics must remain one of our primary objectives. This implies the maintenance and further development of gorse, heather and the indigenous grassland, taking suitable meaures of habitat conservation to prevent the area reverting to scrub land of inferior quality.

Traditionally heaths were managed as common land where animals were free to graze, providing a heath of open landscape free of scrub and taller vegetation. Indeed, many of the early greenkeepers were known to have had four legs! However, with the exception of those courses sited on common land and still selectively grazed, man and machinery have replaced those early greenkeepers.

The characteristic of heathland golf courses has to be the beautiful splash of colour due to flowering heather during August and September, epitomised by Hankley Common Golf Club in Surrey. Unfortunately, on many courses due to competition from scrub, silver birch, Scots pine and grasses, heather has declined and positive measures are required if the trend is to be reversed (see the Ecology Section of this book). Birch scrub must be kept under control as well as competing grasses if the existing vegetation is to survive. At one course in the Midlands, areas of rough which are not in play have been cultivated to disturb the natural seed bank in the soil which has resulted in the natural recolonisation of both gorse and heather. These young plants will be maintained and transplanted around the course and will succeed the older planting which have become "leggy" and beyond regeneration.

The increase in popularity of golf and increased levels of play through 365 days has resulted in many problems with regard to localised wear and tear. Not only have we observed a decline in heather as a result, but soil erosion is also an ongoing problem. Management policies are now in place at some heathland courses to reduce trolley use through the winter in addition to the use of hoops, ropes and white lines to divert traffic around the course.

Many heathland courses are either partially or completely designated as Sites of Special Scientific Interest (SSSI) and as such the management of the course must accommodate the needs of the indigenous flora and fauna. The heathland environment is commonly dry and nutrient-poor, the sand substrate prone to leaching. The sward is naturally thin, providing a "tight lie" which is favoured by the low handicap golfer. To maintain the balance of the finer grasses, it would prove detrimental to add high levels of nutrient, which could dramatically alter the component grass species and lose the character of the heath. On impoverished soils, growth is invariably slow and mowing to maintain the sward may be minimal - do not expect lush parkland turf on a heathland course. Likewise the overuse of irrigation water would affect the balance of species within the sward. During a period of drought the turf will be expected to be dormant, leaving characteristic straw coloured fairways between the more lush-looking greens and tees. However, with the return of more favourable and wetter conditions, the indigenous drought tolerant bent and fescue species would revive.

On areas designated SSSI, the use of pesticides would undoubtedly be restricted, if it is to prove detrimental to the rare species being preserved. Always bear in mind that by applying pesticides we will be killing some beneficial life-forms as well as perceived harmful pests. Cultural practices must therefore be undertaken to reduce the potential for weed or disease activity by focusing on the development of a dense and compact sward. Invariably restrictive practices are only imposed on areas through the green, where tees and greens have been "man-made".

Too many heathland golf courses have become invaded with silver birch, Scots pine, scrub etc, which have taken away the natural open feature of the heath. As a matter of course policy, there must be a phased winter programme of sapling removal, resulting in reduced scrub development with minimal disturbance to the surface. Leaving trees to semi maturity will invariably generate criticism and complaints from members once the initiative to remove them is taken. Selective tree removal at an early stage must be introduced as a management objective so as to maintain the area in its natural heathland state.

Unfortunately one of the biggest problems facing the management of a heathland course is convincing the lobbyists and conservation groups that the invading trees and scrub are the weed elements and if the site is to be "returned to its original form", tree felling and scrub clearance is essential. In all but a few cases, however, this plain fact will fall upon deaf ears and the heathland can only continue to decline.

(ARC : B.185)

PROBLEMS OF HEAVY LAND PARKLAND GOLF COURSES

Back to Fundamentals

Good drainage is essential to successful management and on heavy parkland courses. The answer must, therefore, lie initially with reconstruction of greens, surrounds, tees and bunkers to provide a suitable depth of free draining growing medium, and an under drainage system to take the water away and better designed to shed excess surface run-off and tap sub-surface seepage. On heavy soils and low lying land it is important to raise greens, bunkers and tees above ground level to increase drainage rates, as well as contouring surrounds to deflect water away from putting surfaces.

Fairway Drainage

In respect of fairways the key to success is the installation of an integrated pipe drainage system. How often we see a piecemeal arrangement of pipe drains introduced over a number of years, with haphazard design, limited depth of installation, poor connections and low grade quality profile make-up. To achieve good surface to aggregate drainage rates, use approved sand as a growing medium over the blinding layer/aggregate and after firming each layer finish off with a skimming of top dressing mixed with fine seed to aid seedling establishment. Drain lines may stand out for a period during drought, yet this is a small price to pay for the benefits gained during prolonged wet weather.

On completion of the project the drainage system would then be evaluated over one or two winter periods with a view to assessing the subsequent requirement for localised/overall slit drainage, or just mole ploughing to aid lateral movement of water to drain lines.

The Open Ditch

On more level land with a minimal fall to the outlet, a ditch can be a very effective alternative, both as a carrier of water and as an outlet for a pipe drainage system. The ditch line can also be contoured to enhance presentation as well as providing a feature for the hole. Open drain systems should be cleaned out prior to the winter period to increase water flow.

Spread the Wear!

In respect of golf courses with existing problems, one significant weapon available to the Greenkeeper to help reduce days lost to the weather is the management technique of spreading wear. The essential items here are:-

- Adjusting the landing zone areas on fairways by changing the direction and distance from the tee.
- The provision of alternative tees away from the main areas.
- Look at alternative traffic routes through the semi-rough/rough and woodland rather than using fairways.
- Re-routing walkways taking every opportunity of changing the alternative traffic route from time to time to prevent another worn path developing.
- Regular moving of pin positions on greens, keeping away from lower lying weaker areas during wet weather and strategic positioning to alter traffic route flow on and off greens.

Trolley Ban

During a mild, wet winter there does come a point when the above factors are not enough to compensate for inadequate drainage and in such a situation the best course of action is controlled usage involving a trolley ban for a defined period. It should be appreciated by members that considerable damage can occur over a very short period of time under extreme weather conditions and the aim here is the preservation and recovery of walkways for the main playing season the following year. Indeed, in the worst cases the decision would be to leave well alone by resting the course until such time as the surfaces have dried out sufficiently for the Greenstaff to work on them again.

Catchwater Drain

On steeply sloping ground where cut and fill tees and greens are the norm, surface ponding and stagnation can often be intensified by sub-surface seepage and run-off from higher ground. This situation is best tackled through the introduction of a catchwater intercept drain around the toe of the bank, taking care to avoid pop-up irrigation supply pipes. Ensure the catchwater drain encompasses the whole of the surface run-off area and that there is a fall on the drain of no less than 1 in 200. A drain should also be connected to a positive outlet.

On a Localised Basis

Low lying moisture-retentive sections of green, surround and fairway are further trouble spots where localised aeration treatments should be given to prevent surface ponding and development of stagnant thatch. Within the management programme there is still room for localised hand forking/ hollow tining at close centres and infilling holes with approved medium/coarse sand, although mechanisation offers a quicker and more effective treatment, i.e. a soil ameliorator (locally) or the Verti-Drain (overall). Infill holes with sand for added drainage.

Where design results in major surface ponding around the perimeter of the green, the addition of a spur drain to tap the area, or a solid vertical pipe in the lowest spot connecting the surface with the aggregate, can prove very effective. The pipe can then be covered by a gauze or synthetic grass hole insert to minimise disruption to play. The diameter of the pipe can be varied according to requirement.

A Surface Problem?

High levels of play through a mild winter may well lead to compaction in the immediate soil layers and this invariably leads to surface moisture retention and, hence, exaggerates wear and tear with consequential loss of grass cover, levels and playing quality. A package of aeration treatments including hollow tining and slitting is important to open up the top 100 mm (4") as well as removing thatch, thereafter, the soil profile can be opened up further by degrees through, for instance, Verti-Draining or deep slitting. Ground conditions must be firm enough to take each unit, yet the soil moist enough to gain good tine penetration otherwise resultant damage will nullify the benefit gained.

It is absolutely essential to avoid aeration work, particularly the deeper treatments like Verti-Draining, when the soil profile is saturated to depth and during or after prolonged periods of heavy rain. If the operation is ill timed, then instead of water shedding off the surface or draining away through fissured sub-soil below, rainfall may simply fill up tine holes above the saturated base making the greens or tees like puddings. Wet surface conditions invariably lead to the cancellation of top dressing application, which only increases the speed and severity of the water retention. In such a situation the only real option is to let the surface dry out over a long period before the Greenstaff can take the necessary remedial action. The key here is timing, with the emphasis on anticipation and an earlier response. This is so important, bearing in mind high levels of play and very rapid changes in the weather which have become especially relevant over the last few years. Forewarned is forearmed.

Worm Activity

Prolonged mild, wet conditions through autumn to spring are often linked with an upsurge in earthworm activity. Very heavy worm casting in itself can create extremely muddy conditions which affect appearance, immediate surface levels, drainage, sward density and an increase in weed populations the following year. Accordingly, an early application with an approved worm killer will help to keep the surfaces relatively clean and dry, although with the strictly limited number of active ingredients left on today's market, two or three applications may well be required through autumn to spring.

Beware Poplars!

Willows and poplars in particular are often chosen for tree planting in wet areas of rough as their extensive fast growing root systems 'mop up' surplus water. Nevertheless, it is these very root systems which rapidly invade pipe drainage systems, rendering them ineffective. Accordingly, the policy must be to avoid planting these species as well as keeping tree planting right away from pipe drain lines. A detailed plan of the existing drainage systems on the course is therefore essential. Where poplars and willows exist, systematically replace with approved species.

Summary

Preventative maintenance, including attention to specialised aeration work, along with worm control and spreading wear and tear will help to alleviate problems resulting from high course usage, mild winters and extremes in weather on poorly drained parkland golf courses. However, the timing and intensity of treatment given is essential in gaining the best results.

Nevertheless, this course of action invariably only has short-term benefit and the cure lies with improved design and construction with stress laid on quality of materials used and depth of installation, as well as the provision of integrated drainage systems.

(SJO : B.184)

PROBLEMS OF HIGH ALTITUDE MOORLAND COURSES

Over the Hills

A wild moorland habitat provides a hostile environment for practical greenkeeping and there are a number of difficulties specifically associated with this distinctive type of golf course. The harsh climate and short growing season necessitate a fundamental management requirement which revolves around protecting the grass cover and not upsetting the delicate ecological balance of the site.

Tread Carefully

Developing playing quality within the confines imposed by the weather has to be a slow and cautious process, particularly with a handicap of late growth often not fully developing until June (i.e. a month behind parkland courses). Indeed, late spring and summer turf vigour are rarely strong. A compression of the playing season inevitably puts pressure on the greenkeeper to force growth and intensify treatments such as verticutting, yet this must be resisted as it inevitably leads to regression rather than development. The general aim of maintenance must therefore be to give light and less intensive treatments to take into account the limited growing season, especially in respect of mowing height, frequency of cut, fertilising and verticutting or grooming. Caution is the watchword.

Look Beyond the Golf Course

In a moorland environment many committees look to tree planting as a means of providing a wind-break, yet invariably this is at the expense of the panorama and with a gradual loss of the distinctive character associated with this type of course. Native plant species are replaced by inferior parkland alternatives and this will ultimately be reflected in poorer playing quality. The general message is therefore to preserve the vistas and ensure the natural habitat is not altered, especially as moorland ecology is very sensitive to significant changes in management.

The Importance of Top Dressing

Without doubt, the key maintenance treatment on this type of golf course must be top dressing. The use of quality approved material is ideally suited to protecting the sward in the spring and during drought, as well as improving levels and promoting recovery and development through early growth. Rock near to the surface is sometimes a problem, even on greens, and regular light dressings during the season do very gradually help to build up a significant depth of growing medium. This in turn improves growth and reduces drought stress where topsoil depth is limited.

Living in Harmony

A tie up with common land or a designated habitat of natural beauty is a frequent occurrence which leads to the golf club sharing the course with farmers and/or a body such as the National Trust. As a result, constraints are often imposed on chemical control and removal of material such as turf, which in turn puts added reliance on cultural controls and care when executing project work. For mutual gain, good relationships and regular liaison with all interested parties are so important. Friction leads to restrictions.

In addition, sheep dung or urine scald can be troublesome, especially during drought and there is an increasing problem with sheep cropping the grass tightly on greens and immediate surround. In the case of the latter, top dressing can be helpful as a form of protection and as a barrier, yet even with the addition of fertiliser at the appropriate time, there is a limit to what can be achieved. A mechanical leaf sweeper is essential for sweeping up dung, but for urine scald the application of wetting agent, in tandem with hand watering, will limit the extent of the damage resulting. In severe cases it is a question of resorting to patching using a hole cutter or proprietary unit such as the Turf Doctor. Fencing is unsightly and affects play, whilst proprietary repellents are rarely effective. In any event, these two options are often not permitted within the general terms of using the site for playing golf.

On a Windy Day

The severity of the elements is a major factor on a moorland golf course, especially wind, so it is vital that the number of bunkers is kept to a minimum, instead using mounds and natural featuring to provide the hazard for the wayward shot. Where it is desirable to choose bunkers, select sheltered areas away from the prevailing wind and ensure adequate depth is allowed for to reduce turbulence and hence loss of sand.

Spread the Wear

Even on moorland golf courses the level of play is increasing and it is therefore essential that all measures are taken to spread wear and tear through altering traffic routes (machinery and golfers). Slow growth and limited topsoil depth can exacerbate the problem and therefore, in addition to rerouting, emphasis should be placed on aeration and renovation work where concentrated areas of wear occur.

Conclusion

The general aim is to preserve the moorland habitat, work with other parties sharing the site for mutual benefit and to protect the indigenous fescue/bent turf by slow and careful management, with a very strong emphasis on top dressing.

(SJO : B.184)

WEAR AND TEAR ON THE GOLF COURSE

In combating wear and tear on the golf course, prevention is always better than cure. Within any maintenance programme there should be preventative components, marrying in with operations to prepare playing surfaces. As a result of the effects of all year round foot traffic on the turf, wear and tear problems do develop on greens, surrounds, tees and fairways which require routine renovation to ensure the course will be brought back into prime condition as soon as steady growth starts in the spring.

Winter Work
Forward Planning

A big disadvantage in golf course maintenance is that there is no close season during which routine repairs can be effected as is the case with bowls or cricket. Repairs therefore are generally carried out in a staged process during the autumn and spring, fitting in treatments to greens, tees and fairways as can best be done around the demands of play. In order to develop a balanced routine in this respect, it is often necessary, for example, to build alternative tees, to reshape surrounds, to rebuild bunkers, and to put in drains, so the number of routine repairs which need doing annually in the future will be minimised, keeping each part of the course in play as much as possible. The identification of priorities for future amendments to course layout is generally best done in winter, when a golf course will show up in its worst light. Subsequently, there is plenty of time for planning the implementation of these jobs during the following autumn. With good forward planning, amendments to the course will take a minimum of time and effort.

Bare Ground

Large areas of bare ground should be returfed. When returfing, make sure that the turf being laid will match in with the surrounding grasses. Otherwise it will stick out like the proverbial sore thumb once growth returns and it can stay that way for many years. Also, take care that the soil being brought in at the turf base is not of a fine texture, i.e. not clayey or silty. When compacted, such soils will tend to prevent free drainage.

Finally on returfing, do provide a smooth finish for good presentation and subsequent smooth mowing once the turf has established. Returfing is a lot easier if the turf has been lifted to an even thickness.

Thin Turf

Where the turf has thinned on greens, tees and fairways is usually an area where the topsoil has become severely compacted. During the winter months, when ground conditions are moist but not saturated, it is very important to frequently aerate these areas. This may well involve doubling up with deep mechanical aeration on problem areas, and, on greens, carrying out local hand forking. It is necessary to do this so that as soon as growth weather returns in the spring the turf has the opportunity to grow away quickly and reknit.

On greens, thin areas are usually found to the front, on the line to the next tee, and around prime pin sites within the putting surfaces. To help avoid extra trampling of these areas when ground conditions tend to be wet for prolonged periods (which would result in further damage to the topsoil) careful pin positioning is required. Over the winter period it is essential to use second and third choice pin sites to give well used sections of greens a rest. So, do not just use forward pin positions during the winter, place the flag right around the margin and, to a sensible extent, on slight slopes too. When applying a longer winter cut, and when damper surfaces are prevalent, the greens will tend to be slow, so a ball will not tend to run on and away from less than ideal pin sites.

It may be possible with careful flag positioning to vary the routes taken by players on and off the greens. This will help to spread wear over surround areas.

Paths and Tracks

During the winter there is often a need to deal with muddy paths on a golf course. In helping to dry these up, the choice of material to be used is important as a material which will stay where it is placed is needed but at the same time it cannot be solid. Nor can it be so hard it will damage cylinders or bottom blades of mowing machinery if some of the material spreads out over adjacent mown turf.

Ash, cockleshells and bark are first choice materials for this purpose. Whilst coarse sand can also be effective, it does tend to be expensive and more easily lost into a muddy soil. Gravel will spread out and damage mowers.

Concrete and tarmac tend to be too expensive and ugly for widespread use on a golf course. They have other drawbacks too, in that concrete will not take a spike, so can be slippery, whilst tarmac could be ripped up by spikes if it softens in hot weather.

Bunkers

Many bunkers need routine topping up with fresh sand to replace losses due to wind blow, blast and mixing in with the underlying soil. A minimum of 100 mm firmed depth of sand is required over bunker floors, which represents 10 m³ sand per 100 m² surface area. A good bunker sand is a lime free material, predominantly in the medium to coarse particle size ranges, i.e. with the majority in the size range 0.25–1.0 mm in diameter. A laboratory test will be required to determine the sand quality.

Planning for Spring

In the Office

During January and February there are usually a number of days when the weather is not fit for work on the course, which gives the opportunity for looking through catalogues and preparing for a prompt start when spring arrives. Having all the necessary materials to hand for application as soon as signs of steady growth are evident will make it possible to put a summer finish on the course as quickly as the weather and ground conditions will permit.

Top Dressing

A primary spring treatment on greens, aprons and tees will be top dressing. The purpose of top dressing on greens will be first and foremost to smooth out putting surfaces disrupted by the pitch marking and foot printing which arise due to winter play. Nevertheless, the sandy mix to be applied for this purpose must be carefully chosen, with a view to matching, or indeed improving on, the quality of the underlying topsoil too. An amount in the order of 1 kg sandy compost per 1 m² of green should be provided for this spring dressing.

Tees too will need an overall top dressing in spring as growth begins, primarily to smooth out any superficial bumpiness. However, as a secondary benefit, the compost or soil used may also protect any seed broadcast in combination with the top dressing operation, with a view to encouraging a complete sward cover.

For tees without a means of irrigation a screened sandy soil, or a less sandy mix of sand and soil than would perhaps be used on greens, will be appropriate. Having said that, where grass winter tees have to be renovated, a good sand (e.g. again a medium to coarse, lime free material) will be the more appropriate top dressing to apply, aiming for maximum surface stability during future winter play. For each tee a rate similar to, or even slightly more than, that for greens suggested above should be applied.

Reseeding

While it is usually the case that spring oversowing is not required on greens and fairways, the opposite applies to tees. On main tees, select a seeds mix for this purpose which matches in well with the grasses that make up the turf. In the majority of cases this means using a seeds mixture of fescues and bents for oversowing purposes on tees.

Fertiliser

The spring fertiliser treatment is a key operation for all fine turf areas on a golf course. The need is to promote growth by careful applications of nitrogen to achieve a rapid progression to uniformity after mowing.

Over the winter soluble nitrogen will be leached from the soil and until natural breakdown of the organic content of the soil can start up as soil temperatures rise in spring, there is little if any nitrogen available to the grass plants for the promotion of growth. So, where such applications are cost-effective (i.e. mainly on greens and tees) it is necessary to provide a stimulus to growth by applying chemicals which supply nitrogen. Ammonium sulphate is the principal fertiliser used to encourage each grass plant to grow to mowing height and to encourage tillering, so that worn areas will fill in.

It can be taken as read that each green and tee will require a dressing of fertiliser in spring, but the need for fertiliser application on fairways is minimal. The fairways as a whole receive less intensive wear than greens and tees; the height of cut is not quite as close; and there is no removal of nutrients through boxing off when mowing. All these factors coming together mean that routine overall applications of fertiliser are unnecessary in nearly every case. However, this does not mean that an application of nitrogen on local worn areas will not be appropriate.

Waiting for Warmth

Even if the best overall renovation programme has been carried out during the winter and all is in hand for a prompt start in the spring, little can be done to bring the turf into summer condition until soil temperatures start to rise. The date at which this occurs tends to vary from year to year, depending upon the passing of night frosts.

This means that getting the best effect from spring renovation calls for careful timing, and this is where experience tells in effective golf course management.

(CGC 1 : 10)

LEARNING TO LIVE WITH GOLF TRAFFIC

As the game of golf becomes more popular as a result of media exposure and the success of home grown talent, ever increasing demands are placed upon golf courses. At private clubs, memberships are increasing leading to more play and at municipal clubs up and down the country, annual figures of 70–80,000 rounds per year are not uncommon. When these levels of play are being experienced on courses designed over a hundred years ago, the extent of the problem becomes very apparent.

With increased traffic comes increased wear and tear on all aspects of the course, but problems tend to manifest themselves on tees and traffic routes first of all. Congestion due to poor or old design features often makes renovation a thankless task and some courses are experiencing a decline in standards because of this.

What can be done about this? Clearly something must be done to prevent cumulative deterioration, but it must fall upon individual golf clubs to realise they have a problem before anything can be achieved.

[1] Design

Many golf clubs in the UK were designed during the early part of the century, if not before, when the popularity of the game was dramatically lower than it is today. Small, highly contoured, tightly bunkered greens were the result with small, shaded and tiered teeing surfaces also popular. This was fine for many years but during the 1970's and 1980's as play increased, problems were encountered. Annual meadow-grass (*Poa annua*) which thrives in a thatch ridden, compacted environment took over greens, replacing the more desirable deeper-rooted bents and fescues. Worn and bare areas developed on green surrounds, and approaches often proved inappropriate with bunkering funnelling traffic. Greens and fairway areas experienced more serious compaction problems, resulting in poor drainage and unacceptable winter playing conditions. Many tees rapidly lost their grass cover together with their surface levels, due to an incessant battering on an area which was inadequately sized.

It is amazing how frequently the above scenarios are still encountered today, although many golf clubs have now been forced into recognising that their existing design must be upgraded if the condition and playability of the course is to be improved. Modern green constructions involving drainage carpets and sandy based rootzones, together with large surface areas for pin positioning are essential for success, especially on a poorly drained site. Bunkering must be challenging but at the same time allow free traffic flow and surround and approach contouring must permit

69

the use of ride-on machinery for maintenance. Modern tees must be large and flat, maximising teeing space yet minimising banking and tiering, which are difficult to maintain. The provision of separate winter tees located to change summer wear routes, and preferably landing zones on fairways also, should be the aim where space permits.

[2] Management practices

Machinery has been developed in the past 10–15 years to cope with the ever increasing problems with thatch and compaction. The regular use of hollow corers and Verti-Drains is now an annual occurrence at many clubs, in an effort to maximise the potential of the course and minimise stress, wear and drainage problems throughout the playing year.

Minimal fertilising and watering practices must also be employed in an effort to encourage the more desirable, harder-wearing bent and fescue grass species, which lead to more firm and resilient putting surfaces.

The size of a green dictates how much available pin space there is at each hole, but this must be maximised by the groundstaff utilising all possible alternatives, particularly peripheries, through the winter months. The same can be said for tees and through the playing season tee markers should be moved at least twice per week and maybe even more frequently in some cases. Routine renovation including divoting should be carried out at the same time, preferably weekly during the growing season.

Severe constraints are placed upon golf courses during the winter months, when play is often as intensive as it is during the main golfing season. The use of separate winter tees has already been mentioned and is a priority so that the main tees can be renovated and rested. To combat wear problems on other areas, alternative routings on and around greens, to and from tees and fairways are essential. Courses which introduce white lining 10–15 yards short of every green through the winter, redirecting all traffic around the edges, undoubtedly benefit even in the short-term, with better lies and run-up conditions the following year. It is not uncommon for links courses to close whole fairways for renovation, especially when ball-collecting landing zones become worn.

Many clubs have now introduced trolley restrictions during the winter months in an effort to minimise wear damage. In general, this is successful where implemented and this policy will become more and more important in the age of power caddies and ride-on carts. Both these forms of transport seem to be becoming ever popular.

Where appropriate, the introduction of paths and artificial surfaces is a good idea and the need for more of them will become apparent as years go by. Some clubs consider the introduction of paths as destroying the natural beauty of the course. I agree that there is nothing worse than a badly constructed set of paths, particularly where they comprise differing construction materials. However, it is my feeling that well-constructed paths, consistent with the environment and with each other, can add quality to, rather than detract from, a golf course. On many courses nowadays they are quite simply essential.

On 'in play' areas immediately adjacent to greens, paths cannot be considered, yet many clubs experience wear problems and thin areas. If neglected they not only look unsightly, but often provide very poor lies for a golfer who narrowly misses the putting surface. In this situation there is no option but to undertake renovation during the autumn. Reduction of traffic should be followed by rotovation through depth, incorporation of sandy material if necessary and returfing, reintroducing the area for play the following spring. Frequently aeration techniques such as Verti-Draining, hollow tining and compressed air treatments can also be considered as part of the renovation programme. The application of fertiliser, together with physical protection from top dressing, can also prove beneficial during the playing season by reducing the amount of wear experienced.

Clearly, wear on the golf course is becoming an ever increasing problem and all golf clubs must accept that measures need to be taken to counteract it. Problems are likely to get worse in the next few years and the root of the problem must be tackled if a general malaise is to be avoided.

(AJB : B.183)

ARE TROLLEY BANS REALLY NECESSARY?

Indications are that the effects of modern wide wheels on pulled golf trolleys are minimal on healthy vigorous turf, but if so why do we even have to consider the very contentious issue of trolley bans? This article discusses the effects of trolley use on course condition during the difficult winter months and provides reasoned argument why the use of trolleys may need to be restricted to help preserve the overall year round playing condition of the golf course.

Golfers nowadays expect to be able to play golf all year round. Hence the aim of course managers must be to retain a complete grass cover and playing conditions acceptable to the golfers over all the 'in play' areas of the course through the whole year. However there are several factors which conspire to make this aim difficult to achieve.

Firstly the British climate dictates that grass growth more or less ceases for about four months of the year during winter. Typically this non-growth period also coincides with the occurrence of heavy rainfall. Over several recent years there was a run of dry winters which positively encouraged golf play, but more recently the last few years have forcibly reminded us just how wet a traditional British winter can be. The modern golfer seems to play on regardless however, aided by much improved protective clothing.

Secondly, all courses now have to accept a much more intensive pattern of usage compared to 20-30 years ago and this level continues through the winter period. Indeed the amount of both recreational and competitive golf in winter now seems hardly diminished from the summer season. Consequently in recent winters agronomists and golfers have noticed an increase in the development of poor conditions in areas of high wear around many courses.

During the winter period there is little or no grass growth to repair the effects of wear and even healthy mature turf can be quickly scrubbed out under the effects of very concentrated traffic. The surface conditions can then become muddy and compacted thus preventing drainage and rutting can occur under particularly severe conditions. Once conditions have deteriorated significantly in this way golfers will avoid the poor areas and use immediately adjacent areas leading to spread of the problem. Such affected areas typically occur around greens and tees and also between greens and tees in the areas where traffic naturally tends to become somewhat more concentrated. If the damage is severe then natural repair by grass growth in the spring may not occur, since there is no remaining grass presence and the very poor playing surfaces will remain as an eyesore through the summer season unless renovation work is carried out. Hence it is always desirable to reduce or preferably prevent the development of damage. This therefore requires that wear and hence traffic is spread as widely as possible to minimise the effects on the turf.

But the spreading of wear or traffic may well come into conflict with the use of trolleys. Human nature dictates that golfers will follow the shortest line between one shot and the next, so that a golfer carrying a bag is able to move around the course relatively freely even in the green area and can even cross the putting surface while carrying without undue damage to the turf. In contrast a golfer using a trolley is more restricted in the routes that can be utilised around course features and especially near greens and tees. The result is that golfers using trolleys will all tend to use one route or at best only a very few routes. As already noted it is not necessarily the wheels of the pulled trolley that cause a problem but rather it is the effect of the associated foot traffic that results in damage when concentrated on a restricted area. Powered trolleys however can often have a direct adverse effect which is in addition to the effects of the foot traffic. Power trolleys have an extra wheel of small diameter which leads the main driving wheels and which may be subject to extra loading, leading to soil compaction. These trolleys are heavier because of the motor and battery, but most importantly the driven wheels are liable to slip under wet conditions when starting or moving uphill thus causing direct wear, smearing and damage to the turf. Power trolleys are even more limited in their potential route availability than pulled trolleys. It should be noted that buggies are an even greater potential problem in wet conditions because of their greater weight and speed when turning, so that their general use should certainly be confined to the drier months unless proper buggy paths have been constructed around the course.

When course managers and green committees come to consider the possible necessity for the development of a policy for the control of trolleys at their course they will need to take into account a number of factors which govern the potential vulnerability of the course to damage. Such factors would included:-

- The prevailing weather conditions in their locality - rainfall tends to increase when moving from East to West and as altitude increases.
- The design and layout of the course - tight courses on a limited area have less inherent options available for the spread of traffic.
- The soil type and hence the drainage potential of the course over the winter period - a links or heathland course will be much more free draining than a parkland course on a sticky clay soil.
- The degree of use that the course is likely to be subject to during the 'at risk' winter period.

Only after due consideration of all the factors will a sensible decision be possible regarding the potential damage hazard from trolley use and hence the possible necessity for a policy on trolley restrictions. However restriction of trolley use should not be considered in isolation, but only as a part of an integrated overall management strategy to contain the effects of wear by means of general course protection measures such as the use of preferred lies, separate grass tees or tee mats for winter use, preferably sited to utilise different traffic routes, temporary greens to protect frosted or saturated putting surfaces and direction of traffic away from popular routes into less vulnerable or valuable areas, not to forget of course the option of complete course closure under extreme weather conditions.

If the control of trolleys is deemed necessary then the form of the control measures will need to be decided. A complete ban on trolley use for a specific period can prove simplest since it allows no argument, but some clubs opt for a partial ban allowing the use of pulled trolleys only, or for use of trolleys depending on local day to day conditions. However the very unpredictability of this latter option can often cause problems, argument and complaint from golfers. The use of medical certificates to allow trolley use during a general ban is also problematic since many members will immediately discover a health limitation which makes their use of a trolley imperative.

A better approach must be to educate and explain to members the reasons for a trolley ban making use of photographic or other evidence to indicate the extent of the problem at their course as a result of traffic and trolley use during inappropriate conditions. If this is successful it may prove possible to operate a voluntary system for members to carry their clubs which may produce a surprisingly high uptake. This may prove more effective than the imposition of a total ban which often causes adverse reactions among members. However if the voluntary restriction proves ineffective then there may be no alternative to the compulsory restriction of trolley use.

Thus many busy clubs nowadays will conclude that the only solution to preventing undue damage to the course must be to restrict the use of trolleys during the worst winter months from the beginning of December to the beginning of March approximately. There cannot be an overall country-wide policy and individual clubs will have to work out, often by a process of trial and error over several years, the compromise that is best fitted to the long term needs of their course and their members. This requires the use of common sense, reliance on the advice of course manager and agronomist and an educational programme for the members. Once the trolley use policy has been arrived at, it should be incorporated into the club's Course Policy Document to eliminate further or future argument and so that the policing of the decision is simplified for the club's officers.

Finally, if in any doubt try to allow the needs of the course to come first - it only takes a few hours of intensive use under adverse conditions to cause significant turf damage which may take months and considerable expense to restore.

(NRWS : B.192)

GOLF COURSE WINTER POLICY : ON COURSE FOR WINTER

The Broad Canvas

During the growing season wear and tear from play is offset by a healthy sward, yet through the winter months as grass growth declines the turf becomes prone to thinning and weakening. The situation is aggravated by wetter surface conditions and an increased risk of compaction, impeded drainage and new thatch build up in the immediate surface layers. Deteriorating conditions are normally counteracted by the implementation of a year round maintenance programme and by spreading wear.

In years gone by this was sufficient to meet the desired aims, but increasing levels of play, higher standards demanded by golfers and a succession of mild winters have necessitated an additional factor coming into the equation. This involves enforced protection through resting vulnerable high wear areas such as traffic routes, landing zones and putting surface. Without the benefit of long periods of snow or bone-hard frost to depth to allow for rest and recovery, and with a cold dry April/May to handicap early development of playing quality and presentation, restricting course and trolley usage will have a very real benefit in bringing on the condition of greens, tees, traffic routes and fairways earlier around the start of the main competition season.

The use of winter greens and trolley bans are invariably unpopular with members who regard them as a malicious imposition handed down by the course manager and committee rather than for any meaningful purpose. However, the reasoning behind the declared intention **is** sound!

Many clubs put all their eggs in one basket by picking on a **single** factor as the cornerstone of the winter policy when the fundamental need is to have an integrated approach encompassing **all** aspects.

The Complete Package

Design, spreading wear, limiting course and trolley usage as specific items are dealt with in this issue under separate headings; here the accent is on combining them with maintenance to minimise wear and maximise playing quality and presentation on a year round basis. Looking at the overall picture the salient items are:

[1] *Design and construction*

Some golf course architects still think primarily in terms of aesthetics and the golfing aspect with little consideration given to traffic flow or post-constructional maintenance. Whether the reader is involved in refurbishment, reconstruction or new projects, good design and construction at the outset can play a big part in obviating the need for imposing restrictions on play or trolley usage in the future.

[2] *General management*

(a) Be prepared!

Implementation of a sound management programme in summer and autumn is vital in developing and maintaining a healthy dense sward capable of offsetting wear and tear. In this respect early autumn aeration is particularly valuable if the weather turns wet by keeping the immediate surface open, well aerated and free draining. At the same time guard against overfeeding, late applications of top dressing and raising the height or reducing the frequency of mowing too early which would significantly increase the chances of the sward being vulnerable to wear and tear, winter weather and disease (mainly fusarium).

(b) In the bleak midwinter

The principle requirements in winter are to maintain the aeration programme to keep soil conditions open and free draining, the use of turf tonics such as iron and seaweed extract to strengthen the sward, to keep a watchful eye for disease and top the sward during a mild spell when growth is apparent. In addition, spread wear through careful pin positioning, re-routing traffic and using alternative tees.

(c) Regeneration

Weather conditions in March, April and even May can fluctuate wildly, so a degree of caution has to be exercised when initiating the spring maintenance programme. One has to balance the desire to develop playing quality and presentation as early as possible, without causing short and long term damage through too intensive or frequent a treatment than weather conditions and the state of growth allow. Never-theless, in this situation early light applications of top dressing/fertiliser are very important as well as the ongoing aeration programme and being cautious about the frequency and intensity of mowing/verticutting treatments.

[3] *Restrictions*

When the above methods fail and the levels of play and adverse weather conditions lead to an increased degree of damage, then there is no option but to place restrictions on course usage, especially when weather conditions exacerbate wear, ie. frost coming out of the ground or waterlogging. In such a situation winter greens and trolley bans become a necessity.

Finally

The general winter policy for a golf course must encompass a number of factors including a year round sound maintenance package of treatments, spreading wear and restrictions on course and trolley usage. Remember that good initial design and construction go a long way in offsetting difficulties in the future.

(SJO : B.191)

TOURNAMENT PREPARATION

Organisation is the key word whether preparing for a major Championship or an important Club competition. There must be regular and effective communication between Head Greenkeeper, Committee and any overall Committee organising the event. The aim is to prepare a course with uniform conditions that are appropriate to the level of play expected.

There may be requirements from the overall organising Committee for additional size or length alteration at Championship tees, possibly alterations to bunkers, almost certainly some redefinition to tighten fairway lines, semi-rough and rough. Spectator car parking, pedestrian traffic routes through the course, and maintenance routes will all need planning in advance and marking out.

Where new tees and bunkers are involved, planning and construction may well have to start at the latest two years in advance of a major such as the 'Open'. At least one year in advance, adjustment should be made to fairway mowing lines, steps taken to encourage rough or semi-rough to grow in, and work on fairway bunkers completed.

An overall plan of the course with all the above marked on it is essential, together with checklist, timetable and progress chart.

Checklist
Greens
(1) Potentially disruptive aeration treatments such as Verti-Draining should be completed 18 months to two years in advance of a major Championship where needed. Avoid hollow coring in the spring prior to the event if possible.
(2) Top dress lightly, but frequently on three or four occasions in spring until satisfied with the smoothness of putting surfaces.
(3) Reduce any soft, thatchy build up at least a year in advance. Verticut lightly in spring prior to top dressing, and weekly with growth to within two or three days. Increase frequency of grooming to suit weather and growth.
(4) Apply a final feed ten days in advance so that growth flush is tailing off.
(5) Mow daily for several weeks in advance. Reduce the height of cut gradually over the final 14 days from 5 to 4 or 3.5 mm (bench setting) if using a triple mower. Double cut on the days of the competition, especially where using a triple mower.
(6) Avoid over-watering, aim to produce firm, true surfaces.
(7) Reserve pin positions which will be used during the event at least six weeks in advance. Allow for a balanced selection of placings over the course as a whole, e.g. six relatively hard, six moderate and six relatively easy. Anticipate walk-on and off wear patterns.
(8) Ensure that hole cutters are sharp and cut a perfectly circular hole 108 mm in diameter. The hole cup to be set 25 mm below the putting green surface. Paint the exposed soil white.

Green Surrounds
(1) Maintain surround at a height intermediate between that of putting green and fairway. Mow once or twice a week according to growth in the months prior to the tournament, every day during the event.
(2) Mow collars and aprons twice a week in the month beforehand, boxing off clippings. Verticut lightly, the last treatment being completed 10 to 14 days before the event.

Tees
(1) Top dress with appropriate sandy mixture to provide firm, true and level surfaces.
(2) Adjust use of water to maintain some growth, yet provide a firm stance.

(3) Reduce thatch and eliminate moss over the prior 12 months, especially on little used Championship tees.

(4) Reserve areas of Medal/Championship tees, protect a good part of par 3 tees during any practice days.

(5) During the event mow daily at need, boxing off cuttings.

Fairways

(1) Establish required fairway outlines a year in advance, especially on slow growing links.

(2) Carry out aeration, supplementary watering, renovation and weed control at need during the prior 12 months to provide a uniform and complete grass cover with finer, hardy bents and fescues predominating.

(3) In the run up to a major Championship there is some merit in protecting major landing zones, especially a short iron shot to the green during the prior winter and early spring. Divot repairs should be carried out daily during the tournament.

(4) Reduce height of cut to predetermined level through spring, mow daily during the competition.

(5) Eliminate spongy thatch during previous growing season(s). Light raking or brushing in the spring can be useful to reduce any soft, fluffy thatch.

Rough

(1) Establish required line of semi-rough and rough one year in advance and fertilize if necessary on infertile or very sandy soil to encourage adequate growth.

(2) Control weeds, particularly clover.

(3) Reduce heavy thatch or nap in semi-rough with verticuts or flail scarifiers a year in advance.

(4) Mow at designated heights for Championship at least a year in advance.

Bunkers

(1) Complete all major reconstruction and/or repairs to fairway bunkers two winters in advance. Finalise greenside bunker repair or rebuilding faces the winter before.

(2) Replenish sand, and top dress to provide 100 mm depth minimum over floor area and a skim up faces six months in advance.

Additional Points

(1) Decide on flag colour and that of flag sticks, purchase requirements and spares.

(2) Provide (coloured) boundary stakes, spray paint for definition of hazard boundaries, ground under repair.

(3) Arrange additional manpower for tidy-up jobs, emptying litter baskets, etc.

(4) Arrange back-up/loan of mowing equipment, water removal units. Locate source of mobile pumps for emergency use.

(5) Erect additional bridges as necessary at burns and ditches.

(6) Provide short range radio communication for key staff members.

(7) Arrange for care of greens and bunkers during play.

(8) Co-operate with installers of broadcasting equipment, hospitality tents, stands, temporary car parks and routes.

(9) Check provision of tables, chairs and public address system for awards.

(10) Install traffic route post and rope markers a week before, check daily during the competition.

(CGC 1 : 13)

DIVOT REPAIRS ON TEES AND FAIRWAYS (INCLUDING PITCH MARKS)

Damage on the golf course from the taking of divots is inevitable but if the size of the divots is excessive it very likely reflects on the condition of the turf. Smaller divots are taken on a firmer surface compared to ones taken on a soft thatchy surface for the same club and stroke. Similarly the natural recovery of the turf is far better and there is less cumulative disruption to the surface with shallow divots.

Fairways

Prevention is better than cure and this is true for divot damage. This is a topic in itself. Suffice to say the cultivation of an appropriate turf surface without excessive thatch and with good root and/or rhizome development is an essential element of preventive management. In addition sufficient turf vigour appropriate to the situation must be cultivated in order to maximise the capacity of the turf to recover from the scuffing or divot damage produced by the club. Many factors need to be considered in this context such as the shading over tees or the height of cut for mowing on fairways, the soil nutrients status and irrigation. The other essential element is the way in which wear is spread over the course. The section below on tee repair covers controlling wear on the tee. Similarly, well-positioned winter tees will result in different pitching areas from winter to summer on the fairways.

With our courses under such pressure from high numbers of golf rounds the golfer must be educated to look after his or her course. Club seminars are a useful means of communicating the value of good golf etiquette in keeping the course in condition and helping to reduce repair work. Divots replaced carefully, i.e. as taken and firmed in place will be far more likely to "take" than those replaced later. If this is done roots do not die back and moisture at the cut surfaces is retained encouraging new root development quickly. On the fairway the more fibrous nature of some turf makes it essential that the divot is replaced immediately to reduce the chances of it drying out. Unfortunately when a divot is conscientiously replaced the good deed is often undone by our inquisitive or hungry feathered friends.

On the fairways replaced divots are far more susceptible to drying out if the turf is at all fibrous. Usually the mower reduces failed divots to a mulch but in periods when mowing is less frequent these should be picked up as an accumulation shows poor presentation and gives an unfair surface in prime pitching zones. If warranted the clearing can be done using a leaf sweeper or a flail type scarifier/mower with a collection facility.

Tees

On the tees, replacement of divots when taken is less successful in many cases due to the level of repeated damage on one area. Here some clubs do find success with the provision of bins or tubs containing a mixture of top dressing and grass seed at the par 3 tees at least. It is important for success that the mixture is kept dry and there is scope to ensure there is a means to use the material! This provision is especially of value where tees have irrigation to ensure the grass seed has the best chance of establishing during the busy summer months. Without or with divot bins the worn areas on tees must be repaired frequently preferably as markers are moved to maximise the period of recovery. Generous top dressing and careful luting of the dressing with a wide lute will help to ensure an even surface is maintained and the levels over the whole tee are not allowed to deteriorate.

Even if old divots are collected the value of divot filling is very much underestimated. It should be a continual process when there is moisture about even where the turf vigour is good. It is unfair to expect nature to 'make good' year after year and weaknesses will very likely show up in prolonged dry weather or in winter. Use of a sandy mixture of equal parts of loam and sand is adequate on clay and loam soils. However, it is necessary to be more selective on heathland and links courses where the topsoil is thin and free draining. Here a word of caution. Since this is perceived as a low priority job it is a temptation to use the cheapest materials which are available locally. The use of a sand containing lime is going to encourage worm casting which will prove both costly to correct and at worst ruin a previously dry, clean winter fairway. On lighter soils and where the grass swards are dominated by the fine leaved species use of a sandy loam is likely to be most appropriate or use a mixture simulating this. Soils dominated by fine clay and silt particles used repeatedly in localised areas will spoil the free draining characteristics of such quality fairways. Similarly the use of the wrong materials will change the dominant species in the sward.

Choice of Grass Seed

The choice of grass seed used for repair work on the tee is dependant on the par of the hole, the size of the tee and the nature of the course. Where the swards comprise a mixture of fescues and native grasses do keep to these grasses. In contrast on smaller tees particularly at par 3 holes which cannot be enlarged it is questionable whether any grass other than the better cultivars of turf type perennial ryegrass can establish quickly enough to contribute to the grass cover before the area is once again in play, let alone to have a chance of withstanding the hammering of the club head to regrow!

Choice of a grass seed mixture should reflect the species composition of the swards present. Use the *STRI Turfgrass Seed* booklet to check the ratings of different cultivars, bearing in mind that the importance of disease resistance is of more importance than other criteria which are applied when making a choice for intensively managed areas.

Whilst divot filling is usually seen as a chore, a positive approach to implement an appropriately intensive programme using the right materials is a very effective way of improving weaker fairway swards without resorting to the use of fertilisers. The work does need to be done every couple of weeks between the extremities of the growing season if real improvements to the quality and density of the grass sward are to be achieved.

To effect such a programme is usually easier if part-time helpers carry out this as a sole, or one of a few specific, tasks, although those more fortunate may be able to accommodate such a programme in the routine maintenance programme! On many courses divot repair work is unfortunately not seen as a positive useful job and has to be undertaken by members or juniors who have been bribed or press-ganged into service! Not the best way to get a good job done and likely to be an infrequent occurrence. On most courses divoting is seldom done sufficiently.

Pitch Marks

Another source of damage is the pitching of the golf ball especially from iron shots or elevated tees. Whilst the damage is more evident on the green and apron it should not be ignored on the fairway. A conscientious programme of divot filling will address this. On the greens however, the onus is, and must be, on the golfer. Even when the greens staff rectify the worst marks in the early morning work some areas look like a moonscape by mid afternoon! Since most golfers are happy to complain if their ball falls foul of an unfair hazard, who are the golfers who leave pitch marks (including the one next to their own) without lifting them? One supposes in a similar vein we all claim to be good car drivers – accidents are always someone else's fault!

On some greens due to the elevation of the approach shot or tee height, there is extreme damage on the putting surface. Clearly the damage will reflect the condition of the turf in that a soft thatchy surface will plug deeply and in this case corrective work to reduce the thatch is essential. Light dustings of a very sandy top dressing are a great help in maintaining an even surface and producing a firmer surface as will use of a pedestrian mower. In either case do lift out the plug marks before the work.

If the conditions are to be produced from which quality golfing surfaces are to be prepared conscientious repair of the damage from club and ball is essential. Also, golfers must be educated during seminars and through the golfing media to respect and care for the surfaces for the benefit of those who are teeing off behind them.

(PCW : B.189)

COMPACT TRACTORS

An acceptable definition of a compact tractor would be those machines with a horse power rating of below, say, 26 (DIN). They were originally developed to meet the requirements for a small, economical to run power unit on Japanese farms which only average 1.6 hectares.

UK distributors soon realised the potential for compact tractors in a wide range of applications, particularly on amenity turf areas such as golf courses. Nearly all compact tractors are still manufactured in Japan and include the now household names of Iseki, Kubota, Hinimota and Yanmar, together with those machines which masquerade under Anglo-Saxon names such as Ford or Massey Ferguson. Also, the American compact tractor, the John Deere, has a Japanese engine.

What Are the Advantages?

One of the major advantages of the compact tractor is its extreme versatility. To complement the extensive range of attachments which have been specifically designed for use with compact tractors it is possible to fit implements from other maintenance systems. For example, the Sisis Hydromain implements can be attached directly to the tractor 3-point linkage or adapted for use with a compact tractor by means of a special mounting frame which allows downward pressure to be applied to the implements through the hydraulic system. In addition, the tractor must be fitted with an auxiliary spool valve of the doubt-acting type.

Many Golf Clubs have realised the potential applications of the compact tractor and have purchased a suitable power unit to fulfil a variety of functions around the course. The high power to weight ratio means that a set of three gangs can be towed with relative ease (or driven off the tractor's PTO) yet the tractor can still be used on the vulnerable putting surfaces with safety due to advances in low ground pressure tyre technology.

The more powerful compact tractors can pull five gang units, although it is important not to over-burden the tractor as this will result in a reduction of its effective working life span.

The high ground clearance of the compact tractors enables mid-mounted rotary mowers to be fitted or the option of front or rear mounting of a range of flail or rotary mowers is available for specific models. Fully mounted, hydrostatic-driven mowers have also been developed for grass areas where a higher quality finish is required. This offers the advantage of a purpose-built, self-propelled machine with the bonus of out of season availability of the 'prime-mover' for other work.

Routine turf maintenance operations such as spiking, scarifying, spraying and top dressing can easily be accomplished on golf greens, tees and other fine turf areas by attachment of the appropriate implement. The compact tractor can easily exert sufficient pulling power for carrying out such operations as mini mole ploughing of greens, tees and approaches – which are particularly susceptible to soil compaction. In addition, modern compact tractors have the necessary hydraulic muscle to operate loaders, excavators and similar equipment. Therefore, drainage work can be accomplished, tees can be built, bunkers dug and ditches cleared without the need to hire suitable equipment. Various cultivation operations can be carried out both quickly and efficiently. A special advantage of the compact tractor is that it can accomplish the above functions in areas which may be inaccessible to standard machines while minimising turf wear and damage to the underlying soil structure on peripheral areas or the main traffic routes to and from the site of work.

Safety Must Have Priority

Safety should not be neglected in the interests of economy and a roll bar should be fitted to a compact tractor, particularly if it is to be used on sloping ground, to reduce the risk of the operator being injured in the case of an accident.

Desirable Features

Selection of a suitable compact tractor will depend to a large extent on its intended range of functions. Therefore, certain features may be considered to be of greater importance than others.

Four-wheel drive is highly desirable as this feature will improve traction as well as offering the benefits of a smoother ride and better balance on any ground contours in either muddy or wet conditions. Indeed, four-wheel drive is a prerequisite when using implements which require downward pressure – exerted through a double-acting back ram – to operate efficiently, as this will reduce traction through the rear wheels.

Hydrostatic transmission provides an infinite number of speeds within a defined range so that the pace of the compact tractor can be precisely tailored to implement activity. At very low creep speeds trenching is facilitated.

Direct comparison with integrated maintenance systems such as those produced by Cushman and Sisis or even the larger types of tractor is tempting, although impractical since the role of the compact tractor overlaps into each of these two categories, as well as performing specific functions of its own.

Not a Replacement for a Larger Tractor

Larger tractors, in both horse power and size, take up considerably more room in the shed and cannot manoeuvre or negotiate narrow paths with the same ease as compact tractors. However, they are particularly useful workhorses for carrying out operations such as routine mowing or deep spiking of fairways. Therefore, a compact tractor should not be seen as a replacement for the larger tractor (with a rating of between, say, 35–40 h.p.) but as a complementary unit. Work in the rough and peripheral areas of the course with difficult access or restrictions imposed on manoeuvrability are not 'out of bounds' for the compact tractor if rotary mowing, hedge trimming, post hole boring or cutting back of under-growth is necessary.

Reduced Running Costs

An important consideration which favours the compact tractor is the reduced running costs when compared with their big brothers. In particular, the new breed of highly efficient diesel engines give much improved fuel economy and reduce maintenance costs when fitted to compact tractors.

In summary, compact tractors have the capability of performing a vast range of difficult jobs in combination with a formidable array of compatible implements. This versatility, combined with economy, has been the major factor responsible for establishing a niche for compact tractors on golf courses. **(CGC 1 : 101)**

TURF NURSERIES : THEIR CONSTRUCTION AND MAINTENANCE

A turf nursery is a facility which all golf clubs should possess provided that adequate space is available. With the increased demand for golf and the increased use of many golf courses, the demand for good quality turf for renovation purposes is high. In addition, some clubs are slowly realising that the greens and tees they have are inadequately constructed and/or inadequately sized and as a result cannot cope with modern golfing demands. As a consequence, they are declining in condition and can sometimes only provide good golfing conditions for 6 to 8 months of the year. Reconstruction and enlargement is often the only option and having an adequate supply of good quality, indigenous turf from a well-constructed turf nursery will:-

(1) Minimise layering problems in the soil profile.
(2) Maximise turf establishment, thereby providing a playable surface more quickly.
(3) Exhibit improved wear tolerance upon exposure to play.

Situation and Construction

The first stage in the construction of a turf nursery is to select a convenient location. Ideally, the site should be at least 600 m^2 in size, relatively flat and well-drained. In addition, it should be conveniently located near to the maintenance sheds with easy access and have irrigation provided.

Provided a reasonably well-drained area is chosen, there should be no need to install pipe drainage and gravel carpets etc., but there is a need for a substantial depth of good quality rootzone mix upon which to develop the turf. Initially, therefore, turf and topsoil should be stripped from the designated area with the topsoil being used for another purpose and the turf, dependent upon its condition, discarded. Then a minimum firm depth of 150 mm, good quality rootzone mix should be placed on a firmed, sub-surface formation level, to provide finished levels. Upon a prepared finished surface to which a pre-seeding fertiliser has been applied, seeding should take place. A good quality Chewings fescue/browntop bent seeds mixture should be used at a rate of approximately 35 g/m^2 (1 oz/yd^2).

It is sometimes feasible if the soil type and grass composition are suitable to develop a turf nursery from an existing turf area. Provided the area in question is relatively level it can be scarified and top dressed to improve surface levels, thereby permitting closer mowing. At the same time, the topsoil will be gradually ameliorated with top dressing material improving drainage potential and growing conditions. It should be possible to develop a nursery in 6-12 months with the correct maintenance regime.

Maintenance

The majority of the turf nursery should be given over to green and surround standard turf, although there is no reason why a designated area cannot be set aside for tee standard turf. Following construction and sowing the nursery should be maintained as an immature green or tee, ensuring that fertiliser, irrigation, scarification, top dressing and mowing requirements are met and then integrating verticutting and aeration into the maintenance programme as necessary. Control measures against disease, weeds and earthworms should be carried out as appropriate.

In the case of an average turf nursery the turf is not usually strong enough to be lifted and used for patching or reconstruction work until it is two years old. Younger turf is often used in commercial practice. Allowing the turf a little longer to develop prior to use should ensure better wear tolerance *in situ*. Once removed, the turf should be cut relatively thinly, i.e. to 12-15 mm using a turf cutter. As the turf is removed from the nursery, gaps should be filled with rootzone mix prior to resowing with the appropriate seeds mixture.

The merits of having a turf nursery are self-explanatory and if space is available, all golf clubs should consider developing one, especially in view of the likely demands on the golf course in the years to come.

(AJB : B.187)

MAKING YOUR OWN COMPOST

There has always been some scope for confusion when lay people on a green committee are first confronted with the term composting or compost dressings for greens. They have visions of either the brown, crumbly, thoroughly decomposed product that gardeners are wont to enthuse about – digging their hands into the stuff and raising to the nostrils to admire the bouquet, frequently with the remark "almost good enough to eat" thrown in for good measure. Contrast this with the often wet, coarse, slimy material which resides in the suburban compost heap and which one would, with some justification, shudder at the very thought of putting anywhere near golf greens.

Many strands of horticulture and turf culture are closely related and it comes down to a more precise definition of terms. Whilst "compost" production has been, and in a few cases still is, a regular practice on golf courses, with the aim of producing material akin to that known and loved by gardeners, it is never, ever used on turf as a dressing on its own.

Nutrient Value

Historically, compost was deliberately made rich and to contain a good proportion of nutrients from sources such as farmyard manure, poultry droppings, leaf mould as well as the usual grass clippings and other coarser vegetation, in fact anything that would eventually rot down, together with thin layers of soil. When fully broken down the material was mixed with a proportion of sand, varying from 50-60%. It was used in light, but frequent applications from spring right through the growing season to supplement fertiliser applied from a bag. The latter was often sulphate of ammonia with calcined sulphate of iron and used as much for moss and weed control as its feeding value. This was fiery stuff, prone to burn turf and confined to application in damp spring weather or when it was actually raining in summer, since irrigation in those days was more often a pipe dream for most head greenkeepers than a reality. Such a system worked very well. The mild compost feeding, low in nutrients anyway, suited the finer grass species and there was no risk of scorching. The hotter sulphate of ammonia based fertilisers were used in spring when supplementary nitrogen was needed and for early moss and weed control – in those days there were no selective herbicides.

The compost top dressing could be made too rich, especially when the base compost included quantities of bullock-yard or stable manure, or after the war, dried sewage from treatment plants. Heavy and particularly late top dressings following autumn aeration could often trigger severe disease outbreak.

Nowadays, the nutritional value of top dressing is of low priority although the organic content and soil, together with the right type of sand, can still give us an ideal material for top dressing golf greens, to maintain that resiliency of turf surface and trueness which are the hall marks of good putting surfaces. Sand alone rarely does this and there is always the danger of root breaks developing, particularly where a coarser particle size sand is used with a view to helping improve drainage.

Preparation

There is a good deal to be said for a golf club producing its own compost for dilution with sand and ultimate use on greens and tees as well as for divot repair where needed. Home-produced material, especially where the local topsoil is available in sufficient quantities and good enough for use on greens, does ensure a good match when diluted with sand with the natural topsoil, for the vast majority of golf greens were built with soil found on site.

This aspect is particularly important with seaside links courses, where often the soil element can be kept very low indeed and in that situation a mixture of rotted seaweed, grass, vegetation, a little soil and sand are built as heaps to gradually rot down before final preparation, with yet more sand to achieve the very sandy, finely-blended material needed for top dressing.

Building a compost heap requires a relatively dry, free-draining site, especially these days when the materials used will be handled with a tractor and front loader. The chosen site should be convenient to the course maintenance buildings and for preference there should also be a simple roofed structure – a lean-to, open on three sides, into which well-decomposed material can be stacked for final drying before processing and mixing with sand.

Building the Heap

Construct the heap with alternating layers of organic material and sandy loam topsoil. The organic element can comprise partially rotted leaf mould, grass clippings (which is an excellent way of recycling the large quantity of vegetable matter arising from this source), along with coarser grass, even stable or farmyard manure provided you are prepared to wait until all components have fully decomposed. Spread the material about 150 mm thick and cover with a thinner layer of topsoil. Repeat until the heap is complete and built up to a convenient working height, capping it off with soil.

The heat generated within the stack, especially if coarser vegetation has been included, will provide for at least partial sterilisation, usually enough to see off most, if not all, weed seeds and fungal spores.

It helps to turn the heap after 12 months to incorporate the sides into the centre and ensure more uniform breakdown, but this is not essential. Often the heaps are merely built in sequence, one each year and the 2 or 3 year old stack is opened for current use.

Initial Preparation

Once the organic material in the compost heap has decomposed nicely, it can be chopped down with spades or a fore-end loader during the late summer and loaded into a loose stack, preferably under cover, e.g. an open sided lean-to, allowing wind and air movement to dry the material further to an easy working, friable condition.

From this stage, pass the now fairly dry compost through a soil shredder or processor to break it down even more finely and at the same time help remove stones or coarser un-decomposed material. This finer product should now go indoors where it must be kept dry.

Final Preparation

Although by now well dried out, the friable and crumbly material is certainly not yet ready for application to turf. It must go through a further stage, which perhaps is the most crucial in making it suitable for use on golf greens.

For fine turf areas which are expected to be in use virtually 365 days a year barring frost or snow, maintenance of good drainage or where necessary, improvements to the draining properties of the growing medium on greens is all important. This means our compost has to be well-diluted with sand (and a carefully chosen sand at that) to provide the right textural characteristics for the drainage requirement.

The sand used must have a fairly uniform particle size range, basically between 0.2 mm and 0.7 mm for fine turf areas on inland type soils and it should be lime-free. On the links a finer type of "wind-blown" sand is acceptable since this will more readily match the naturally occurring, finer sandy soils on links. Here lime in the form of shell fragments is often present and in this situation is acceptable.

The amount of sand to incorporate with the compost will depend entirely on the quality of the soil used in building up the heaps and its particle size distribution. We want an end product which will improve, or at the very least match the existing soil, even as it provides additional organic matter arising from the normal growing cycle of grass plants, i.e. dead roots, stems and leaves. The top dressing compost will usually be sandier than the existing growing medium, with never less than three parts of suitable sand to one of screened compost and often four parts of sand or more are required. The ultimate criterion has to be the mechanical analysis of the end product which should contain less than 20% fines (i.e. those particles below 0.125 mm), less than 10% silt and clay particles and have between 1% and 3% organic matter. The appropriate quantity of sand can be added before or after the final screening of the compost, although passing both materials through the screen helps with mixing. The material is now ready for use and should be stored dry until conditions on greens permit application and working in. Its preparation provides a most useful under-cover job for staff during inclement periods in the winter.

To do the job properly, the first essential is to have available the right sort of materials of consistent quality. It is necessary to invest in appropriate handling equipment, including tractor front-loaders, soil processors, screens etc. as well as having available sufficient storage accommodation for the final screened product. Home-produced compost, provided it is consistent year by year, can be at least as good as, if not cheaper than, bought-in material. At the very least you have the option of producing sufficient material to meet full requirements rather than having to limit dressings because of financial considerations. Unfortunately, nowadays the sheer difficulty in obtaining suitable supplies of topsoil has led to a decline in the practice of building compost heaps and thereby recycling things like grass clippings, although the current vogue for recycling as much as possible may reverse this trend in the future.

Certainly, whatever top dressing product you use on golf greens, it is vital to ensure that the material is consistent year by year so that you build up a uniform and free-draining upper soil profile.

(DFB : B.187)

WHY AERATE?

The Basics of Life

Golf greenkeeping has become a high-tech business but the very basic essentials for grass growth have never changed. Sunlight, water and air are the three factors essential for the growth of all plant life. Although we can improve accessibility to sunlight in shaded situations, we are not able to regulate the number or quality of sunlight hours during the day but there is a single management operation that directly influences the availability and quality of the latter two factors. That operation is aeration. Other maintenance procedures may improve the quantity and quality of the grass cover and playing surface, e.g. feeding, mowing and top dressing, but aeration is the key to producing the foundation upon which additional treatments can work. Ask any greenkeeper or knowledgeable golfer "why aerate?" and the first answer will probably be to improve drainage. Whilst this may be a primary reason, aeration also helps create the general environment essential for healthy grass growth.

The Growing Medium, Air and Water

Soil is the growing medium. This is not the absolute truth. Whilst the soil provides physical support and anchorage, grasses actually grow in the spaces between soil particles. Roots grow down through air pores and drainage is, essentially, water movement through air spaces. Healthy soils have an inherent balance between air space, water content and the physical soil component. Ideally, there should be an even proportion of air to water in the pore space between the solid soil particles. This balance is disrupted by compacting forces brought about by play and maintenance. Under compaction the air spaces within the soil become compressed and this depresses drainage rates and the ability of the plant to extend its root system. If air occupies less than 10-15% of total soil volume there are likely to be problems of poor soil aeration. Adequate air volume is one thing, but there must also be a good circulation of air so that the soil air does not become "stale".

Grasses need water for life. Water is not only an integral requirement for life in it's own right but acts as the carrier for nutrients, i.e. the plant's food supply. Water is held in soils by clay and organic fractions, hence the slow drying of soils with a high content of either. Water uptake into roots is an active process, termed osmosis, and the ability of plants to extract water is affected by soil type. Soils which tend to hold large amounts, e.g. clays, retain it with great tenacity and plants have to exert tremendous forces to obtain it. In sandy soils water is lost far more readily via gravity and evaporation but water is, generally, more accessible to the roots. Plants can tap water from sands at much lower soil water contents than is possible from loams and clays. Effective uptake of water and nutrient by a plants roots is, therefore, dependent on the flow rate of water through the soil and this is directly related to the volume, and size, of air space. Water saturation of a soil is not good news for turf as the anaerobic condition that ensue causes stagnation and a most inhospitable environment for growth.

Other Life in the Soil

Plants do not grow in isolation. There is a vast array of other life forms in a soil, from microscopic fungi and bacteria to invertebrates such as worms. Many of these have a working relationship with the grass, for example, the presence of microorganisms has a positive effect on soil fertility by their influence on the decomposition of organic material, e.g. thatch. All soil life is affected by changes in the soil air to water ratio as is grass growth. Microbial activity is suppressed in anaerobic conditions and is controlled by the availability of moisture. Worm casting may increase in wet conditions and worms require soil moisture to prevent them from desiccating, they are also adversely affected by waterlogging of soils in addition to being driven to the deeper regions of the soil profile during very dry periods.

So Why Aerate?

The processes described above are far more complex than outlined here but, hopefully, this much simplified glimpse at life processes within the soil will, without further explanation, answer the question "why aerate?" It is worth emphasising certain points which have a bearing on year round turf condition and the beneficial results of the entire management programme.

Drainage is a vital aspect of good turf management, not only from the viewpoint of keeping golf courses open through wet periods but also in enhancing free movement of water through the soil profile all year round. This will keep nutrients in circulation and increase the effectiveness of summer irrigation. Aeration relieves compaction and improves water penetration into and through the soil. Autumn and winter aeration treatment are obviously beneficial to promoting drier surfaces capable of taking play.

Spring aeration may also be accepted as a means of relieving compaction from winter use. It is, unfortunately, rare that routine aeration is considered as a summer operation. Compaction is a constant factor whenever there is play and the need to irrigate through a dry summer can add to stress rather than decrease it if the water applied is retained near the surface. Shallow rooting can result, favouring annual meadow-grass and a growing reliance on irrigation.

Root development is limited by water and nutrient availability and also by the physical reduction of air space through compaction. Aeration increases, or should we say restores, the air: water: soil particle ratio and, hence, improves conditions for root extension. Although root growth peaks spring and autumn, aeration through the rest of the year is equally important to encourage new root.

Aeration as Part of an Integrated Maintenance Regime

So, aeration helps sustain the backbone of the growing medium by retaining the proportion of air within the soil through compaction relief. Aeration maintains the supply of fresh air and water to the plants roots, a vital function for healthy growth and the life-support mechanisms of many metabolic processes that are carried out in a plant, e.g. photosynthesis. Aeration prevents the concentration of carbon dioxide and other gases in the soil from reaching toxic levels. In waterlogged conditions, nitrous oxide, sulphurous gases and methane may be produced by micro-organisms, poisoning grass roots. Aeration promotes healthy growing conditions not only for the turf but also for the soil microflora which have a direct influence on the "fitness" of the soil as a growing medium.

Aeration contributes to drier playing surfaces directly and, to a degree, indirectly by producing the conditions for absorption and amelioration of top dressings. Specific forms of aeration, e.g. hollow coring, serve a basic purpose in allowing soil exchange where poor soils are partially replaced by better draining mixes of soil and sand. As a consequence, aeration has an influence on the quality of any turf but also an influence on the make-up of turf by helping produce the growing environment that favours bent and fescue grasses at the expense of annual meadow-grass.

Aeration aids the penetration of irrigation thereby enhancing deeper root structure and nutrient uptake. Aeration increases the drought and wear tolerance of turf. Conventional forms of aeration, e.g. solid tining, serve this purpose well. The relatively new development of the HydroJect, which injects water into the soil under pressure, gives extra weight to this benefit from aeration.

Aeration can reduce the susceptibility of turf to disease by helping regulate environmental conditions that favour pathogens such as fusarium patch and take-all patch.

Aeration should not be seen as a treatment in isolation. As part of a sound maintenance package it can produce all of the benefits outlined, enhancing the performance of many other components of management policy. There is hardly an area of golf turf maintenance that is not affected by the nature of the aeration regime, aeration is that important. Like everything else, aeration can be overdone but there is far more danger to turf quality in under-achieving in so far as aeration is concerned. So, the next time you see the greenkeeper aerating any part of the golf course remember that it is for the good of the turf and, hence, the good of the golfer. Aeration should be seen as a positive measure, not merely as a disruption to putting surfaces.

(SPI : B.189)

AERATION – BEYOND THE BASICS

Introduction

The increasing level of play on golf courses throughout the year requires constant attention to alleviate compaction and the ills it fosters; impeded drainage, thatch, stagnation and poor root development. Aeration is the means of combating compaction and a conventional programme involves winter slitting and summer solid, shallow slit or chisel tining, backed up by the occasional intensive treatment to relieve severe problems. Carrying out aeration practices which can disrupt the smoothness of a green is a cause of debate within Clubs, particularly during the months of greatest competitive golfing activity, i.e. April-October. As a consequence there is a move to less disruptive aeration treatments but these must prove effective if the ravages of play are to be countered. Looking beyond the basics of slitting and solid tining, what aeration methods are available, how effective are they and what can be done to minimise interference for those playing the game?

Verti-Drain

Despite technical advances in other aeration methods, Verti-Draining remains the most valuable form of deep-seated compaction relief. Verti-Draining can create most disruption where rooting is poorly developed, often the exact condition where maximum benefit may be attained. For an initial operation setting the machine properly should minimise damage; employing a pressure roller behind the tines, working short of the maximum possible depth, using worn tines and minimal, if any, lift. Of utmost importance is regulation of travelling speed and ensuring perpendicular penetration and removal of tines. It should be safe to work deeper with greater heave during subsequent passes.

Timing of the treatment becomes ever more critical as the soil to site becomes heavier. Due to the demand on golf courses Verti-Draining is often delayed to October-November when Verti-Draining a wet clay soil is likely to promote a smeared tine hole which will hold water and reduce effective drainage, the hole closing over rapidly at the surface from the effects of play. For such a site an operation in late summer-early autumn when the soil is just moist is essential to achieve fissuring of the soil and must be followed by top dressing to retain porosity at the surface. Remember too that recovery from the treatment will proceed much faster if completed when there is still vigorous growth. Top dressing is desirable following Verti-Draining but if site conditions permit a late treatment, more acceptable to the golfing fraternity, then delay top dressing until the spring. Autumn treatment on most sites is best, giving the greatest likelihood of suitable soil con-ditions for effective fissuring, improving drainage going into the winter and any disruption from the procedure is likely to be more acceptable pre-winter than immediately before the start of the main competition season.

Spring Verti-Draining may promote stronger root extension and relieve winter compaction but poses greater dangers, being less sure of ground conditions and increasing the likelihood of surface disruption going into the summer competition season both from the operation itself and if it turns dry the tine holes can remain exposed for some time. Fairway treatment is often the exception to this rule, it make take a winter to soften the ground to achieve a reasonable depth of penetration. Verti-Draining may be necessary annually on greens, alternatively it may only be needed on an ad hoc basis, perhaps looking to treat individual "problem" greens more often. Routine treatment elsewhere on the course will not go amiss, particularly where traffic is concentrated. Regular Verti-Draining has now extended to approaches, tees and fairways and the cost of hiring a Verti-Drain has led many Clubs to buy their own machine, allowing more frequent use around the course and the ability to time each operation when ground conditions are most suited. Hollow tines are available but the primary value from Verti-Draining is heave, and this is only attainable with solid tines. A dappled appearance can result in the months following Verti-Draining, stronger rooting and top growth through tine holes providing a positive visual advertisement for aeration, if disruptive to smoothness in the short term. (Note that the general term "Verti-Drain" is now applied to a number of competing models of the same basic sub-aerator.)

Hollow Tine

Hollow tining is nothing new but does seem to come in and out of favour. Reasons for hollow tining include: a means of thatch removal, soil exchange and relief of compaction near the surface, though there are now machines capable of working effectively to 150 mm. Although never out of favour at the Institute, hollow tining as an integral part of aeration programmes, beyond the conventional "once every three year" dictate, is a consequence of the dramatic increase in play seen at most golf courses. The frequency of hollow tining necessary on greens is related to the level of play at a golf course. Care needs to be taken as too frequent hollow tining can lead to soft surfaces. Hollow tining in combination with Verti-Draining is becoming common practice. If working to such a system the hollow tining should be completed in the autumn a month or so before Verti-Draining or it can be delayed to the spring to alleviate compaction following the winter's play.

The advent of ride-on and tractor-mounted equipment has extended the benefit of hollow tining out to surrounds, tees and even fairways. New golf course construction projects have brought about a further outlet for hollow tining where greens have been turfed, importing soil which is foreign to that used for the growing medium. This can lead to capping and to a longer-term rootbreak so hollow tining is often employed in the first couple of years after laying to exchange the soil imported with the turf for a dressing compatible with the growing medium. Disturbance from hollow tining can be minimised, if removing thatch or foreign soil imported with turf which lie less than 50 mm from the turf base, by using mini-tines as there is little point to taking out cores to greater depth, removing good top dressing applied through past years in the process. Mini-tines are also useful for overseeding and more frequent treatment, including summer work, if thatch or other surface impediment poses a real problem. For very thatchy turf and soil exchange, the best tines to use are those that remove the greatest volume of soil in a single pass. There will be a point of diminishing returns where a similar material is being removed as is applied in the subsequent dressing. The most time-consuming and disruptive element of hollow tining is removal of cores. Hollow corers on a closed drum collect cores as the job proceeds and there are conveyor belt systems to harvest cores. On tees and fairways it may be possible to break up the cores and work them back in if soil exchange is unnecessary – such a process must be completed in dry conditions.

The choice of top dressing after hollow tining or leaving tine holes open will depend, to a great extent, on timing and the primary purpose of treatment. If late in the autumn, say when grass growth has declined to an insignificant level, top dressing will cause smothering and disease and tine holes are best left open. Where thatch removal is the main reason for hollow tining, on greens that have a sandy growing medium, it can be useful to leave the holes open to facilitate greater air movement through the turf base, provided the ground is not too soft. If contemplating leaving tine holes open then care must be exercised in selecting tine width and spacing to minimise disruption to the playing surface. On greens spring treatment must be followed up with dressing to restore a smooth putting surface. When changing pin positions long after hollow tining, beards of root can be seen working down tine holes, often promoting patchy growth of more vigorous grass, though a uniform appearance is rapidly restored as warmer weather returns.

Vibrating Mole Plough

Carrying out intensive aeration to a shallow rooted turf or a site with a limited depth of topsoil poses great difficulties. Hollow tining will remove some of the valuable topsoil and Verti-Draining may prove too disruptive. The use of a vibrating mole plough could be the answer with a working depth limited to 125-175 mm. Where severe compaction precludes other aeration options the mole plough can be a useful precursor to future Verti-Draining. A combination of the two operations can have value on heavy soils where the mole plough, applied a month or so after Verti-Draining, assists channelling of surface water away, though this does require a consistent fall across the ground so treated. A vibrating mole plough can prove useful along the top of ridges on undulating fairways (run along the length of the ridge) where even penetration of other types of aeration can be difficult. In combination with hollow tining, mole a month after hollow tining. The secondary operation can facilitate more effective compaction relief and promote even migration of sandy dressings. There are a variety of machines available for this type of aeration work, select carefully if employing on greens to limit disruption. A pressure roller following the tine is a must to prevent lifting of the turf. The plough leaves a continuous slit along its run and it is best employed late autumn to early winter when surface healing will be more rapid. If taking the run from rear to front of green a final run across the approach should be made to divert water from the approach. Obviously the direction of run through a putting green will be restricted by the positioning of bunkers and other design features far more than for other techniques. Insert and withdraw the unit at least a metre beyond the green, as it is at the start and end of each run where the dangers of ripping and more severe levels disturbance are greatest.

Compressed-air

The air-exhaust of such units expels air under pressure to 45 cm to 1 metre depth, deeper than other treatments, and has proved beneficial for work on wet ground or dry patch, though mostly restricted to local treatment as the operation is relatively slow. Depth of treatment can be varied but it is wise to remain below 250 mm as the closer to the surface the greater the danger of disturbance from the unpredictability of the pressure flow. Solid or hollow tining is often recommended prior to use, the perforated surface acts as a release valve for the surge of air. This method is not an option where the tine penetrates into a gravel carpet or naturally free-draining substrate as the air is dissipated through the greater pore space of the stone. Where moisture is retained in the top few inches and the soil is dry below, often seen on traffic routes and in a wet autumn following dry summers through green approaches and fairways, this technique may be effective in promoting freer water movement through depth without smearing the surface, as might happen with Verti-Draining. A pedestrian operated tool may be worth purchasing if the course is suited to its mode of operation as it can be used frequently through most weather and soil conditions. Back-filling the tine hole, funnelling in coarse sand or fine grit, can provide a more persistent drainage channel than merely relying on fissuring. Larger tractor-mounted units can relieve compaction in areas of high wear concentration where a Verti-Drain or hollow tiner would bounce along. As such the compressed-air unit is a valuable precursor to other forms of aeration. Research has looked into the possibility of injecting fungicide through the probe of a compressed-air device and this is of value in regulating fairy ring activity, though the effect is fairly short-lived.

Drills

A slow operation mostly restricted for use in treating local dry patch or severe compaction and can be employed through the summer as surface disruption is minimal. Of value in aerating poor constructions if it is possible to work down to an underlying drainage layer, by-passing the impermeable root-zone material above. Semi-permanent drainage channels can be formed if holes are backfilled with coarse sand or fine grit. This technique has value as a precursor to fairy ring control or wetting agent application. The action of the drill leaves a pile of soil at the turf surface, so the operation is best done in dry conditions for the soil is to be lifted or worked back in cleanly.

High Pressure Water Injection

Perhaps the most innovative approach to aeration developed in recent years. The primary applications for this technique are for treating dry patch, black layer and to facilitate summer aeration with minimal surface disturbance. The operation leaves pin holes at the surface but water disperses below ground to produce a fan effect. Compaction relief tends to be short lived after each treatment. The only disruption to play comes from the hose depositing clippings and this does leave a bit of a mess that has to be cleared with a mowing pass once the surface has dried. Confined to dry and warm times of the year when the irrigation is on tap, be wary of too frequent use which may promote loss of soil structure through migration of fines. It may be best restricting use to two to three operations per year and advisable to combine summer water injection with autumn hollow tining or Verti-Draining. Sensible use of this procedure may preclude or at least reduce the need for the more disruptive solid and chisel tining through the summer. Specifically designed to work on greens, the machine has used successfully to promote better playing conditions on drought-stressed approaches. The water injection mode of aeration is a potential source of much research to assess its true benefit and potential pitfalls. Could it be used as a means of reducing irrigation and thereby of stressing annual meadow-grass yet sustaining fescue and bent? Is it possible to introduce wetting agent or fungicide through machine without damaging the unit or covering the golf green with a foam carpet? What is the effect of regular use on soil structure and fertiliser leaching rates?

Vibrating Solid Tines

A recent innovation where studded discs vibrate to relieve compaction in the top few inches. Disturbance to the surface is great and this technique has limited potential on golf courses. Main navigation routes, either for golfers or maintenance vehicles, where renovation is required may be the only ground where this aeration technique has an application, though such areas seem to be increasing all the time.

Summary

Adequate aeration is needed to combat the damaging effects of heavy play. Treatments for specific circumstances must be seen as part of an aeration programme which will still incorporate conventional techniques. Deciding which tool to use (and when) is the secret to healthy turf and maintenance of quality playing surfaces. During the course of our advisory work we are asked, mainly by golfers, "why punch more holes into the greens when they are just becoming good?" There is no substitute to regular attention to aeration; occasional exhaustive treatments may relieve compaction that has built up over time but the benefits are relatively short-lived and are unlikely to sustain healthy growing conditions between treatments. There is a political benefit to be had from implementing aeration techniques that limit disruption during the summer competition season and relying on more intensive work later to fully alleviate the ills of compaction while weather and ground conditions remain suitable in the approach to winter. A balance can be attained between what is good for the grass and what is acceptable to the golfer but the Greenkeeper must not compromise too far. It should, however, never be necessary to go out of your way to antagonise the golfing fraternity. There are less disruptive options and means of getting the best out of potentially damaging operations without excessive disturbance, yet golfers must accept that there will be times when some disruption to play cannot be avoided and that, in the long term, the work being undertaken is for their benefit.

(SPI : B.181)

VERTI-DRAINING

Drainage and the Verti-Drain

An open, well aerated, free draining growing medium is of paramount importance in sports turf management and a package of aeration treatments is the major basic maintenance technique to help achieve these criteria. The Verti-Drain was first introduced from Holland in 1982 and its use is now well established throughout the British Isles, with a number of competing firms producing versions of the machine. The Verti-Drain is a specialised tractor-mounted unit primarily designed to deal with deep-seated compaction which conventional aerators cannot penetrate far enough to reach. The operating principle is similar to hand forking where deep aeration of the soil profile is combined with levering up of the compacted layers. Verti-Draining followed by top dressing also provides the opportunity to create vertical drainage channels which have a lasting effect.

About the Verti-Drain

There are currently four types of the original Verti-Drain available which are commonly referred to as the Popular, Greens and Sports Ground machines (two available widths). The former two units are predominantly employed on fine turf areas, the Sports Ground machine on winter games pitches, racecourses and golf course fairways. The availability of a variety of solid tine sizes, working depth (to a maximum of 400 mm), tine spacing and overall working width, enables a wide range of problem situations in different sports to be tackled. Hollow tines are also available to carry out a deeper soil exchange which cannot be achieved by the use of more conventional equipment. Many contractors now hire out the above units with an operator, although an increasing number of Verti-Drain machines are being purchased by individual clubs or local authorities who want freedom to choose the timing of operation and have the need to use it on a regular basis on a number of areas.

How to Achieve the Best Results....and Avoid Disasters!

As with other forms of aeration, the best result with the Verti-Drain occurs when the soil is no more than moist. A dry soil will hinder deep tine penetration and often result in tearing of the turf. To offset this condition, the application of an approved wetting agent can help to moisten the turf prior to the arrival of the Verti-Drain on site. Verti-Draining a wet soil will inevitably lead to smearing down the sides of tine holes and reduced fissuring of the soil.

The Verti-Drain must travel over the surface at the correct creeping speed (between 0.25 and 0.65 miles per hour) to achieve an even lift, otherwise surface rippling will occur – a condition difficult to remedy. The operator should be aware of any shallow pipe drainage or irrigation supply pipes. Worn tines will reduce the effectiveness of the unit and bent or wrongly aligned blocks of tines will invariably result in surface damage. Altering the angle at which the tines enter the soil decreases or increases the soil-heaving effect of the unit.

The Verti-Drain will cope successfully with a limited number of small stones in the soil profile but areas with significant stone content and rock near to the surface should be avoided. Renovation work on localised areas of damage **must** be organised in advance and completed quickly and efficiently, removing obstructions and making good levels with sandy compost or equivalent. On fine turf a light rolling is given just to settle the surface before top dressing takes place.

Top Dressing

As well as relieving deep-seated compaction, Verti-Draining also provides an opportunity to give distinct, long lasting vertical drainage channels between the surface and (hopefully) freer draining layers below, i.e. a drainage carpet or free draining subsoil. These channels often act as a by-pass through more heavily compacted and destructured soil, allowing better movement of air and nutrients. Improved root growth and natural breakdown of thatch through bacterial action follow as a result of the above work. To maintain this connection it is therefore important to top dress either just before or just after Verti-Draining. However, on larger areas cost may well restrict the extent and amount of top dressing applied.

The most commonly applied material is sand, although it is better to use sandy compost on fine turf areas such as golf greens. For sand top dressing, a good quality medium/fine lime free material with a narrow particle size distribution range is recommended, although a similarly specified medium/coarse sand is often preferred on thatchy greens with deep-seated compaction in the soil profile. It is vital that as much sand as possible is worked down tine holes to make the connection between the surface and sub-base as well as avoiding a layering effect further down the profile in years to come (i.e. a sand rootbreak). Apply a dry sand to a dry surface and work in immediately, this makes the above desired aim much easier to achieve. Larger diameter solid tines or hollow tining further aid the working in of sand. In general, the Institute would prefer a sandier top dressing material to be used, rather than pure sand.

Applications on Golf Courses

On the golf course, the specialist use of the Verti-Drain on golf greens during the early autumn period is now well-established but with the increasing levels of play, especially during the winter, and better standards expected by players, alleviating localised areas of heavy wear around the course has now become a routine necessity. This has extended the range for Verti-Drain use on the golf course as an integral part of the autumn/winter renovation programme with special emphasis on approaches, tees and traffic routes. Sections of, or whole fairways can also be Verti-Drained with advantage and a dressing of approved sand or sandy top dressing is advised prior to the treatment where surface drainage is poor or algal growth affects surface traction. To avoid disruption to play, top dressing with sandy compost or sand on golf greens is completed after Verti-Draining using in the order of 1.5 to 2 tonnes per green. Following settlement in the holes, a further light dressing may be required but care will have to be taken in respect of timing to avoid smothering the turf or encouraging disease. If in doubt, leave until the spring. The Greens Verti-Drain fitted with 12 or 18 mm ($^1/2$ to $^3/4$ in.) tines is used primarily on greens and tees, the Sports Ground unit fitted with 25 mm (1 in.) tines on approaches, traffic routes and fairways.

One word of caution – Clubs considering Verti-Draining should not gain the impression that the results are impressive in all situations, as this is not necessarily the case. Taking a specific situation, where a limited depth of heavy loam soil overlies clay subsoil on a green, then if the profile is saturated Verti-Draining would have little benefit with no significant fissuring and with water backing up the holes from a saturated sub-base. In this situation where the green also has a uniform slope, a combination of hollow tining, deep slitting and Vibroslitting or mole-ploughing to a positive outlet could well be a better option although the real answer is fundamentally one of reconstruction, including installation of an under-drainage system.

(CGC 1 : 28)

VERTICUTTING,GROOMING & SCARIFICATION

Introduction

The control of lateral grass growth by a combination of verticutting, grooming and scarification is as important as the mowing for the sake of turf vigour, playing quality and presentation around the golf course. The debilitating effects of such growth are many and varied. Procumbent grass stems have an adverse effect on the smoothness and pace of the putting surface, in extreme cases producing a definite grain or nap across the green where the ball travels at a slower pace against the grain than with it. Bent grasses and annual meadow-grass are prone to flattened leaf growth, far more than fescue and this can be a major impediment to providing a visually attractive surface, particularly on new greens containing a high proportion of the bristle-leaved grass. Often the poor quality of putting surface provided by a mixed sward of this nature encourages closer mowing and the rapid loss of the desirable fescue. Meadow-grass seed heads and distinct patches of coarse grass (Yorkshire fog and perennial ryegrass) also detract from playing quality and a visually uniform turf, yet can be regulated with an appropriate vertical mowing programme. If not lifted by mechanical means lateral stems and other plant parts will bed down at the turf base, evolving into thatch with all the problems that entails. This rundown of potential ailments is not restricted to greens, turf will be prone to more variable growing conditions if thatch is a problem anywhere on the course. Should too great a depth of thatch develop the turf can be prone to water retention and contoured ground affected by differential drying patterns. Such a situation in approaches can produce unpredictable bounce characteristics, a tremendous irritation to golfers. Surface moisture encourages shallow rooting and a drought prone turf, together with the promotion of annual meadow-grass at the expense of bent and fescue. Coarse grass species can be found in all areas of the golf course creating the greatest nuisance where present on through the green areas dominated by a tight knit turf composed of desirable species. Many a blasphemous outburst has been heard when a golfer, contemplating a tricky chip shot over a bunker, finds his ball sitting tight against a prominent patch of ryegrass. The presence of a fibre layer on fairways has had a direct bearing on the extremes of drought damage seen on some courses over the last two to three years, restricting penetration of moisture and consequently recovery, enabling moss invasion which then competes with emerging grass seedlings. With all the troublesome effects from the presence and uninterrupted development of lateral growth there can be no doubting the benefits from what is essentially a single operation, vertical mowing. Accepting the need for mechanical regulation of such growth what is the difference between the terms verticutting, grooming and scarifying, and when, where and how should each be employed?

Verticutting

Verticutting is akin to a light raking operation and is the most effective means of regulating thatch accumulation and thinning patches of coarse grasses. Regular verticutting improves smoothness and pace of fine turf by cutting out flattened stems and stolons, promoting tillering, denser turf and a more erect growth structure in the process. Verticutters should be set to lift loose litter bedding down at the turf base, not working into the existing compressed thatch layer. If the blades are set to cut too deeply scalping will occur and be exaggerated on contoured greens. Set up properly the marks from verticutting should grow out within four to five days of treatment. Verticutting is conventionally carried out weekly when there is reliable strong growth. Setting the verticut units higher can produce a lighter treatment and operations twice a week or a double-cut once a fortnight, particularly where coarse grasses a problem, can have a dramatic effect on turf quality. Verticutting frequency tends to be cut back if grooming on a regular basis. However, the two operations perform different functions and verticutting must remain part of the routine management programme, perhaps treating greens once a fortnight. A lighter, less frequent verticutting operation should be carried out when initial stress from climatic factors occurs, postponing verticutting altogether when growth rate significantly declines. Avoid verticutting drought-stressed turf, though when drought breaks verticutting can facilitate recovery and moisture penetration. For new greens which have been seeded avoid regular verticutting until organic debris has built up at the turf base to protect the growing point of the grasses. Even for turfed greens 12 months of limited verticutting post-laying may reduce thinning, particularly of fine fescue, and help control meadow-grass ingress. The pattern of operation with verticutting is similar to mowing, aiming to vary the direction of cut as much as possible and to complete the exercise when the turf is dry, for a better finish. Always verticut in straight lines as turning a curve with the units in operation will promote severe scuffing. As the potential for loose thatch production is greater on less worn perimeters the best option is to make an overlapping cut into the green fringe rather than avoiding the green edge. Sharp, pointed tines should be employed as worn, rounded ones will prove ineffective or necessitate setting the blades dangerously low. It may be necessary to renew the cutting reel annually. Verticutting employs separate units on a triple mower to those used for mowing and this requires changing heads on a regular basis through the growing season. This vertical mowing practice lifts a lot of organic debris which must be boxed off or picked up by a following trim with the mowing unit. The most efficient means of completing a verticutting programme is to have two triple mowers available, one to verticut the other to follow with a clean up cut. When buying a new greens triple mower it is a sensible procedure to retain the old triple, if mechanically sound, to carry out verticutting duties as the strain on the power unit is far greater when driving verticut reels than when operating mowing heads. The new innovation of an interchangeable verticutting cassette for a pedestrian mower is not thought suitable for busy golf courses due to the time factor of verticutting, though may be an option for quiet and impecunious 9 hole courses. As a precursor to top dressing application, verticutting will increase the rate of absorption of the material. Avoid verticutting for at least four to five days after top dressing or fertiliser application as much of the material will be lifted. Verticutting can be of great value to promoting a uniform texture to green run-ups and tees. Avoid using greens verticutting units elsewhere than on the greens as beyond the putting surface wear on the cutting reels will be increased, not only by the greater area to be covered but also by a greater likelihood of treating coarser grasses and hitting more debris. Buy a separate set of heads for a back-up triple mower or a suitable compact tractor-mounted scarifier for verticutting aprons and tees. The timing of such work will be regulated by climatic effects on growth rates but treatment through spring and autumn can be as frequent as fortnightly, backed by occasional summer work when there is adequate growth.

Grooming

The basic principle regarding the use of groomers, i.e. the ability to maintain a good pace whilst keeping the height of cut at a sensible level, holds true despite problems seen with experience of their employment. Ribbing, scrubbing and scalping, and excessive wear around green perimeters has been a recognised complaint against groomers. A combination of reasons is often the only way of explaining the severity of much of the damage, relating to the design of machine and abuse from the user. One manufacturer has redesigned their original grooming unit and another has produced an attachment to adjust the operating mode of their machine in an attempt to improve the performance of the grooming attachment. Researched and developed in the USA, groomers are intensively employed in States where strong growth can be relied upon, requiring as much as daily treatment. In Britain this approach is totally inappropriate, though a similar tack was initially advised by the manufacturers. Groomers should be treated as a polishing tool for fine turf akin to brushing, lifting stems lying at the turf surface into the cutting cylinder that follows as well as cutting off a proportion themselves. In many cases damage to turf has been due to ignorance of this basic purpose, setting units to work too deeply or working when the ground is too soft, and employing the groomers too frequently for UK growing conditions. Experience suggests that grooming should be limited to two to three operations a week when grass growth is vigorous. Initial ribbing is often seen adjacent to leaking automatic sprinkler heads, evidence that the increased weight of the cutting unit with groomer is at least partially to blame. A cutting reel with grooming attachment is substantially heavier than one without. Perpetually following the same route on the perimeter cut stresses turf; this stress factor is exaggerated when groomers are operating, even more so on soft surfaces where the weight and vibration of the unit adversely affect the smoothness of the cutting operation. As a consequence some manufacturers are now recommending restricting grooming to a straight line cut as for verticutting, though this means missing out the tidying perimeter cut. This practice can only be done once, and at most twice a week without a noticeable deterioration in presentation. Although it is possible to lift grooming reels out of operating mode, the upper setting is not much above the turf surface and on undulating greens the groomers may turn even when not in use, adding to the scrubbing effect. Following a grooming treatment it should hardly be possible to see the tine marks, indeed the mark produced by the grooved roller can easily be mistaken for that from the groomer. It is possible that the grooved rollers are responsible for much of the scrubbing on green perimeters. One of the options suggested to those suffering from "the curse of the groomer" has been replacing the grooved roller with a smooth one. This is only an option for those models with the grooming unit set away from the front roller and the question must then be asked, does this reduce the effectiveness of the groomer? Grooming is a stressful treatment and should be postponed through dry spells when a reversion to light verticutting will sustain the regulation of lateral growth without damaging the turf. If long sections of stalk are collected in the grass box during grooming then either verticutting is being neglected or the groomer has been set to work too deeply. If grooming and verticutting are performed at an adequate frequency the clippings should be of a similar length to those from mowing. Perhaps an exception to this rule would be at the start of the growing season or at recommencement of grooming following occasional summer postponement. Being irrevocably attached to the mowing head, groomer clippings are always boxed off and this joint operation with mowing provides for a more efficient treatment, as far as time is concerned, than does verticutting.

Despite the problems associated with grooming attachments, though it has to be said there are few complaints relative to the number of groomers now working on golf courses, groomers are very effective in improving appearance, pace and the lifting of meadow-grass seed heads. The visual disturbance from patches of coarse grasses appears to be much reduced with grooming though this is may be misleading, merely taking off lateral shoots, making coarser grasses appear less obvious rather than refining their growth pattern as is achieved with the severer forms of vertical mowing. Grooming should be postponed for a few days following the application of top dressing and fertiliser, otherwise much of the material will end up in the grass box. Groomers are available on pedestrian cylinder mowers but as groomers should only be used during the summer when there is often inadequate time for hand cutting, these may be an expensive luxury. New greens may benefit from occasional grooming rather than verticutting in the initial two years of establishment to lift flattened stems without cutting into the base of the immature sward. Grooming units are available on some surround/tee mowers and self-propelled fairway gang mowers. Such mowers work exceptionally well on the more prestigious and manicured courses in the USA, and even on the few falling into this category in this country, where very frequent cutting of such areas promotes minimal stress on the turf and machinery.

Scarification
A deeper treatment to those already considered, scarification physically lifts accumulated thatch. Scarification has perhaps become rather neglected on greens with the introduction of less disruptive verticutting and grooming. There is a danger in this in that, although surface impediments to smooth and pacy greens may be controlled, long term turf health and green speed may deteriorate without comprehensive thatch regulation. Even if undertaking verticutting and grooming, it can be valuable to scarify at least every other year to clean out the turf base. Being a relatively destructive treatment it is important to time scarification to coincide with vigorous growth in order to promote recovery, generally restricting to the autumn and spring. Scarification reels can be set to work as lightly as a groomer or to cut into compressed thatch, though working deeper than 3 mm or so may seriously thin turf cover. More than one pass during a treatment may prove of value, though consecutive runs must be carried out at an oblique angle and the total number of passes during any single treatment regulated by the potential for recovery, a couple usually being the maximum. As part of the process of preparing ground for overseeding anywhere on the golf course, three to four passes may be undertaken. Occasionally careful summer scarification can be contemplated if thatch poses a serious problem. Such a necessity usually indicates underlying problems, often related to compaction and drainage difficulties. Wet summers, excessive irrigation and over-feeding promote thatch so the development and presence of dense thatch requires a wider perspective for control involving other aspects of maintenance, particularly aeration, top dressing and limiting fertiliser application and irrigation. As highlighted previously, thatch production and other problems for which scarification and its derivatives are beneficial are not restricted to putting surfaces. Through surrounds, tees and fairways frequency of treatment is regulated by the ability to positively manage turf through dry summers, i.e. the availability of irrigation. However, lush growth must not be promoted just to facilitate vertical mowing. Monthly light scarification work on surrounds and tees during the growing season can prove most beneficial, with work on fairways mainly confined to the autumn and spring. Semi-rough and rough should not be totally neglected either, perhaps looking to an annual or bi-annual treatment here. Scarification is an operation that is not carried out as diligently as it should, even more so beyond the putting green, as Greenkeepers are often faced with a Catch 22 situation, wanting to scarify but erring on the safe side, forever wary of causing deterioration to playing surfaces. Though understandable, if this approach persists too long, greater disruption may be necessary in order to control thatch. For greens and limited work within surrounds and small tees, a pedestrian scarifier still has a role though compact tractor-mounted

scarifiers are necessary to efficiently complete a verticutting/scarification programme. On fairways, scarification has to be completed with larger tractor-mounted units and the debris lifted by a sweeper. Combination sweeper/scarifiers are available and do a good job, but are slow as regular emptying is necessary and such combinations do not follow contoured ground as well as floating head units on hydraulically-driven tractor-mounted scarifiers or detachable scarifying heads on gang mowers.

Summary

The growth of grass is not two-dimensional. Flattened stems look unsightly, produce a bumpy surface, a slow pace and contribute to thatch accumulation. Prevention is better than cure and a combination of grooming and verticutting as a frequent exercise is less disruptive than relying on occasional vigorous scarification to lift bedded organic litter. However, experience has shown that if vertical mowing concentrates solely on grooming and verticutting, ignoring scarification, the result can be softer, thatchier turf. Vertical mowing must be seen as a package of the three treatments. If individual operations are carried out too vigorously the turf will be stressed and thinning can occur. Each of the three processes has its own, if variable, limits to setting depth and frequency of operation. Using grooming units as verti-cutters, or verticutters as a scarifier, will have disastrous consequences. The reverse scenario is feasible and in certain situations, where turf is under stress, positively desirable, but for routine treatment operating a vertical mowing attachment in this way will prove less effective than employing that designed for a specific task. Timing of each treatment must also be regulated to avoid damage, rarely if ever contemplating vertical mowing outside the main growing season and imposing further limitations to intensive verticutting and scarification.

(SPI : B.181)

IRRIGATION WATER SOURCES AND SUITABILITY

The irrigation of turf is becoming a more and more expensive operation as mains water charges increase. Now some golf clubs and, to a lesser extent, other sports clubs are looking towards using alternative sources of water for irrigation purposes. This may be a nearby pond, stream or river. In some situations an underground aquifer is present which could potentially be used as a water source. There has also been interest in the use of water from sewage treatment works as a source of irrigation.

However, a number of steps and precautions should be taken before "taking the plunge".

Availability and Quantity

In considering the use of a local stream, river or pond as a source of irrigation water the total quantity which is available for use must be assessed. Almost certainly a licence will be required from the National Rivers Authority (NRA) in England and Wales to abstract or impound water. In many instances a licence may not be granted because of the effect on local water courses. Even where a licence is granted, during periods of low summer flow restrictions may be put on its use. In Scotland the local authority should be contacted regarding water abstraction and in Northern Ireland enquiries should be made to the Department of Environment, Environment Service. In the Republic of Ireland a licence should be obtained for water abstraction from the District County Council.

A licence is also required to sink a test bore hole into an underground water source.

Even where there is a sufficient water supply present for irrigation needs the amount which is permissible for use may be limited in order to protect ground water resources.

Water Quality

Once permission has been obtained to use a water source, the next step is to have the water analysed chemically and, in some cases, biologically.

For any type of turf it is important to ensure that the water is not over-saline. High salinity could cause discoloration of the grass leaves and, if extremely high, could kill the turf. Different species of turfgrass have different tolerances to salinity. For instance slender creeping red fescue (*Festuca rubra* ssp. *litoralis*) is relatively tolerant to saline conditions, perennial ryegrass (*Lolium perenne*) shows average tolerance whereas browntop bent (*Agrostis castellana*) is very intolerant of salinity. Therefore, along with the actual salinity value of the water, the grass species present should be taken into consideration.

High salinity in the irrigation water can also have an effect on soil structure. This would be of importance where salinity in the water is due to high sodium levels and there is a significant amount of clay in the soil. The sodium in the water may cause the clay to disperse within the soil leading to blockage of drainage pores.

If salinity is found to be excessive then there are techniques available, such as reverse osmosis, for its reduction. Another possibility is to dilute the saline water with the mains supply in order to reduce the salinity to a safe level.

The acidity or alkalinity of the water may have a significant effect on turf quality. Again this should be measured by laboratory analysis. On fescue-bent turf the application of highly alkaline water on a regular basis is equivalent to the application of lime. Thus problems may occur with fungal infection by fusarium and take-all patch diseases. Such a problem is more likely to occur on very sandy rootzones.

Alkalinity in the water can be reduced by the use of an acid dosing system which injects nitric acid into the irrigation water prior to application. However, other means can be used to counteract the effect of alkalinity; in particular the application of ammonium sulphate as the nitrogen fertiliser source. This produces acidity at the soil surface.

On perennial ryegrass or smooth stalked meadow-grass dominated turf, irrigation with an alkaline water source is unlikely to cause any problems with regard to turf vigour.

Salinity and alkalinity measurements are the two most important for irrigation onto turf. However, if it is suspected that the water source is contaminated by industrial effluent then it is necessary to analyse for metals such as cadmium or zinc and for organic pollutants such as phenols. These materials, if present at high concentration, may adversely affect growth in turf. In treated effluent from sewage works the concentration of boron should be measured also.

If effluent from a sewage treatment plant is being considered as an irrigation source then biological tests need to be carried out in addition to chemical analysis. This is to ensure that the presence of any human pathogenic bacteria is kept to a minimum. Such water sources are not commonly used for turfgrass irrigation in Northern Europe, but in Spain, Portugal and the USA treated effluent is used on a number of golf courses.

On a number of newly-constructed golf courses water from drainage in the greens is recycled as irrigation water. Because the water picks up soluble materials as it passes through the rootzone it becomes saline with time. It is therefore important to regularly monitor the water's salinity level.

All the tests mentioned above can be carried out by the laboratories of the local water company or National Rivers Authority. Chemical analysis of water for proposed irrigation use is also regularly carried out at the laboratories of the STRI.

(DML : B.188)

IRRIGATION SYSTEMS : SERVICING AND MAINTENANCE

At a time when many areas have experienced severe drought conditions and stringent controls on water usage have been introduced, it is essential to get the best out of your irrigation system.

The quantity and frequency of watering are clearly critical to turf management and conservation of water. These topics continue to generate lively debate, but before these matters can be considered it is essential to ensure that your irrigation system is in good condition.

The following guidelines are particularly appropriate to golf courses, but the main points are equally important for smaller, less complex systems.

During the winter months the system should be fully overhauled and serviced in preparation for the next year.

Over-Wintering

The system should be drained to avoid frost damage, paying particular attention to any exposed pipework at the storage tank or stream crossing points. It may be necessary to blow the system out to ensure it is fully drained using a compressor with similar output volume to the system. This should not be done too quickly to avoid surges and water-hammer. Allow about half a day for a system on an 18-hole course.

Floating suction pipes with a foot valve for abstraction from a reservoir will be damaged by frost and should be removed in winter.

Steel storage tanks should be drained, but tanks with butyl liners should not be fully drained as the liner can be damaged. The water level should be reduced to about two thirds of the normal level, ensuring that the inlet ball valve is fully open. The tank can be protected from frost damage by placing a large piece of polystyrene foam in the tank. The level of water should be checked periodically as a leaking roof can cause the tank to overfill.

Pumps should be drained. The drain plug should be removed from the pumps, but should be replaced loosely once the pump is drained. It may be necessary to remove the air valve at the top of the pump to ensure that it is fully drained.

Floating pumps should be removed from lakes unless they are made of materials which are not affected by frost.

Some pumps incorporate a heater and should not be isolated. If the pump is switched off, a tag should be placed over the switch to prevent the pump being run when dry.

Leave power to the pumphouse switched on so that a thermostatic heater can switch on, if fitted, to provide frost protection and reduce condensation, which can cause corrosion of electrical equipment. Allowing some ventilation will also help to reduce condensation.

The electricity supply to the controller should not be switched off as some types of controller require power to retain their memory. Some controllers also have built-in heaters to prevent corrosion. The transformer will also generate some heat which may be sufficient to keep the equipment dry.

Pressure tanks should be drained as well as all pressure-relief and pressure-regulating valves.

Manual hydrant valves should be opened to ensure they are fully drained.

Maintenance

Careful attention to maintenance and repairs during the winter period will help to avoid problems during the irrigation season which could be costly and result in damage to the turf.

If any servicing or repairs are required, these should be attended to as soon as possible to ensure that spares can be obtained and the work completed before irrigation is needed.

During winter, solenoid valves should be operated occasionally to ensure that the plungers and springs are free. Setting the controller to syringe will operate the valves.

Sprinkler heads should be checked and serviced if necessary. Check the arc and speed of rotation of the heads, check that they pop-up and retract fully, and clean out any filters.

The system should be started up before irrigation is required to allow time for all necessary checks and final servicing.

Reconnect and check the pumps, replacing all drain plugs and check all the seals.

Check all pressure switches, valves and reservoir float switches and adjust if necessary.

The system should be filled slowly by operating the pump manually with purge valves open. On an 18-hole course it can take up to 8 hours to refill a system, it may take a few days to clear all air from the system.

Close the purge valves and check air release and pressure relief valves, as well as pressure vessels and gauges.

Check all sprinkler heads for correct operation and ensure there is sufficient clearance around the heads and that they pop-up to the correct height.

Check the controller and test the sprinklers to ensure they are adjusted and working correctly to cover the required areas.

Finally, make sure there are no leaks or a drop in pressure in the system.

These are general recommendations and you should carry out all maintenance and repairs in accordance with specific instructions which your irrigation installer should provide.

It is essential that your irrigation system is maintained and functioning properly when it is most needed without wasting water.

(RE : B.179)

TURF IRRIGATION MINIMISING DROUGHT STRESS AND CONSERVING WATER

GENERAL

Good maintenance practices will encourage the development of a vigorous healthy sward with a deep root system, which will be able to withstand the effects of drought better than a weak sward with shallow rooting.

It is essential that irrigation systems are properly maintained. Servicing and repairs should be carried out during the winter months so that the system is working efficiently on starting up in spring. Check for leaks. Ensure that efficient use is made of all available water sources on the course.

WHILST LIMITED WATER IS STILL AVAILABLE

[1]   Make sure your watering system is working efficiently. Check sprinkler arcs, nozzles, etc. Water only the essential areas.

[2] Do not water during the day.

[3] Reduce the frequency of watering and water more thoroughly each time, to get moisture well into the soil.

[4] Do not allow puddles to form or surface run-off to occur.

[5] Improve infiltration of water by spiking (not slitting) and using wetting agents, particularly where thatch is serious and on high spots. (High spots may require a hand-held hose with attachment for wetting agent.)

[6] Wetting agents are usually most effective if first applied in late spring with additional applications through the growing season, according to the severity of the problem and water availability. Water in after application, to avoid scorch.

[7] Raise the height of cut. Where appropriate, return grass clippings to help to act as a mulch.

[8] It could be helpful to mow fine turf with pedestrian machines, if practicable.

[9] Reduce the frequency of mowing as growth slows down.

[10] Spread light applications of compost top dressing on golf greens and similar fine turf areas, and work in gently with a mat.

[11] Keep pin positions to the margins of golf greens.

[12] Reduce wear on turf by varying the position of pathways and closing off sensitive areas.

NO WATER AVAILABLE

When all watering is banned continue with points [7] - [12] as conditions dictate.

[13] Do not apply pesticide or fertiliser.

[14] Stop verticutting or grooming on golf greens and similar fine turf areas.

[15] Do not carry out any aeration work.

[16] On small areas of newly established seed or turf, use perforated plastic sheet or netting to conserve moisture (but beware heat stress under covers).

[17] Be prepared to close golf greens or similar areas to avoid long-term damage which will require costly reinstatement.

AFTER THE DROUGHT

[18] Reinstate any severely damaged areas as soon as conditions and water availability will allow.

[19] Wetting agents can be used to help with rewetting of drought-damaged or water-repellent turf.

[20] After the immediate problems have been dealt with it may be necessary to revise the management strategy to minimise future problems. The following points should be considered:–

- Alleviate compaction to encourage deeper rooting and water infiltration.
- Eliminate excessive thatch by a combination of scarifying, hollow tining and top dressing with sandy compost.
- If possible, manage turf to favour drought-tolerant species and to develop deep root systems.
- Update the irrigation system to improve efficiency.
- Investigate alternative water sources; it may be possible to intercept and store surface water to boost reserves.
- Increase the water storage capacity.

(IS No.17 Ref. 02/04)

THE VALUE OF SUB-AERATION

The Problem

Test hole excavation into golf greens or other areas of the golf course suffering from drainage problems often shows excessive compaction existing to a depth of several centimetres below the turf surface and this frequently accentuates the naturally slow drainage of soils with poor structure. The problem is most commonly found on older established inland greens where the hindrance to water penetration aggravates the problems caused by thatch where such exists. The slow infiltration of surface water to lower levels is a serious contributory factor in the development of thatch.

In more recent years the need for increased aeration has become much more accepted and modern equipment has speeded up and simplified the task of relieving compaction. Unfortunately, examination of soil profiles often shows that the depth of penetration obtained by orthodox aerating tines is not sufficient to fully penetrate the compacted region. Where this situation exists, deeper forms of aeration must be considered as a supplement to normal aeration, and not as an alternative.

The procedure found to be effective is to treat the green or other problem area with a machine fitted with a mini-mole plough or subsoiling tines and these can be either of the rigid or the vibration type. Within reason, the greater the depth of penetration that can be obtained the better, and with machinery presently available this means working at a depth of 130-180 mm. The tines should be drawn through the green at 230 mm (no more than 300 mm) centres, at an angle of some 20° across maximum fall. Wherever possible the tines should be drawn right through the putting area and drawn through the surround preferably on to land which falls away from the green. Where this is not possible the low end of the slits running through the putting area should be linked up by two or three additional slits cut on a line which will run out of downward sloping ground. If the maximum benefit is to be obtained from the sub-aeration, the work should be done in the very early autumn, e.g. September and before the soils become wet as a result of late autumn and winter rains. This is important as work done when the soils are wet has a similar effect to passing a knife through a block of spreading cheese and little or no shattering of the compaction is obtained. The appearance of the slit lines (i.e. brown lines) on the green's surface following the work may concern some golfers but they do not really affect putting and they can quickly disappear.

It should be realised that, unlike complete cultivation, the effects of the above-mentioned forms of aeration are only partial and therefore to gain real benefit some continuity of treatment from year to year is necessary. In many cases the use of the Verti-Drain machine would be preferable. Experience shows that quite considerable progress can be made in three years but the effectiveness of the green's under-drainage has some influence on the progress made. If the under-drainage is unsatisfactory due to the presence of a slow-draining clay subsoil, the penetration of water draining to lower levels is again impeded and this could apply even where complete cultivation is carried out. In these cases the reconstruction of the green may have to be considered.

(CGC 1 : 27)

FERTILISERS FOR FINE TURF

Of the three main plant nutrients for fine turf, nitrogen is the most important since it is the element primarily responsible for encouraging the growth of stem and leaf. Phosphate affects all plant growth processes and is particularly involved in root development. Potash rarely produces obvious benefits in turf though it is linked with the health and general functioning of the plant, and is said to encourage resistance to disease, to drought and to severe winter weather, particularly when there are high nitrogen levels.

Early Trials Demonstrate the Necessity for N and P

All three elements are therefore needed in the nutrition of turf, albeit at appropriate levels. None of them should be omitted completely. Some of the older readers of Institute publications will remember the famous 'Set D' trial at Bingley, now no longer with us unfortunately, since after some 40 years it had outlived its usefulness as an experiment and needed to yield place to trials of a different nature. Set D was a fertiliser trial set up in the early days of the Research Station and consisted of a whole series of fertilisers like sulphate of ammonia, superphosphate and sulphate of potash, alone and in all manner of combinations with other fertilisers both organic and inorganic. It was shown by the experiment that quite good turf could be maintained just by sulphate of ammonia alone, provided that periodic dressings of lime were given to counteract over-acidity. Better turf (still *Poa annua* free) was produced when superphosphate was added to the sulphate of ammonia, being more free from moss and having greater resistance to drought. The addition of potash made very little difference to the appearance of the turf except in drought (when the plots with potash were outstanding). We think a little potash is always useful in the main fertiliser mixtures for the reasons given above.

Sulphate of Iron

Apart from these N, P and K, there are other major and minor elements which are essential in plant nutrition, though it has been extremely rare to find any deficiency of any of them in golf turf. The situation needs watching however, particularly with regard to USGA-type rootzone mixes. Iron is one minor element which really is of definite value if included in fertilisers for most kinds of turf since it helps to give the grass a good dark green colour and to reduce weed, worm and disease troubles.

Avoid Alkaline Fertilisers

All fertilisers for regular use on fine turf should, as a rule, be slightly acidic or neutral in their effects. Alkaline materials like Nitro-chalk, if used regularly, will influence the botanical composition of the grasses in the sward for the worse and encourage weeds and worms.

The Value of 'Organics'

There is not the space here to describe detailed fertiliser programmes for the various types of golfing turf. Suffice it to say that a general complete fertiliser for spring application to fine turf might include sulphate of ammonia, superphosphate, sulphate of potash and sulphate of iron (in the calcined powder form), together with such suitable organic forms of nitrogen and phosphate as are available like dried blood, hoof and horn meal and bone meal. However, phosphate and potash fertilisers should only be used after chemical analysis of the soils on the greens. These organic forms help to produce a mixture which releases its nutrients more slowly and also have considerable 'conditioning value' in that they promote a greater friability of the fertiliser mix and prevent the mixture caking too quickly.

A Variety of Fertiliser Needs

Follow-up dressings through the rest of the growing season might consist of nitrogen alone – a simple mixture of sulphate of ammonia, dried blood and/or hoof and horn meal. There is, however, a tremendous amount of variation in the fertiliser require-ments of different golf courses. Some good golf greens receive virtually no fertiliser whatsoever, whilst other good greens, especially pure sand greens, may receive each year 14–28 g nitrogen per m^2 with corresponding amounts of phosphate and potash. On golf courses where there is a good supply of fertile home-made compost, actual fertiliser applications to the greens need to be minimal. The turf manager should always be interested in producing the correct results in terms of turf performance; yield of grass is not the aim.

Home-Mixing of Fertilisers

In the quantities normally required on golf courses the mixing process is not really difficult but is now seldom undertaken due to time and labour considerations – proprietary products are usually thought more convenient. The appropriate quantity of each fertiliser is spread out in turn on a hard, smooth surface such as a clean floor. The heap should be shovelled so as to turn and mix, the operation being carried out three times. In order to increase the accuracy of application, thus reducing the chances of scorch and to produce a fertiliser mixture which (subject to the compatibility of the ingredients) will keep under good storage for a considerable time without physical deterioration, it is good policy to mix the fertiliser thoroughly in turn with a carrier of screened dry soil or compost (at least twice as much carrier as fertiliser).

Choose Carefully Your Proprietary Fertiliser

Many turf managers these days prefer proprietary fertiliser mixtures to the home-mixed variety for the sake of convenience and despite the advantages of home-made mixes in terms of material cost and individual 'tailoring'. These fertilisers are commonly available in powder form but sometimes as small pellets (mini-granules or mini-crumbs). They are usually complete fertilisers and there is a wide range of nutrient contents, of plant food ratios and of constituents. Firms typically sell two products, one for spring/summer and one for autumn/winter use, the former being relatively high in nitrogen, the latter relatively low. When using proprietary products one is relying heavily on the background knowledge of the manufacturer, so it is important to buy the most reputable products and to use them generally in accordance with the manufacturer's recommendations. The Institute does not recommend the use of autumn/winter fertilisers, as a general rule.

Variation in Contents

It should be borne in mind that the ingredients used in proprietary fertilisers are not necessarily constant, being governed by market and other considerations. In view of the scarcity and price of organics, some manufacturers are now including a proportion of one of the newer slow release nitrogen fertilisers. Some contain sulphate of iron and some do not. Some products have magnesium compounds added and an odd one or two have added trace elements. Proprietary fertilisers are normally formulated so as to be suitable for application without dilution with compost or soil but there are still advantages to be gained by so diluting in order to facilitate spreading without scorch.

Fertiliser/Weedkiller Formulations

Several proprietary fertilisers contain selective weedkiller also. These are really of more interest to the home lawn owner than the professional turf manager.

Storage

Fertilisers should always be stored in dry conditions, but especially so if they are kept in containers other than polythene bags. Care should be taken to protect bags from sharp points or jagged edges and bags should be dropped flat rather than on their corners. To maintain dry conditions it is wise to have a platform of duckboard or similar between the floor and the bags and to ensure ventilation around the bags and in

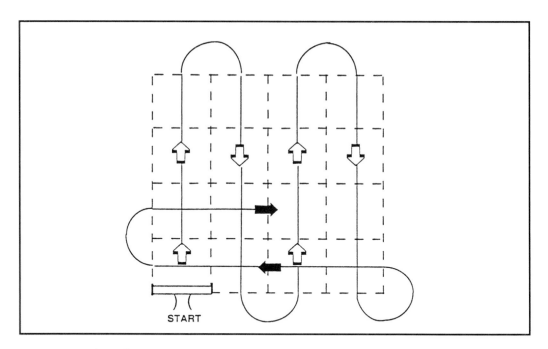

FIGURE 9: Using a linear type distributor.

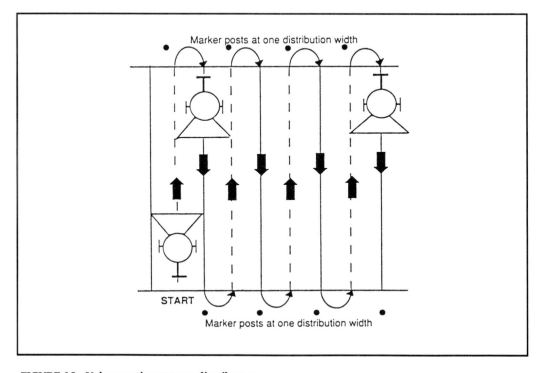

FIGURE 10: Using a spinner type distributor.

105

the building, though doors and windows should be closed in damp weather. The most convenient arrangement is usually to have the bags stacked in a criss-cross manner, keeping the height down to about six bags and certainly not more than ten bags. Always close a part-used bag to conserve the remainder of the fertiliser in good condition.

Timing of Application

Good turf should be uniform, and even application of fertiliser is highly important. Uneven spreading results in uneven growth and colour, and excess application (such as caused by overlapping) may damage the turf severely. Fertiliser dressings should preferably be given during a dry spell in broken weather, when rain can be expected to fall shortly afterwards to wash in the fertiliser. If no rain falls within one or two days, generous watering should be undertaken where practicable to achieve the same end.

Application Methods

For relatively small areas like greens hand application is still possible, the fertiliser (suitably bulked out with the carrier referred to above) being divided into two and the two halves broadcast by hand in two directions at right angles to each other. However, even on fine turf, fertiliser distributors are normally used but it is a mistake to assume that these will automatically do a good job. Linear-type distributors spread fairly evenly within their width (subject to uniform fertiliser in good condition, evenness of ground, etc.) but great care is needed to achieve correct marrying of successive widths and to avoid difficulties at the ends of runs. It often pays to go off the site to turn, or to have at the ends polythene sheets on which to to this. For first-class work it is wise, even with good distributors of this type, to divide the fertiliser into halves and apply these in transverse directions at right angles. The small distributors of the spinner type used on fine turf commonly give more fertiliser in the middle of their spread than they do at the outside and so to improve the evenness of spread it is wise, once again, to divide the fertiliser into two but to work so that all the turf is treated twice **in opposite directions**. This is achieved by making successive runs **half** a breadth away instead of a full breadth of the spread (see Diagrams).

(CGC 1 : 33)

THE USE OF SULPHATE OF IRON

Sulphate of iron has been used for well over half a century as a turfgrass treatment. During this time the benefits of applying this chemical to turf, either alone or in fertiliser or lawn sand mixtures, have been recognised and consequently its role in turf management is now well-established. This article describes how sulphate of iron may be used to discourage moss, algae and weed invasion, earthworm casting and certain diseases.

Effects of Sulphate of Iron on Moss, Algae and Weeds

Sulphate of iron applied at 5 g/m^2 is a traditional treatment for moss control, applied alone or in conjunction with sulphate of ammonia and a carrier such as sand. Moss is killed very quickly by sulphate of iron although duration of control is generally short. However, as it is very cheap to purchase it is probably the most cost-effective material for moss control available. Sulphate of iron applied at the moss killing rate may also be effective against algae in turf. However, whilst some suppression of algae may be achieved by repeated application, long-lasting control will only be achieved by correcting the cultural conditions (shade, poor drainage etc.) which favour algal growth. Additional benefits of regular sulphate of iron application may be gained in the control of broad-leaved weeds, especially when used in conjunction with sulphate of ammonia as a fertiliser treatment.

Effects on Earthworm Casting

Earthworms cannot tolerate acidic turf, so applying an acidic material such as sulphate of iron will keep earthworms away from the turf surface and thus keep casting to a minimum. Thus, the problem of earthworm casts providing seedbeds for weeds, creating muddy conditions and interfering with play may be reduced. In a recent trial at STRI applying sulphate of iron at rates between 4 and 8 g/m^2 in the early winter months has inhibited earthworm casting for 2 to 3 weeks. Statutory bans on the use of many formerly popular wormkilling chemicals have encouraged the search for safer materials and it is possible that sulphate of iron may play an increasing role in earthworm management programmes in the future.

Effects on Disease

During cool wet weather, fusarium patch disease may cause serious damage to fine turf. The fungal pathogen which causes fusarium patch, *Microdochium nivale* is most active under neutral or alkaline conditions at the turf surface where the fungus is active. Consequently, sulphate of iron by acidifying plant tissues and thatch to which it comes into contact will help control the disease. Although not as effective as a fungicide spray, regular use of sulphate of iron will help minimise incidence and severity of fusarium patch and thus reduce the need for fungicide application. As well as fusarium patch another disease, namely take-all patch, is favoured by an alkaline turf surface. Re-acidifying the turf surface with sulphate of iron may limit the spread of take-all patch disease.

Other Uses for Sulphate of Iron

Sulphate of iron is widely known for its darkening effect on turf colour, thus producing a more attractive sward. The greening effect is mainly due to a darkening of dead material at the base of the sward which makes thin or bare areas less noticeable to the golfer. Several liquid formulations of iron combined with sulphur and urea are now available designed specifically to have a cosmetic effect on the turf. Initial tests at STRI have indicated that these liquid iron products may darken the turf colour very rapidly and also give some reduction of fusarium patch disease and earthworm casting.

(CGC 1 : 38)

HYDRAULIC OIL LEAKAGE

The advent of hydraulic systems on so many machines used on fine turf areas (and not only triple mowers although of course these are the major users) has inevitably led to an increase in the type of damage caused by hydraulic oil. Leaks occur in several ways, such as faulty valves, seals or hose failure. Clearly, regular pre-use checks of the equipment are essential and an annual maintenance overhaul is a 'must'. Operators must be fully aware of the damage likely to occur on fine turf from hydraulic oil and must be alert for the first signs of any leak. Damage is caused to the grass by ingredients in the oil but also due to the oil temperature. To minimise damage, the leaking unit should be driven off the most vulnerable areas, usually greens and approaches, as quickly as possible and into adjacent rough. Speedy follow up treatments can also help a lot, especially where only a smear or light mist of oil exists on the grass leaves. With a heavy leak, quite severe turf damage is likely, but even so prompt treatment can aid recovery and reduce the extent of repair work ultimately needed.

Within 10 to 15 minutes of the leak occurring the affected area should be scrubbed for one to two minutes using a sponge and a solution of liquid non-ionic wetting agent or non-phosphate containing detergent diluted 1–10. Follow up by washing off the residue with a hand-held high pressure hose.

Normally scorch damage after a spill will be apparent in 48 hours and the maximum turf loss at about two weeks. If treatment has been prompt, some recovery should be noticed after three or four weeks of reasonable growing weather and an assessment of repairs needed can then be made. Where partial recovery has taken place indicating minimal oil contamination of the soil surface, the thin areas can be helped to thicken up by close shallow forking and light raking followed by rubbing in a mixture of sandy soil and fine grass seed. If the turf has been completely killed then oil has damaged the growing points of the plants and contaminated the soil to such an extent that seed is unlikely to be successful. In this case immediate plugging with a hole cutter or turf repair tool, or in very severe cases patching with turf in autumn is the only satisfactory answer.

(CGC 1 : 29)

PLATE 2: **Top dressing a golf green with a modern tractor-drawn spreader. (Courtesy SISIS Equipment (Macclesfield) Ltd.) One of the most basically essential of all golf green maintenance operations.**

SECTION 3
THE MAINTENANCE OF GOLF GREENS

❖❖❖

Top Dressing & Fertilisers

Mowing : Scarifying : Aerating

Soil Compaction & Surface Drainage

Thatch & Fibre

*The Care of
the Golf Course*

TOP DRESSING FOR GOLF

The general term 'top dressing' can be described as the application of a bulky material with a view to improving or maintaining the qualities of a playing surface. Top dressings should not be confused with fertiliser treatments, as the former may or may not have any plant food value.

The main reasons for applying a top dressing material are:-

(i)   that it is an effective method of building up a true surface and thus improving the efficiency of mowing. This is a much more effective way of producing smooth levels than rolling, over-use of which induces compaction and subsequent drainage problems. This factor is of most importance to those sports that require a smooth running surface, such as golf;

(ii)   top dressing can also be of benefit by increasing the drought resistance of freely draining constructions. Conversely, applications of very sandy top dressings can assist surface drainage when carried out in conjunction with deep aeration treatments;

(iii)   in some cases application of appropriate top dressings can alter playing qualities, such as resiliency;

(iv)   newly seeded areas can be protected from the elements and also bird damage by covering them with suitable top dressings;

(v)   the top dressing which is applied to the turf surface may have a small plant food value, thus reducing the amount of artificial feeding required.

Top dressing work is generally confined to relatively small areas such as golf greens owing to the quantities of material involved. The timing of top dressing is important, as there should be some growth on the area to be dressed to avoid smothering the turf, and conditions should be reasonably dry.

Golf Greens

On fine turf areas such as golf greens the best material for top dressing purposes is usually a friable sandy compost. Proprietary composts are available for fine turf use, being made up from varying mixtures of sand, soil and perhaps fine grade peat. Some golf courses have their own compost-making facilities, thus enabling them to produce large quantities of top dressing material comprising a mixture of light topsoil, sand and some form of organic matter which will break down rapidly, forming an homogeneous 'soil', such as farmyard manure or grass clippings. Once a steady supply of home-made compost has been made available, then regular light applications should be possible throughout the main competition season, helping maintain smooth and uniform putting surfaces.

A major limiting factor with home-made composts (and also with the proprietary types) is the quality of the topsoil used in the mixture. If the soil contains a high proportion of fine silt and clay particles, then this can create further problems, particularly if used in high rainfall and poor drainage areas. Therefore, if the only available topsoil is of a heavy nature, then adequate amelioration with a suitable sand will be required in order to achieve the required drainage characteristics. In many cases heavy indigenous soils should not be used as top dressings, even when mixed with large quantities of sand. The quantities of sand and soil used in the final mix can be determined by laboratory tests carried out at the Institute.

As the supplies of good, light topsoils dwindle, there has been a trend in recent years towards the use of sand/organic matter mixtures. When used under appropriate conditions, these types of top dressings can have beneficial results, although their usefulness is also dependent on the qualities of the sand, soil and peat used in them, which can be quite variable. The peat must be very finely ground so that it will become an integral part of the soil structure – fen peat can be an ideal component of a top dressing.

On golf courses, several top dressings may be given throughout the year, although the two main applications are made in the autumn after the main competition season and a lighter one in the early spring to help smooth out any unevenness in the surface caused by the winter frosts.

There has been some controversy over the use of pure sand on fine turf areas, particularly when the turf contains a deep thatch layer. There is no doubt that an application of sand will help to firm up a soft thatchy turf, especially during a wet spring. However, if this practice is repeated, alternating this with normal compost top dressings, then problems will arise with the formation of root breaking layers in the soil profile. A soil component in the compost mixture is also a useful source of the micro-organisms responsible for the breakdown of the thatch material. The problem of root breaking layers is not only confined to situations of irregular use of pure sand dressings. If the source, and type, of top dressing material is not consistent year in year out, then layering of top dressings may occur in the soil profile. Such a situation could not only restrict rooting depth, but may also impede drainage. Our basic advice would be: if you have a good source of a suitable top dressing, stick to it – do not chop and change your top dressing.

The exact proportions of each component of your top dressing should be determined by the soil already on site, and by what you are trying to achieve with the dressing. If the soil under the greens is sandy and naturally free-draining, then the top dressing should also be sandy in nature, with the majority of its particles lying in the same range as those of the soil on site. On the other hand, if the soil on site is rather heavy and relatively slow to drain, what is the point of adding more of the same? In this instance, we are looking to improve site conditions by applying a dressing of a sandy compost to facilitate freer drainage. For either situation the amount of organic material in the dressing needs to be closely monitored. Too great an organic matter input will tend to hold water at the surface – you will merely be adding to any organic thatch layer that already exists. In extremely free-draining situations, a small amount of organic matter can help increase drought resistance. Generally speaking, more than 10% organic matter in a top dressing is considered too much, and there is usually enough organic material in the soil constituent of a top dressing for the requirements of most situations.

In most instances a sand/soil mix with the proportions of 3 parts sand : 1 part topsoil or possibly 4 parts sand : 1 part topsoil could be used depending on the nature of the topsoil available. The type of sand used should be one of a fine to medium category, that is with the majority of its particles lying in the 0.125–0.5 mm range, and it should also be lime-free, except for links golf courses based on limy sands. For situations where thatch is a major problem, then sands with the majority of their particles lying in the 0.25–1.0 mm range can be used.

Summary

Clearly top dressing is an essential aspect of maintenance on golf greens. However, for this operation to be successful, a certain amount of skill is required in judging the appropriate material to use, adequately preparing the surface beforehand and choosing the correct weather and growing conditions in which to carry out the work. Tests on samples of top dressing materials in the soil physics laboratory at the Institute enables our Advisory Service to recommend the correct dressing for each individual situation, and greatly reduces the risk of applying a material that could turn out to be detrimental to the condition of the playing surface in the long term.

(CGC 1 : 31)

SANDS FOR TOP DRESSING GOLF GREENS

On areas of fine turf the main purpose of top dressing is to preserve a true and level surface and to dilute the build up of thatch. Ideally an annual application of 5-6 kg/m^2 of top dressing material will be used, with this quantity being divided into several applications to avoid excessive amounts of material on the surface at any one time. If the playing surface is on a heavy soil with poor drainage or has excess thatch, larger quantities should be applied in conjunction with a programme of hollow tining so that the drainage and aeration of the surface layer can be improved.

The composition of the top dressing material may vary depending on the type of construction and the availability of topsoil materials or composts for the top dressing. Where a green has been constructed with a special rootzone mix it is important to use a top dressing material which matches the mix in terms of the quantity of sand and the sand type. This will preserve a continuity in the profile of the green. In the extreme case of a pure sand construction the size and uniformity of the sand should match that of the rootzone sand.

Where a golf green has been developed from a native soil which may have a relatively high silt and clay content, it is sensible to use a relatively light (sandy) top dressing material in which the clay content has been diluted by sand to below 5% and the total silt and clay content should not exceed 10%. The use of a sand dominated by the medium or coarse sand size fraction (0.125–0.5 mm diameter or 0.25–1.0 mm diameter) is preferred for the preparation of this type of top dressing mix.

Sands with a high content of fine material should be avoided as these can clog the surface and excessively coarse sands are not popular as it is difficult to work sand grains above 2 mm in diameter into the turf and coarse particles such as these will damage mowers and are unpopular with golfers.

Consistency in the use of top dressing materials on fine turf is important and for instance, use of pure sand for perhaps a year followed by reversion to a sand-soil mix can form a root break. This thin layer of sand can have significant effects on the vertical movement of soil moisture and the penetration of grass roots will tend to reflect the moisture distribution within the soil.

In fine turf areas, the lime content of the top dressing material is critical. If the sand contains large quantities of shell or other calcareous material the pH of the surface layer will increase. This can have important effects on weed invasion, earthworm activity, turfgrass disease and the composition of grass species within the turf. In particular annual meadow-grass (*Poa annua*) will tend to invade the turf at the expense of the fescue (*Festuca*) and bent (*Agrostis*) species.

(CGC 1 : 30)

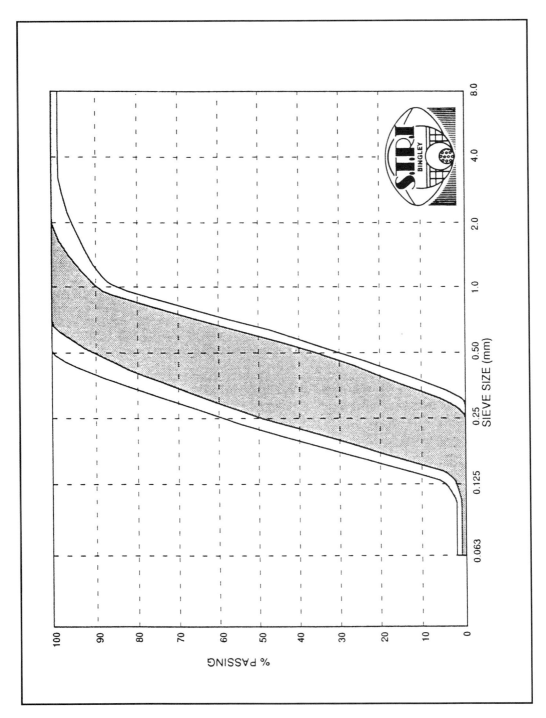

FIGURE 11: Grading curve defining recommended and acceptable limits of sand size for golf greens.

MOWING : PEDESTRIAN MOWER VERSUS TRIPLE

In the course of our advisory work during the past 10 to 15 years, a popular question at golf clubs, raised both by green committee members and by greenkeepers, has been "what do you think of triple mowers for greens"? Indeed, the question is still raised frequently but nowadays it is sometimes substituted by "is it true that some clubs are returning to using the small pedestrian-operated machines for cutting greens"? Concern at using the right equipment will always be uppermost in people's minds but differing outlooks and priorities, depending upon perhaps whether you are a green-keeper or green committee member, can lead to different conclusions. Whichever camp you are from, however, there is no disputing facts and of these there are plenty to help decide whether triple or hand mowing is to be preferred in a particular instance.

Initial Considerations

Fine turf triple mowers are highly manoeuvrable and capable of turning within a very small area. Even so, the best is achieved from these triple mowers when fairly extensive areas such as 9 or 18 golf greens each of 500 m^2 or more have to be cut – very small areas of fine turf can be rather awkward to mow, particularly if the triple mower has to be turned on the actual putting surface due to surrounding banks or other obstructions. When mowing golf greens, the aim should always be to turn the large triple mower on the collar or surrounds if at all possible. Wet and soft fine turf can tend to mark due to regular turning with a triple mower within a confined area, although much depends on the care and skill of the operator – even small pedestrian machines will mark a tender surface if care is not taken.

The size and shape of the area may also limit the number of directions in which one can mow with a large triple mower; remember that changing the direction of cut is considered an important aspect of mowing practice.

Advantages

Assuming there are greens of the right size and shape and that club finances are good enough to acquire a triple mower, then there are a great number of advantages to be obtained by using a triple machine. Time and labour saving are two major selling points with triple mowers and hopefully the time and labour that has been gained can be channelled into other aspects of management. It has been noticeable at some busy golf clubs with a small labour force that the introduction of triple mowers on both greens and tees in recent years has produced enormous course improvements and, with present demands upon staff, it is difficult to see how such clubs could manage otherwise.

Besides saving time and labour in relation to mowing, the fine turf triple mowers can, of course, be adapted to other purposes, i.e. machines are capable of light verticutting (vertical mowing) and also grooming. Indeed, the term mowers in the name should not be over-emphasised as these machines are multi-purpose. The verticutting units for the triple mower should always be considered a necessary purchase.

The Debatable Points

The narrow swaths produced with small pedestrian machines often seem to be preferred on greens – the narrow bands on a green may psychologically help the aim!

On the question of actual finish, both the fine turf triple mowers and the best hand machines achieve an excellent cut. In the long term, however, the floating head principle of the fine turf triple mower *may* tend to produce a softer type of playing surface and use of the verticut units must not be neglected, particularly if there is a history of thatch and fibre troubles. Hand machines often seem to leave a firmer surface – maybe the rolling factor has some effect. The softer and perhaps occasionally slower putting surface sometimes found in the case of golf greens cut with triple mowers can also be attributed to the actual setting up of the cutting units. Experience has shown that with identical bench settings, fine turf triple mowers tend to leave a slightly longer grass cover than hand machines (again probably the difference of a cutting unit floating over the surface as compared to one that settles into the turf and drives through it). In other words, fine turf triple mowers will probably have to be set slightly lower than the hand machines to leave a similar length of grass. Setting up the three units on a triple mower so that they are all producing an identical finish is an important point that must receive close attention.

Some older triple mowers used on slightly coarser turf areas such as golf tees, surrounds and approaches, etc. do not have grass collection facilities and obviously this may be detrimental, particularly on tees. However, modern tee machines do have collecting boxes fitted. The larger hand machines used in these situations, besides having grass collection facilities, also produce a significant rolling effect which is often considered to be beneficial on areas such as tees.

On the question of maintenance costs, repairs will be expensive, irrespective of what type of mower is in use. It is really surprising how in the course of advisory work one sees such an enormous difference in machinery reliability and presentation. Some golf clubs seem to think that after three to four years a new triple mowing machine is the norm, but five miles down the road, the same type of machine doing similar work but receiving completely different attention can often look and perform in peak condition after six to seven years use.

Maybe a Compromise

After having had experience with both types of machine, i.e. triple and hand mowers, most golf clubs find circumstances have so developed in the last few years that the triple mower is the only machine which can cope with requirements. At other clubs, however, committee members, golfers and greenkeepers are finding that a combined approach of hand and triple mowing is perhaps the best answer, e.g. in the case of a golf green, cutting two or three times midweek with the small machines and then cutting Saturday and Sunday with the quicker, less labour demanding triple mowers. Similarly, on the tees, cutting every now and again (say one week out of every three or four) with a hand machine seems to reverse any detrimental effect resulting from constant use of the triple mowers.

(CGC 1 : 17)

TURF GROOMERS

The search for pace on putting greens without the need to mow too closely was provided with a valuable aid some years ago with the introduction of turf groomers into this country. Close cutting of greens, to 3 mm or even lower, generally makes greens putt faster though long term weakening of the sward is the result if the practice is prolonged. This leads to deterioration in quality of sward by encouraging annual meadow-grass invasion, this species can seed below 3 mm! Moss and prostrate weeds are also likely to take advantage of a weak grass cover. Established bentgrass will grow quite happily at a 5 mm height of cut during the growing season, so will the fine fescues. It is normal to raise the level to 8 mm for the winter. Routine mowing at these heights means leaving more grass on the greens, producing a slower putting surface. The main advantage of implementing these sensible cutting heights is retention of ground cover and, long term, smoother putting surfaces. There is an added problem of lateral growth of shoots and leaves, promoting grain or nap, particularly with bentgrasses and annual meadow-grass which can produce a bumpier surface and thereby reduce pace. The use of turf groomers cuts down on lateral growth, stimulating vertical growth and a denser sward by the encouragement of more shoots, providing smaller and more plentiful leaves, over which the ball will travel smoothly and truly. Grooming units will also fine down patches of coarse grasses in the sward and pick up annual meadow-grass seed heads more efficiently than verticutters.

What are Turf Groomers?

Basically, turf groomers are a refinement of verticut reels. Verticutting has been around for many years as a routine treatment – vertical mowing cuts down into the turf surface to lift procumbent (flat) growth and organic debris, reducing the rate of thatch build up. On green triple mowers, verticutters are separate to the cutting units and are interchangeable with them. Changing over the units is not overly time-consuming, but this does produce a situation where the same mowing machine may have to carry out two functions, reducing its useful life through extra wear and tear and reducing the time it is available for its primary function of mowing the greens.

Turf groomers are reels that are fixed to the cutting unit, allowing the two operations to be carried out simultaneously. The device was invented by Lawrence T. Lloyd, Course Superintendent at Rancho Canada Golf Club in Carmel, California – he sold his patents to Jacobsen in 1985. The original Turf Groomer as manufactured by Jacobsen consisted of 71 blades providing 261 tempered steel knives mounted spirally on a powered roller set behind the front roller of the mowing unit. Each knife rotates through a groove of the front slotted roller. The 0.64 mm thick, 54.0 mm diameter blades are driven at 3000 rpm, slicing stolons and horizontal shoots which are lifted by the bevelled edges of the preceding roller. Jacobsen later introduced a new groomer reel which had 85 blades, retaining the spiral mounting set into the front grooved roller to 11 mm. The next grooming reels to feature on a green triple were produced by Toro, working on a similar principle to the Jacobsen. The main differences were that the grooming reel on the Toro unit was set so that there was a gap between it and the front roller, and the grooming blades were individual rather than in a continuous spiral. With this arrangement, the Toro implement was not restricted to the use of a grooved Wiehle front roller, Swaged and Full roller options are available. The Toro unit also had variable blade spacing, 6 mm or 19 mm, whereas the Jacobsen was obviously confined to the gap between the grooves in the front roller. The reel with the closer spacing had 76 blades, whilst the wider spacing had 26. Each blade had six cutting teeth. The Toro blades were 0.71 mm thick and of 53.9 mm diameter, driven at 3200 rpm. A further grooming unit reached the market in the form of the Ransomes Verti-Groom for their GT green triple mower, introduced in 1989. Ransomes redesigned the original groomers by placing the grooming reel ahead of the front roller. This set up rather went against the original principle, whereby the bevelled edges of the grooved roller lifted trailing stems into the path of the groomer blades. Ransomes would argue that the speed of rotation of the groomer should ensure an efficient vertical cutting action while the following grooved roller lifts any remaining lateral growth into the cutting reel. The Ransomes Verti-Groom had 35 hardened steel blades each with five cutting teeth. The blades were of 60 mm diameter, spaced at 15 mm. The Jacobsen and Toro groomers formed part of the free-floating cutting unit, whereas the Ransomes groomer was free-floating in a manner independent of the cutting unit. Groomers later became available on pedestrian cylinder mowers; the Jacobsen 19 and 22 in. Walking Greens Mowers, the LF 100 Lightweight Fairway Mower, the Ransomes 51 and 61 Super Certes and Greens-Pro, and the Toro Greenmaster 1000. The Bunton and John Deere pedestrian cylinder Greensmowers have a thatching attachment based on the groomer principle. Groomers have more recently appeared on other competing mower designs, such as the Hayter-

Beaver Greens Triple and the Lloyds Paladin and Saxon pedestrian machines.

Using Turf Groomers

Turf groomers will complete the task they are designed for if set correctly and used as and when growing conditions permit. These implements were originally designed to work in conditions found in North America, where growing conditions tend to be more consistent. Grooming reels tend to be of variable depth and adjustment, 5 mm above front roller to 5 mm below front roller on the Ransomes. It is important to know the lower extreme setting for efficient use of this fine tuning implement, not too deep when it will serve as a verticutter which is not its intended purpose. Such treatment will not only be severe, but will reduce the working life of the groomers considerably. Settings of 1.6 mm above to 1.6 mm below the bottom blade will usually be appropriate, the exact setting being determined by the strength of the sward, growing conditions and the degree of lateral growth. Frequency of grooming must also relate to the prevailing growth and weather. During the first season of use it is suggested that groomers be used as little as once a fortnight, gradually working up to three or four operations per week. Remember that daily grooming, as practiced in the USA, may over-stress the grass in our variable, cooler climate. Reduce frequency and raise the setting when the green sward is under stress, say during drought conditions or when growth is less predictable in the spring and later autumn. Toro recommend using their reel with close spacing during periods of faster growth and the wider spaced reel when growth is slow, e.g. in the autumn. If grooming reels are set correctly, it should be possible to make the final perimeter cut with the units in action, though great care must be taken to regulate travelling speed to compensate for not travelling in a straight line, and also to lay off grooming in perimeter area which may weaken quickly, e.g. undulations in drought and main traffic routes on and off greens.

Dangers of Groomers

It must be stated that many of the early problems reported were a result of misuse, mainly incorrect setting – treating groomers like verticutters or, even worse, scarifiers – and too frequent use. If you are contemplating purchasing grooming units, make sure that your supplier provides full details of performance and use. In many instances it will be a case of trial and error to obtain the exact setting for your situation, the setting likely to vary with season, but you should be provided with sufficient inform-ation to ensure that your errors do no damage to the putting surface or the grooming blades. It is a good idea to carry out your tests on the practice putting green where any problems can be corrected before risking work on the main greens. With the necessity to regulate the use of the groomer, it is important that the grooming reel can be disengaged quickly and raised above the cutting height so as not to run along the turf when out of action.

As more and more grooming units have found their way on to golf courses, a few difficulties have arisen which are related to design rather than misuse. The use of coarse top dressing materials can create a problem with some units. Coarse sand or fine gravel particles can lodge in between the grooming blade and the roller into which it is set, possibly bending the knife or even snapping it off. Such damage not only means the cost of repair to the machine, but also to the turf which may be scalped, particularly on the perimeter cut. Our advice is not to use groomers after top dressing for at least four to five days, or as long as it takes for the majority of the dressing to migrate from the turf surface. If this procedure is not followed, you may not only risk damaging the groomer units but will also lift, and waste, a lot of top dressing.

The same principle applies to the application of fertilisers, particularly mini-granule or the larger granule slow release forms. On the Toro unit, setting the groomer away from the front roller has produced a wider roller base so the unit will not follow contours as closely. However, unless your greens have severe, tight contours, this should not be a problem except perhaps around green edges where undulations are often found, or on a severe Mackenzie two-tier green.

Summary

Turf groomers are here to stay and, if used sensibly and correctly, can be a valuable aid to producing smoother, faster greens. Jacobsen even go as far as to state that an immediate increase in green speed of up to 10 per cent or more can be achieved after just two passes, and that regular use can gradually increase green speed by as much as 25 per cent without lowering the height of cut. Whether these figures are applicable to the average British golf green has to be resolved scientifically, but there can be no doubt that groomers can have a noted positive effect on green speed, as well as helping to control annual meadow-grass by seed head removal and fining down patches of coarser perennial ryegrass or Yorkshire fog more efficiently than by verticutting. Groomers do not replace verticutting units, they should each have a role in greens management. Once a grooming programme is established, then the frequency of verticutting can be reduced. If you are thinking of purchasing grooming units for your current triple mower, then, in the majority of cases, we would support your decision. If you are looking to purchase a new triple, then we would recommend serious consideration be given to obtaining cutting reels with groomers. In such a situation arrange for demonstrations of all the market leaders to provide the best for your course, and a machine that your greenkeeping staff are happy to work with. Do not fall into the trap of believing that groomers are going to solve all of your problems, indeed there will be problems with the use of the units if you do not set them correctly or if they are over-used – grooming units are a conditioning tool and should be treated as such. Groomers are available to promote smoother and faster putting conditions without the need to sacrifice grass cover through over-close mowing, and we have probably reached the day when Clubs that do not own grooming attachments for their greens mowers are now in the minority.

(CGC 1 : 16)

MANAGING WET, ANAEROBIC GREENS
The "Iceberg" Syndrome

Golfers often perceive the presentation and playing quality of greens solely in terms of the turf cover and immediate putting surface. Like an iceberg the surface may only be $1/6$th of the story with $5/6$th being hidden underneath and the latter invariably poses the main threat. By definition anaerobic is "living in the absence of free oxygen" which gives the clue to the heart of the problem and mode of attack in terms of management. Indeed from research, experience and on-site evaluation it is clear certain factors are common to wet stagnant conditions.

Cause and Effect

Compaction of heavy textured soils and lack of any under drainage system invariably leads to saturation or near saturation of the growing medium with the result that oxygen levels fall. The natural progression of this escalating snowball effect is a switch to anaerobic bacterial action. Here a reducing, rather than oxidising, process takes place with the anaerobic soil bacteria's respiration utilising other compounds in the absence of oxygen. In the presence of sulphate in the soil sulphides are produced, e.g. hydrogen sulphide, along with other noxious compounds. Being highly toxic the result is the death of roots and ultimately the grass plant (annual meadow-grass first, followed by browntop bent). As well as the putrid smell a visual appearance of a black layer within the soil profile can occur plus an accumulating surface thatch problem. As the black layer increases a knock-on effect of sealing and further compaction plus moisture retention adds to the management difficulties.

The above deterioration can be accelerated by high rainfall, low light and evaporation rate levels, especially in winter months, as well as reduced wind flow (shading) and increased course usage. Design can also exacerbate the effect through encouraging surface water run-off from higher ground into moister retentive hollows on greens. In addition, it should be appreciated that anaerobic conditions are not just confined to heavy silt or clay soils and subsoils; the phenomenon has also been observed on pure sand, or very sandy constructions and at the interface where layering occurs.

Prevention

In a perfect world where prevention should always come before cure, a number of positive decisions taken during the design and construction phases can help avoid anaerobic conditions occurring in the future. These are:-

[a] The design of greens and surrounds should be to shed excess surface run-off water and avoid moisture retentive hollows. The introduction of catchwater intercept drains would be appropriate where the land contours make this aspect difficult to achieve.

[b] Design of the putting surface must include sufficient area to help spread wear once the green comes into play and hence reduce compaction and impeded surface drainage. In addition, ensure there is a uniform slope from the back to the front of the green.

[c] Choose a top-quality, high-specification growing medium whether it is to be a sand/soil or a sand/peat mix.

[d] Avoid inconsistency by:

- not introducing less than the recommended depth and/or an uneven depth of growing medium;
- poor mixing of growing medium components;
- ensure top dressing is the same as the growing medium or at least compatible;
- avoid excessive handling of growing medium and suspend construction work when ground conditions are wet.

Management

When the course manager is presented with wet anaerobic greens as a starting point, management techniques are required to reduce the problem until improved design and construction can be implemented. Several maintenance practices are important, but the most vital aspect is the introduction of an intensive aeration programme to increase the oxygen supply to the soil and hence reverse the anaerobic condition. In addition, the aeration treatments will have the benefit of loosening the soil profile and encouraging root growth, speeding organic matter breakdown and improving drainage. Hollow tining in particular will speed up the rate of progress, especially using the larger diameter tines and should the layer be at depth, one option available is the Verti-Drain fitted with hollow tines. The frequency of treatment depends on the severity of the condition and other forms of aeration being considered, yet two or three treatments per year for two or three years may well be appropriate. It is also important that aeration encompasses the whole profile on a year-round basis using a combination of surface slitting (summer), deep slitting, mole ploughing or vibroslitting, a soil ameliorator (air blaster) and the Verti-Drain.

Monthly light top dressings during the growing season (say $1\text{-}1^1/2 \, \text{kg/m}^2 - 2\text{-}3 \, \text{lb/yd}^2$ on each occasion) will help to increase the oxygen flow near to the surface and encourage breakdown of organic material. If a sandy compost material used for top dressing contains a medium-fine sand then consideration should be given to changing to a medium coarse sand, yet always remembering to be careful to avoid layering by careful integration, i.e. hollow tining the first time the material is employed.

With an inherent, very slow drainage capability it is vital that irrigation is limited during dry spells, particularly in the late summer period. The general message is always to err on the side of caution. Whilst not of primary importance, it would be wise to keep a regular check of the pH level and reduce the number of fertiliser dressings containing sulphate and iron, i.e. inclusion of liquid organics. During periods of good growth more emphasis can be placed on verticutting and grooming to remove this season's dead and decaying organic material and so help to prevent future thatch build up.

Spreading wear as evenly as possible through careful pin positioning will dilute the effects of surface compaction, and thinning out surrounding trees growing near to greens to increase light and air flow over greens can only have a beneficial effect. With the millstone of an ill-draining soil prone to compaction, as well as unhelpful design features, annual meadow-grass can be favoured and consequentially it will be difficult to maintain and improve upon the bent component of the sward. Nevertheless, we must not abandon the principles of management which favour bent at the expense of annual meadow-grass, rather to persevere and accept that the increase in the amount of bent can be very slow and limited and annual meadow-grass will always make up a percentage of the sward cover.

Conclusion

Any management technique for increasing oxygen supply to the soil profile will be beneficial in reducing anaerobic conditions. Based around aeration the improvements can be significant, but at the end of the day any defects in design and green profile make-up will inevitably put a limit on the level of success that can be achieved. Golfers must be made aware of this fact and that the condition of the putting surface is far from the whole story; there is always a potential iceberg lurking below!

(SJO : B.187)

COMPACTION ON THE GOLF GREEN

It seems that in the last few years there has probably been more words written and discussion undertaken about golf green compaction than most other greenkeeping topics. As a result of such concentrated attention, compaction is a word that most green committee members are familiar with but unfortunately the mechanics of compaction problems are often still not fully understood by golfers. The more practical guardians of our golf courses, the greenkeepers, do however present a different story. There is no doubt that the great majority of greenkeepers understand most of what there is to know about compaction and its associated problems.

What are the Problems

Soil compaction occurs when a force (a moving weight), such as a machine or players' feet, pushes soil particles very closely together, thereby closing the pore spaces between the particles. With reduced soil pore space there is less oxygen available and any moisture from rainfall or irrigation may not flow through the soil. Compaction can occur in both the subsoil and in the topsoil. Where topsoil compaction is encountered there is usually a good chance of solving the problem with various management practices, such as hollow coring or slitting, but compaction in the subsoil is more difficult to correct and in these circumstances major reconstruction work may be needed.

Compaction on a golf green usually means slow drainage and impeded root action, and this results in a change in botanical composition and vigour of the grass cover. Annual meadow-grass with its shallow roots survives on a compacted turf surface, at the expense of the deeper rooting bents and fescues. The build-up of thatchy material at the base of the turf is also another condition associated with golf green compaction and the secondary effects of thatch development are considerable not only as far as the turf is concerned but also the playing characteristics of the green.

Factors Affecting the Development of Compaction

Compaction problems on many of our golf greens today undoubtedly go back to the original construction. On very old courses the original constructional techniques were often entirely satisfactory at the time, bearing in mind comparatively light use and management, but with today's heavy usage and vastly different maintenance these old constructions are often inadequate and compaction problems are often a consequence. Many of our old courses do not have efficient drainage within their greens. When the soil is moist the soil particles slide together much more easily and with an applied weight from feet or machinery, soil compaction soon results. There is also another consideration that should not be forgotten, namely just the passage of time itself can lead to soil compaction, particularly in the lower levels of the topsoil or subsoil. Fine soil particles may collect together at a particular depth and then, maybe with the weight from just the soil above, compaction may result.

Sadly, in any discussion about compaction on newly-constructed golf greens one has to say that often workmanship, particularly when using heavy equipment for levelling purposes, is frequently the cause of the problem. It is vital that where there is a possibility of compaction, especially in the subsoil, during the construction of new golf greens, that the Contractor undertakes subsoil cultivation at some suitable stage in the development.

Besides constructional work, design features can also have a significant influence on the development of soil compaction. Golf greens should have at least 70% available pin space to spread out the wear and thus avoid concentrated continual play on a relatively small area. Narrow entrances into greens or limited walk-off areas towards the next tee are other design features which may affect the development of compaction.

Mention was made earlier of how compaction is produced, i.e. the soil particles being pushed together, often with a significant reduction in pore space. Compacting processes proceed much more easily and much more quickly with certain types of soil and, to generalise, one could say that soils with a high clay content are much more likely to compact as compared with sandy soils. To avoid possible compaction problems when constructing golf greens, great importance should therefore be given to a well-drained base and a free-draining sandy topsoil, preferably with a sand/soil mixture.

Curing Existing Problems

Poor drainage caused by subsoil compaction on an established green has in the past almost always required major remedial works which involved taking the green out of play for several months. In desperation, as an alternative to reconstruction it has not been unknown for some clubs to try something like deep mole ploughing, but the disruption to the playing surface was so great that this sort of work has been found valueless. Nowadays however, with the introduction of the Verti-Drain machine and compressed air injection techniques, deep compaction can be relieved with little surface disturbance.

Where topsoil compaction is a problem there should be two objectives in view;

relief of soil compaction by mechanical means, and the possible amendment of the topsoil characteristics.

Elimination of compaction by mechanical methods means aeration. Golf green aeration should be carried out frequently (once or twice per week) and as deeply as possible, fitting tines appropriate to the time of year and bearing in mind playing commitments. Hollow tining in the autumn at the end of the main competition season is a good way of helping to relieve compaction – again the deeper the better, especially where there is compaction at depth. The frequent use of solid or slit tines is also invaluable for allowing air into a compacted turf and soil, and there is no denying that the availability of machines such as attachments for compact tractors, the Sisis Hydromain and the Cushman System has been a great stride forward in enabling green-keepers to aerate regularly up to 200 mm in the fight against compaction. If deep compaction is a problem, then the use of the Verti-Drain machine is most beneficial.

Besides the more conventional tine-type aeration equipment the development of mini-mole plough devices has been another welcomed development in recent years, enabling greenkeepers to form continuous aerating slits up to 175 mm below the surface without upsetting the playing surface significantly. Before leaving the subject of elimination of compaction by mechanical means, do not forget the hand fork. Localised compaction on golf greens is often just as much a problem as overall compaction and there is no denying limited localised hand forking still has a significant place in golf green management. Small and compacted dry patches which can be a problem on some courses in the hot summer weather are the ideal sort of areas for hand treatment.

Amending topsoil characteristics with the aim of producing a free draining growing medium will also more than likely be a necessity when dealing with compaction. The use of a very sandy compost, particularly after deep hollow tining, is an essential part of anti-compaction treatment, especially where the topsoil contains a large amount of clay.

Other Important Considerations

Heavy play on a moist soil and turf is more likely to produce compaction problems than play under drier conditions. Use of irrigation systems should therefore be closely controlled to avoid excessive applications of water, this being particularly true with automatic systems. Regular aeration should supplement any irrigation work, partic-ularly if the soil on the greens tends to be rather slower-draining than one would wish.

Winter play is another factor which unquestionably has contributed to compaction problems at some courses, particularly where drainage is not very efficient. At sites where wet conditions are quite common in wet weather, the preparation of temporary greens should be considered – these temporary greens being brought into play when very wet conditions occur on the main areas and when play under such conditions seems to be causing significant damage and likely compaction problems.

From time to time the point is raised about various pieces of maintenance equipment contributing towards golf green compaction. Triple mowers are favourites for this particular point of concern. It is unlikely that any piece of modern fine turf management equipment used in Britain today would encourage and produce compaction if the equipment is used under the right operating conditions. One should not forget that nothing produces more concentrated weight (and therefore more potential compaction) than players' feet.

Prevention Better Than Cure

This old proverb is certainly very applicable when considering compaction on golf greens as once you have the problem and its secondary effects the cure is not always straightforward. However, with the wide range of efficient deep aeration equipment available to greenkeepers at the present time, there is probably a greater chance of them winning the fight against compaction than ever before.

(CGC 1 : 24)

FURTHER OBSERVATIONS ON THE SUBJECT OF COMPACTION ON THE GOLF COURSE

Within our golf clubs attention has been focused on the problems associated with compaction due to increasing levels of play throughout the year. To define what we mean by compaction, it is basically a soil condition whereby the particles of soil are pushed together, primarily by the pressure exerted by the golfers on the turf surface above. Maintenance equipment also contributes to compaction but this is minimised by fitting low-ground-pressure tyres and is certainly not as significant as the concentrated weight imposed by players' feet, especially during wet weather. The weight of the topsoil alone may also result in the development of deeper-seated compaction over a prolonged period of time.

The direct consequences of the process of compaction are reduced soil pore space, impeded root growth and reduced drainage rates. The development of excessively soft, wet and thatchy playing surfaces dominated by annual meadow-grass testifies to the adverse effects of compaction on many of our golf courses and to a lack of remedial work in the past. Outbreaks of anthracnose (*Colletotrichum* basal rot) have become more prevalent in recent years and this is often indicative of the weak state of growth of the annual meadow-grass on highly compacted soils. Reinstating healthy grass growth by improving the supply of air to the roots will usually be sufficient to remedy the problem.

Compaction should not be seen as a difficulty confined to the golf green as all areas of the course are susceptible to a varying degree, especially traffic routes such as walk-off/walk-on to greens and tees. However, when formulating management strategies to minimise the adverse effects of compaction, the most vulnerable areas should have priority, notably the greens, tees, approaches and main traffic routes.

Combating Compaction

Having identified the problems associated with compaction, how can we best combat this undesirable condition on the golf course? The most effective answer would be to remove the golfer from the course, thereby eliminating the primary cause of soil compaction. This course of action is unlikely to receive universal approbation, but fortunately there are less radical methods of minimising compaction!

The philosophy of 'prevention is always better than cure' is certainly applicable on the golf course. Therefore, a system of 'traffic control' should be initiated to re-direct golfers away from heavily used routes and thereby spread the weight of golf traffic more evenly. The provision of **separate** winter tees, placed well away from the main summer tees, will help in this respect as the well-used spring and summer traffic routes from green to tee and tee to fairway will be rested. Temporary greens are never popular with the golfers but, if conditions dictate, should be employed to protect the main greens at critical times, e.g. when soil conditions are saturated and therefore most susceptible to compaction. To reduce the resistance of the golfers to the use of 'temporaries', putting surfaces comparable to the main greens must be prepared.

Good Drainage Helps

All soils are prone to compaction but heavy clay soils, which are inherently poor draining, are particularly susceptible. Many of our old-established courses based on heavier soils were designed and constructed for much lighter use. Consequently, the efficiency of their drainage does not meet the demands of the game today. Indeed, golf greens were actually shaped to hold moisture, prior to the installation of modern automatic irrigation systems with their capacity to put on large quantities of water at any one time. To avoid possible compaction problems when constructing new greens, emphasis needs to be placed on introducing a free-draining base, over which a sand/soil mixture is placed to ensure consistently high rates of drainage. Elevation of tees usually precludes the need for the introduction of a comparable drainage system to that advocated for greens. However, modifying the topsoil by ameliorating with an appropriate quantity of sand is usually necessary as the free-draining topsoil produced will be less susceptible to the adverse effects of compaction. To circumvent poor drainage on fairway areas, additional drainage may also be necessary in the form of pipe drainage or ditches, perhaps augmented by slit drainage in situations where percolation through the topsoil is extremely slow.

Influence of Design

Design can have a significant influence on soil compaction. Golf greens should be formed so that at least 70% of the putting surface is available for pin positioning in order to avoid concentrating play, and thus compaction, on localised areas. The undesirability of creating narrow entrances into greens restricted walk-off areas or 'bottlenecks' (where many traffic routes converge) must also be taken into consideration when designing or modifying a course layout as these will also affect the development of soil compaction.

Aeration Treatments are of Fundamental Importance

To counteract existing compaction, aeration work should be seen as an ongoing process which must be carried out with modern, efficient equipment to achieve optimum benefits from individual treatments. At one time, hand forking performed once or twice a year was considered satisfactory, but this is totally inadequate on golf courses today which have to contend with 50,000 to 60,000 rounds of golf per year regardless of weather conditions.

The bulk of aeration work should be carried out during the autumn and winter months when soils are most susceptible to compaction. Deep penetration should be the objective (minimum 150 mm) to allow air in, facilitate water infiltration to lower levels and encourage deeper grass rooting. Without good gaseous exchange and movement of surplus water out of the system, excessively soft, thatch-ridden playing surfaces dominated by shallow-rooted annual meadow-grass will be perpetuated. On fairways, much deeper penetration is now possible with spiking units which operate on the tractor hydraulics, thereby forcing the tines into the ground to their optimum working depth.

Hollow tine aeration still has an important role to play in combating soil compaction within the top 75-100 mm of the soil profile - which is most susceptible to the condition. If hollow tining is followed by top dressing with a sandy top dressing mix, then more freely draining surfaces will result. In addition, hand forking should not be disregarded as this is particularly useful for treating localised, highly compacted areas.

Besides the more conventional aeration equipment, there are specialist forms of aeration which shatter the compacted soil and thereby restore freer draining, better aerated soil conditions. The vibratory mole plough - a development of the rigid mole plough - comes into this category which is designed to work in the depth range of between 125 and 175 mm. For alleviating deeper seated compaction (below the normal working depth of routine aeration equipment), Verti-Draining is invaluable and this operation has become an integral part of the aeration programme on many courses. If maximum benefit is to be derived from these particular treatments they must be applied before ground conditions are excessively wet, as in these circumstances the effect will be like passing a knife through butter – there will be little or no shattering of the compacted soil.

Spring/Summer Aeration Work

Although the importance of autumn/winter aeration work has been emphasised, spring and summer treatments should not be neglected, particularly on the slower draining sites. There is often resistance from within the golf club to applying aeration treat   ments to greens at these times, but the use of solid tines should minimise disturbance to the smoothness of the putting surfaces, particularly if conditions turn dry.

The development of drought-susceptible areas within greens can often be associated with highly compact soil conditions beneath. In these circumstances, localised spiking treatments of the affected areas are invaluable for aiding moisture penetration and thereby reinstating uniform turf conditions.

Irrigate with Discretion

Excessive irrigation can be implicated in the development of topsoil compaction, therefore close control must be exercised when using automatic watering systems. In addition, regular aeration should be seen as a complementary treatment to irrigation to ensure that water infiltration is not confined to the uppermost layers of soil as this feature will create, with the passage of play, an impervious 'cap' over the soil beneath.

(CGC 1 : 25)

THATCH ON THE GOLF GREEN

The accumulation of a layer of fibrous material is a natural feature of turf development and cannot be entirely prevented. Total prevention would in fact be most undesirable as a surface with no underlying fibre would lack resiliency and would easily become muddy in wet weather. However, when fibre builds up to an excessive degree it becomes a problem. About 15 mm of matted material would be acceptable on the golf greens, while a 25 mm layer would begin to prove troublesome. The 100–150 mm layers which are not infrequently seen make turf maintenance and the formation of good playing surfaces extremely difficult.

Most people who are experienced in turf management will realise that there is more than one form of thatch or fibre. In the past, words like mat, thatch or fibre have been used very loosely and more precise definition of terms would therefore be of value. The following classification could be a guide:

(a) *Litter*

A loose and fluffy accumulation of grass clippings and decaying leaf bases and sheaths in between the grass stems at the base of the sward. Litter is not usually seen on intensively used or well-managed turf but is more characteristic of old and neglected lawns which are perhaps cut weekly without boxing-off clippings and which receive very little additional treatment.

(b) *Fibre*

Fibre resembles coconut-matting, being tough and wiry in texture and brown in colour, and consists of old roots and other organic debris. Fibre usually overlies dry soil, the turf becoming very dry indeed and difficult to re-wet under drought conditions. Fibre is most commonly found under acidic conditions on fairways and semi-roughs where the sward is bent and fescue with a tendency to invasion by acid-loving weeds like sheep's sorrel, bedstraw and wood-rush.

(c) *Thatch*

Thatch is waterlogged throughout most of the year and smells strongly of decay and stagnation. It is yellow/brown in colour with black streaks showing the activity of anaerobic bacteria. The underlying soil is wet, compacted and usually of clay with restricted drainage. Annual meadow-grass invariably predominates in the sward with perhaps some surviving bent. Thatch can accumulate to layers several inches thick, particularly in water-collecting hollows on heavily played parts of golf greens, etc.

Accumulations of organic material of this kind are widespread in many plant communities. In any natural system, whether grassland or woodland, two processes may be traced – production and decomposition. Organic matter accumulation may therefore be caused either by excessive production or by insufficient decomposition. In the case of sports turf, fertiliser treatment increases production, sometimes excessively. The employment of fungicides and wormkillers together with maintenance of acidic conditions reduce decomposition so that there is a pre-disposition towards thatch formation.

Different grass species tend to produce thatch at different rates. The desirable fescue grasses, for example, tend to have leaf bases which are resistant to decomposition and are therefore prone to encourage fibre. The common weedgrass, annual meadow-grass, also tends to produce thatch probably because of fast growth under moist, fertile conditions.

Earthworms

It has been stated in the past that earthworms are primarily responsible for thatch breakdown and that the feature appears under golf greens as a result of eliminating earthworm populations. This view is probably over-simplified or possibly totally false as it seems that earthworms may lack the capacity to digest thatch, although they do move soil around and may therefore slow the formation of distinct thatch layers. It seems more likely that microscopic fungi and bacteria in the soil tend to be the prime cause of underlying thatch breakdown and that the use of fungicides for controlling plant disease hence encourages thatch by limiting these useful organisms.

Fertility, particularly as far as nitrogen is concerned, plays an important part in plant production and decomposition. If the ratio of carbon to nitrogen becomes too high, organic matter breakdown is slow. This is why the addition of nitrogen to compost heaps fosters fast breakdown. Even when nitrogen is added to turf it may be rapidly leached out of the thatch layer and no longer available to the flora which cause decomposition. Acidity is equally important as there is less activity of soil organisms in very acid turf.

Moisture Effects

Temperature, moisture and aeration all affect soil biology and hence thatch. Very dry conditions will slow thatch breakdown because of lack of moisture limiting the growth of soil organisms. On the other hand, excessive moisture has the same effect as soil fungi and bacteria require air for their growth and air is very limited in waterlogged turf. Temperature also has some effect in that there is less soil microbial activity at a low temperature.

Thatch Control

As with many other problems, the prevention of fibre or thatch formation is more satisfactory and much less laborious than curing an established problem. In practical greenkeeping, it is possible to slant maintenance towards minimising the chances of serious thatch accumulation. Fungicidal applications should, for example, be kept to a minimum to avoid killing off useful soil fungi. Obviously, it is necessary to use fungicides to cure damaging diseases like fusarium but the damaging effects of fungicides should also be borne in mind.

Vertical mowing using rotary scarifiers is useful in preventing the accumulation of new thatch and, to some extent, in increasing the aeration of the very superficial layers. Frequent scarification using tools like the thatching reels or groomers on triple mowers is particularly important if carried out frequently, say every seven to ten days. It should be realised, however, that scarification can do little to remove thatch which is already accumulated, possibly to a depth of several inches. In the past, attempts have been made to remove such thatch by very severe scarification usually using pedestrian rotary scarifiers. Often this merely disrupts the putting surface and although considerable quantities of organic matter may be removed, the operation does nothing to attack the causes of thatch build-up and so the material tends to accumulate again quite rapidly to its former level.

A more effective approach to thatch control involves the use of aeration equipment – conventional spikers fitted with flat or hollow tines, or more specialised sub-aeration machinery. Aeration is particularly useful in letting air down into waterlogged thatch layers, so increasing the activity of useful soil organisms. Its effect on drainage is also significant in that getting water away into lower soil layers also increases the air supply and fungal activity in the upper layers. Top dressing with sand compost is most desirable both in firming and diluting spongy thatch layers and in improving surface drainage. In some situations waterlogging of the surface may be caused by deeper compaction or poor drainage at lower levels than may be reached by surface aerating equipment and in such cases reconstruction of the green or the introduction of a better pipe drainage system may be the only answer.

Since annual meadow-grass swards seem particularly prone to spongy thatch formation, reducing the proportion of this grass in the green should be useful. Annual meadow-grass is, in any event, undesirable in a golf green from other points of view. Annual meadow-grass is encouraged by excessive nitrogen fertiliser treatment, and by the over-use of phosphate. It is also favoured by heavy summer watering which in itself tends to increase fibre by reducing soil air. Annual meadow-grass should therefore be discouraged by limiting fertiliser and by keeping swards as dry as possible each summer.

In the case of moorland golf greens where swards are naturally bent and fescue, hard brown layers of fibrous thatch are quite common. Here, there may be no waterlogging or slow surface drainage, indeed such fibrous thatch is often associated with dry conditions. Sometimes over-acidity is the cause and lime treatment cannot be entirely ruled out as a method of control. The use of lime on golf greens can, however, have many undesirable side effects and should only be undertaken after very careful thought and as a last resort. Moorland fibrous thatch layers often respond well to frequent scarification and aeration work and it is probable that such mechanical treatment is the best method of reducing the problem in these circumstances.

Really serious thatch problems have in the past sometimes been tackled by thinly stripping off the turf, physically removing the remaining thatch then cultivating the underlying soil and relaying the green. It should be realised, however, that unless the cause of the thatch is eliminated in this operation the thatch layer will merely tend to accumulate once again after the turf has been replaced. Certainly, soil cultivation may eliminate soil compaction and hence waterlogging, but unless this is the prime cause of the problem such work can be an expensive waste of time. It is better to see if the problem can be tackled by less extreme means before such measures are considered.

Associated with dry moorland thatch is the condition known as 'dry patch'. Here, the surface becomes very dry and difficult to re-wet with poor grass growth and moss activity. The problem is often associated with fungal growth. In such cases aeration work and treatment with wetting agents may be useful, together with elimination of surface high spots which tend to shed water.

(CGC 1 : 14)

PLATE 3: Scarifying a putting green with a pedestrian-operated rotary scarifier, in this case the SISIS Auto-Rotorake Mk.4. Groomer and thatching reels attached to mowers provide alternative methods of carrying out lighter scarification or vertical mowing work. (Courtesy SISIS Equipment (Macclesfield) Ltd.)

SECTION 4
THE MAINTENANCE OF GOLF GREENS FURTHER INFORMATION, WITH PARTICULAR REFERENCE TO PUTTING QUALITY

--- ❖❖❖ ---

Irrigation Management

Winter Play & Frost

Pin Positions

The Speed of Putting Surfaces

The Care of the Golf Course

WATERING GREENS : PRINCIPLES AND PERSPECTIVES

Principles

Is Watering Necessary?

Looking at this subject from a purist point of view, i.e. solely in terms of quality of grasses on greens, the answer is probably, "No". If one is lucky enough to have bent/fescue or even just bentgrass dominated greens, the turf will be sufficiently drought tolerant to survive most of the stretches of dry weather we (occasionally) experience in this country, if other maintenance practices are adapted to take account of minimising drought stress. Also, a measure of drought stress can give the most desirable turfgrass species a competitive edge over less drought-tolerant grasses such as *Poa annua.*

However, taking a more realistic line, some ability to control moisture availability beneath greens is virtually essential if putting surfaces are to be produced to a consistently good standard to meet the demands of today's golfers. Indeed, it is not unrealistic to say that any course which is played more than moderately (say 30,000 rounds per year and above) really does need a sophisticated automatic irrigation system if necessary watering is to be carried out adequately without interrupting the throughput of play.

Losses of water from the soil due to evaporation and transpiration can be as much as 2.5 mm per day in a British summer. Watering becomes necessary when rainfall is inadequate to compensate for this and when soil moisture reserves are depleted to the point where the grass will start to show signs of drought stress. A small degree of stress, however, is not always undesirable. For example, if a slight moisture deficit is allowed to develop in the spring, this will encourage deeper rooting as the plants are forced to search below the top few inches for water. Such a sward would then be better prepared to withstand dry summer conditions than one with only a shallow root system. However, watering usually becomes necessary at some time during dry spells even when there is a fairly deep root system. There are various ways of determining just when to start watering. One technical approach is to use tensiometers installed in the soil to give an indication of the soil moisture tension (i.e. the amount of work which grass roots must do to extract water), but this method is not commonly used. Most experienced greenkeepers can judge when watering is necessary by probing the ground, examining soil cores and keeping a close watch on known drought sensitive areas which show signs of droughting before the rest of the turf.

Objectives of Watering

In an ideal world there would be two objectives to be gained from watering greens:-

- to maintain a uniformity of playing surface characteristics between each and within each putting surface during spells of dry weather;
- to prevent a lack of moisture from restricting top growth during dry weather and leading to turf damage through management and wear.

These two points summarise the total need for water on golf greens, and it will be evident that there is no mention in the above of 'holding qualities' or 'speed' or 'colour'. This is because if control of watering is dependent on all or each of these three latter factors, the whole approach to watering is more likely than not causing actual long-term harm to the greens in respect of their year-round usability. In addition, inadvisable watering can ultimately cost the Club a lot of money too, from the aspects of creating a need for larger course budgets, together with the possibility of loss of revenue.

Perspectives

Dangers to be Avoided

There are two problems which can arise from routine watering of greens: over-watering; and under-watering. Remember that the former can be as damaging as the latter. Over-generous irrigation produces an environment in which only shallow-rooted grasses can survive, the result of which is:

— *Poa annua* dominated turf with the desired grasses precluded
— and heavy thatch build up at the base of the sward.

In playing terms, this does not mean a club cannot have satisfactory greens through the summer (once *Poa annua* seeding has ended) but for the remaining eight months of the year the club can be left with yellow, wet, soft, foot-printed, disease-riddled, mossy, weedy, pitch-marked, worn, muddy putting surfaces. Temporary greens will be the rule, not the exception, in such circumstances.

Providing a remedy to such problems is by no means as easy as creating them. A cure can take years of hard work and can cost a great deal of money. It should be noted too that working through a cure can also be a very painful process in terms of the loss of surface which can arise in summer as a result of trying to change the botanical composition of a green back to what it should be.

It must always be remembered that a green is not a 'static object', it is a living system, and what can be produced on the surface depends very much on the year-round quality of the sward's environment.

How to Avoid the Pitfalls

Correct policy for watering greens in spells of dry weather through the summer is to imitate frequent light summer showers (rather than frequent or even occasional tropical monsoons) simply to hold moisture (not free-running water) through the topsoil profile. So, watering needs to be done lightly but with sufficient frequency, both overall and on drought-sensitive patches, to maintain a uniformity of moisture availability and a receptiveness to applied water over the whole of each green surface.

Saturating the soil and keeping it saturated creates the environment of the peat bog beneath the putting surface, while simply dampening the top while the soil underneath remains dry gives a competitive edge to shallow-rooted turfgrass species.

However, striking a balance to achieve the above criteria is easier said than done:–
- what is happening on the surface in dry weather often bears no reflection of the moisture availability in the sub-surface.
- Even the most sophisticated pop-up watering systems cannot automatically put water just where it is needed,
- and where pop-ups are not available, there is the constant battle of trying to water greens carefully and adequately while a constant stream of players is either switching off the sprinklers or throwing them off the green.

Further factors which have to be taken into consideration when devising and managing a watering programme are:–
- the soil type beneath greens, as some soils are more receptive to applied water than others.
- Variations in contouring, aspect, siting, shadiness, etc., of **each individual** green site.
- Constantly changing weather conditions affecting the rate of evaporation and transpiration.
- Whether or not moisture availability is a limiting factor to growth. (Could it be soil temperature instead?)
- Keeping an eye on the weather so that prolonged rain does not saturate greens

which are already moist as a result of watering.

All the above call for constant checking and adjustment of watering practice.

Sprinklers

The size and shape of the area to be covered usually determines the choice of sprinkler. There are rotary, impact drive types which give a circular coverage and are suitable for use on golf greens. Pop-up sprinklers are permanently installed in the ground and only appear above the surface when in use. They give circular or part-circular coverage and systems can be designed for most sports areas. They are popular on golf courses where they can be used to irrigate tees and fairways as well as the greens. Pop-up systems are expensive but they have advantages as they save labour and they can be set to operate at night when there will be no interference with play.

Water Supplies

The commonest source of water for irrigation is the mains supply. This is perhaps the most convenient source, but the supply may be cut off or usage restricted when it is most needed. Bore holes, rivers, streams and ponds are also used but permission is usually needed from the catchment authority. With these sources it is important that sufficient quantities are available and that the water is free of injurious contaminants. Water from bore holes sometimes contains appreciable amounts of lime, whereas there are some cases of over-acid supplies from surface streams and ponds. A soft water is best and it is always a good idea to check the quality of any bore hole or surface water supply from time to time.

Irrigation Management

When irrigation is necessary the amount of water applied should be enough to maintain no more than a sufficiency of moisture at the rootzone, say the top 150 mm (6 in.) of soil. The irrigation system should have the capacity to supply the equivalent of about 25 mm of rain per week and the rate at which the water should be applied depends on the infiltration rate of the surface. Run-off should be avoided as it results in waste and causes over-watering of hollows, leaving high spots dry. On fine turf areas overall solid tine aeration is a useful preliminary to watering as this will aid penetration and help get the water through to the roots where it is needed. Round solid tines are recommended in preference to slit tines because with the latter the slits can dry out in the hot sun and open up, thus producing an uneven playing surface.

It is important that an adequate amount of water is applied – a minimum of 11 litres per m^2 on each occasion. There are two approaches to watering. One is to water quite heavily two or three times per week so that on each occasion the water gets well down to the roots and allowing the surface to dry in between. The alternative approach, which has become popular where there are pop-up systems also has merit. This involves very light watering (sometimes every night in dry weather) to maintain a moisture level at the roots which has never been allowed to get too low. This technique of more frequent watering is often necessary on areas with a very free draining sandy construction which tend to dry out rapidly. With both methods it is very important to make sure that the water applied actually gets down to the rootzone. One problem with pop-up systems on golf courses has been over-watering. This is because the operation has been made so easy and also because decisions have been made to use the system frequently in attempts to justify its initial cost. Careful use of any irrigation system is important as there have been cases of annual meadow-grass and thatch build up where only light surface sprinklings have been given. If only the surface soil is kept moist this will encourage the shallow-rooted annual meadow-grass. This grass will produce thatch which will in turn hold more water at the surface and so the problem builds up. Most greenkeepers are aware of these problems now and there has been a change to more sensible use of irrigation systems.

As with many other aspects of turf management, irrigation is not always as straightforward as it first appears. Dry patches can develop during drought which do not respond to normal watering. These are caused by poor water infiltration and may be due to the presence of a dry fibre layer at the surface, raised features (on a golf green), compaction or the development of 'dry patch' which has been associated with fungal activity. Where such problems do occur, specialised local treatment should be provided. Carry out plenty of solid tine aeration at close centres using a hand fork. In addition to carrying out routine sprinkling, more often than not there will be a need to be making good use of spot watering techniques and plenty of wetting agent.

Wetting agents are detergents (materials which reduce the surface tension of water), the use of which assists the penetration of water into soil. There are now many proprietary turf wetting agents on the market. Wetting agents can be used on a routine basis on turf areas subject to dry patches, at intervals throughout the summer months. They can be of particular value as spot treatments on high areas or banks where water tends to run off. The point of using them is simply to make watering that much more effective in sustaining uniformity of the turf area.

Such an approach to watering is obviously labour-intensive, even where there is an automatic irrigation system installed. To be able to keep this labour input to a minimum, it is essential to have a well-designed watering system, but unfortunately many of the pop-up irrigation systems installed from the early days in the late 1960s and right through the 1970s do not meet the necessary criteria. The end result of inadequate design is poor distribution of water – local areas of greens getting drenched while the rest remain dry. With such systems, unless there is a good appreciation of their defects, and there is a high labour input to compensate for their deficiencies (nearly as much as if stand-pipe sprinklers were being used), then over-watering **and** under-watering problems are going to develop simultaneously.

There is ground swell within golf clubs to modernise out-dated pop-up systems, but up-grading is expensive and it is difficult to demonstrate the need for such improvements to committees and memberships in general. Nevertheless, if any club is to obtain full value from the insurance the installation of a watering system provides, and is to achieve the best from organisation of labour around the course as a whole, up-grading of watering systems to the minimum specification of the British Turf and Landscape Irrigation Association is vital.

As well as being needed for irrigation during dry spells, water is also needed for routine operations such as weed and worm control and the watering in of fertilisers for fine turf.

Finally, a note on maintenance. All irrigation systems should be regularly checked and any faults dealt with as they are found. Proper maintenance can eliminate many problems. Pumps and ancillary equipment should be serviced regularly and all pipes prone to frost damage should be drained before the winter.

(CGC 1 : 18)

THOUGHTS ON HAND WATERING

Demands for the perfect putting green at every hole become ever more exacting year by year. Running parallel with this is the weight of responsibility placed on the Course Manager in providing for the demands of Committees, whilst at the same time managing his greens in such a way as to obtain and maintain a technical base of high quality upon which to build presentation according to needs from week to week. From this a conflict arises in 'distance of vision': the golfer takes his assessment of greens on an average of day to day condition; while the Course Manager is aiming to balance this short term assessment against the longer term requirements of the course, looking months, or indeed years, ahead.

One of the flashpoints of this conflict of aims and ideas concerns use of water, that is whether or not water is over-used, or indeed under-used. Few involved in golf course management would argue that a high percentage of courses have not suffered some adverse effect from excess use of irrigation water on greens over the past 20 years, and the vast majority of Head Greenkeepers fight against over-watering. But those in the know are heavily out-numbered by others whose reaction to firmer putting surfaces and the odd brown patch is to apply more and more water to give lush greens and soft plugging (holding) surfaces.

Given that high capacity pop-up watering systems are here to stay, many courses have the potential for over-watering greens. So, what techniques can be applied to keep the pressure for damage to a minimum? The classic advice is always to pick out the 'hot spots' on greens – patches which drought early in dry weather – and as these dry out, start a watering programme. There is a lot to be said too for routine probing of greens to examine moisture availability within the top couple of inches of the profile. The use of a moisture meter to measure water availability within the rootzone can be valuable too. While the exact numbers may be meaningless, they are useful for comparison, and taking measurements or readings does give a good impression of professionalism.

There is no doubt anywhere that successful watering of greens depends upon starting early in a dry spell and keeping the moisture just topped up to nearly moist, but no more. This does run contrary to the conventional agronomic theory that occasional wetting and drying cycles favour the more desirable grasses and deeper rooting. But it has to be accepted too that theory does not always meet needs in practice.

One of the main objectives of golf green maintenance is to produce good uniformity in terms of density of grass cover, completeness of cover, and quick green speed both within each and between every green. When you have the typical situation of 18 greens with varying degrees of featuring, soil type and soil depth, and a constant risk of being caught out by unexpected heavy rain just after watering, no greenkeeper can really afford the luxury of a wetting and drying cycle approach to watering if he can possibly avoid it. Also, where the little-and-often practice is applied well, there seems to be little detriment to the production of good bentgrass turf.

It would therefore seem logical to be as flexible as possible in the capacity to put water on to greens, just when and where it is needed. Watering high spots whilst avoiding low hollows, or damping down areas and greens prone to baking, or selectively watering greens open to the sun (or worse still wind), whilst avoiding shady, sheltered, low lying places, before droughting problems set in, keeps back the need for a blanket approach until there is a general drying. When there is general drying one needs to use pop-up sprinklers, but hand hoses will be adequate beforehand.

It is important to stress that we do not advocate such watering with the aim of maintaining softer, easy to hold greens – quite the reverse. A flexible hand hosing programme helps to keep use of water to the minimum overall, whilst helping to keep the golfer satisfied. There are less likely to be complaints concerning hard greens if the development of brown patches can be kept to an absolute minimum, while at the same time the turf itself need not be lush green either.

Beyond the early stages of a dry spell there is a continuing need for hand-held hosing in that no pop-up system is automatic in the sense of being self-regulating. Again the shape, siting, aspect, featuring, soil type and soil depth of each green (and its apron), together with the quality of the design of the watering system itself and the effects of rain, mean results of pop-up watering can never be perfect. Minimum damage, with maximum benefit, calls for use of pop-ups as the lowest common denominator, i.e. watering those places well covered, which may well not be enough for individual areas of green, and these have to be topped up by hand hosing.

Judicious use of hose pipes has extra value too in getting maximum benefit from a wetting agent programme. To be effective in containing the major problem of dry patch, wetting agents have to be applied frequently (as often as every two to three weeks in serious cases), the programme of wetting agent application has to be started early in the year, and the detergents have to be washed in and backed up by ongoing watering. Allowing for spot treatments of wetting agent gets it just where it will have the best value, whilst keeping the costs to an essential minimum. The use of wetting agent applicators in conjunction with hand hosing is beneficial in controlling dry patch.

Lastly, in putting forward the case for hand-held hosing as part of the greens irrigation programme, the Institute is well aware that some course managers apply this technique already. Also, that it is very common at clubs which are using this technique just to use open hoses with the traditional thumb to break up the spray. Thumbs tend to get cold and/or tired. Then, open hosing jets water across the surface rather than encouraging it to sink in where it is needed. Some 'sophistication' can be achieved with a bent piece of copper pipe in the end of the hose, but why not large shower heads fitted with a tap – cheap technology!

(CGC 1 : 19)

GOLF GREENS IN WINTER

The British climate is never kind to winter golf and the heavier the soil on which the course is built the more numerous the problems. With new courses, though the local soil may be clay, the actual greens are often built with light sandy topsoil mixes (the proportions pre-determined by laboratory tests) with special provision for under-drainage. Some are made almost entirely of sand. Sadly, though, there are green-keepers still nursing along sets of golf greens built perhaps 50 or 60 years ago of heavy clay soil with no drainage layers and few drain pipes. There are plenty of such golf courses north of London (on the London clay) and elsewhere, providing golfers and management with many more headaches during the average winter than the courses on lighter soils, like the Bagshot sands in Surrey for instance.

Hole-Cutting

In wet weather the greenkeeper must have a regular programme so far as changing the pin holes is concerned. Never wait until the turf is starting to show wear before cutting a new hole. Use pin holes which are likely to be tolerated in winter to a greater degree than in the main golfing season. Here is a chance to put the pin nearer the edge where there is probably more spongy fibre, simply due to lack of wear. Moss and patches of Yorkshire fog do not like the concentrated traffic round the pin hole and cutting the hole in a mossy area can often be useful in reducing it.

The Value of Temporary Greens

Some golf clubs site the pins on the front of the greens all through the winter, keeping the rest of the green free from play until the spring, and never use temporary greens. This is certainly one of the options but, especially on the clay greens, there is a strong case for using the greens more or less in the normal way through the winter (though with more of the less favourite pin placements) but coming off the greens on to temporary greens when the surfaces are exceptionally wet and soft or when there is any frost either in or on the ground. For this to be done without an abnormal number of entries in the suggestions/complaints book, temporary greens must be available where putting surfaces are not vastly inferior to the main greens. They should be sited well to the right or left of the main greens where practicable (not directly in front as seems to be the case quite often) and should be carefully prepared, well in advance of use, by fertilizing, weedkilling, scarifying, spiking and top dressing – in fact, by similar management to that of the main greens.

The greatest harm is done following frost when a green is beginning to thaw out after a hard frost: this is when the grass roots suffer most.

Prevent the 'Beaten Tracks'!

Keep an eye on the surrounds for signs of undue stress caused by processions of trolleys. Be ready to re-route, possibly with the aid of real physical obstacles like hoops, or with plastic white strips inset in the turf or similar, depending on the degree of co-operation from the members. It would seem that rolls of barbed wire would be needed to turn some golfers from their usual route!

Breaking the Ice?

Some winters are bad for golf greens, especially 1979/80 and 1962/63 when many golf greens suffered severely, perhaps the worst affected being those in North West England. The difference between 1979/80 and 1962/63 lay in the fact that the turf was covered with snow for lengthy periods at a time in 1979/80. In 1962/63 there were alternate thawings and freezings which resulted in the complete destruction of the grass in the hollows where the frozen water lay. Wise after the event, we formed the impression that it was probably better to break the ice in the hollows than to adopt a policy of "laisser faire".

Mow When Needed

Grass growth does not stop completely in a normal winter, coarser grasses like Yorkshire fog and perennial ryegrass in particular growing away from the rest if allowed. Occasional topping of the turf with the mower on a relatively dry surface is good for both grass and golfer. Top at about 8 mm and use a pedestrian mower rather than one of the combination triples when the surface is at all inclined to be soft.

Spike When Dry Enough

Regular winter spiking, preferably with a machine fitted with sturdy long slit tines, whenever weather conditions permit, is always a great help in preserving good drainage and encouraging root growth. If possible, slitting should take place at weekly or two weekly intervals.

Sandy Top Dressings Useful

After spiking, a top dressing principally composed of a suitable medium lime-free sand (with a small admixture of sandy compost or topsoil to avoid the risk of producing a rootbreak at some future stage) can be most helpful in firming up a green which is soft in winter, although probably the chance has gone by this time; such dressings are better given in the autumn when the weather is more open and dry.

Don't Let the Trees Take Over!

Trees have a substantial contribution to make to the charm of many a golf course and to the character of the holes, but they *will* keep growing! Winter is the time to do some cutting back where necessary. A thick stand of trees to the side or behind a green will often shut off the sunlight entirely through the winter, keeping the green damp and soft, subject to diseases like fusarium patch and invasion by moss and algae. Rain dripping from overhanging branches will injure the grass directly by sheer physical impact (in some areas it also carries down pollution deposited on the tree). Tree roots enter the green and in summer rob the grass of its fair share of water and plant food. Winter is the time to assess the position objectively, rating turf first and trees a bad second, and to chop or trim where necessary for the green's sake. Where tree roots are a problem in the green, and several greens are affected, it might be worthwhile hiring one of the small trenching machines for a period and using it to cut a narrow slit round the greens, severing roots during the process. It is also useful to place a thick (1000 gauge) polythene sheet in the trench wall to prevent further root invasion.

Compost Making

Winter is the time for building the new compost heaps which are needed to maintain continuity of supply, for turning over the heaps which are half-way to maturity (having already been standing out in the open for 12 months) and for breaking down the heaps which are mature (after standing for two years or so), bringing the compost under cover for drying, riddling and storage for eventual use as top dressing. Good natural compost derived from compost heaps made by stacking alternate layers of sandy topsoil and organic material (preferably farmyard manure or horse manure) is not seen around on golf courses these days as often as it used to be. There is perhaps nothing to beat it, and greens where the basic treatment consists of plenty of sandy compost with the minimum of 'artificial' fertiliser are those, as a rule, with the best turf. In order to make good compost though, adequate weather-proof buildings are needed of suitable size for entry and exit with tractor and trailer, a hard floor for mixing and mechanical equipment for screening. Commercial top dressings of acceptable quality are, however, available nowadays, and the majority of clubs prefer this option as opposed to the home-production of compost. The labour costs of home-production are considerable, and increased levels of winter golf mean that staff have less time to spare during the winter than was formerly the case.

The Problem of Cold Springs

The main top dressing is usually done in early autumn but it should not be forgotten that remarkable benefit can be obtained from a compost dressing applied about the end of February or the beginning of March to repair imperfections in putting surfaces caused by winter play and (perhaps more important still) to provide some early encouragement to growth. Early spring is a bad time for golf greens. Many greens in this country have a turf which is mainly a blend of bentgrass and annual meadow-grass. In March or April, before the soil has warmed up appreciably, there is often a period when there is uneven growth related to the mixed composition of the sward since some grasses start growth earlier than others. This gives rise to bumpy putting surfaces which persist until the annual meadow-grass catches up with the bent. An early top dressing does wonders in helping the slower-growing grasses to catch up and also incidentally gives the grass a better colour – try top dressing just half a green with a good top dressing material in the early spring and the proof will be clearly seen.

Timely Fertiliser Application

Before the end of the winter thought should be given to the spring fertiliser and arrangements made to have it ready when required. Springs have been late in recent years and many greenkeepers, waiting for the warmer weather which was so late in coming, left the spring fertiliser dressings too late. Whilst it is true that fertilisers may, up to a point, be wasted if they go on before the soil warms up sufficiently, to wait too long is just as bad and can leave the golfers to struggle with unfair putting surfaces right into June.

(CGC 1 : 22)

GOLF GREENS – SPRING DEVELOPMENT

Is it Spring, Or Just an Extension of Winter?

The spring is probably the most difficult time of the year for the greenkeeper in this country. This is not just because the weather can be at it's most unpredictable and inclement but also because golfers are emerging from their winter's torpor expecting good playing conditions. Few golfers appreciate, or indeed seem to care, that the demands of growth in the spring and the demands of the golfer tend to be incompatible. It does not help that the professional golfing season swings into action in April with the US Masters on our TV screens in April. This is golf at its most ornate and has the average member drooling over the velvety texture of the fairways, never mind the greens. Comparison with their own course is always unfavourable and wholly unfair as how many courses in this country enjoy the climate, never mind the low level of play and huge resources for maintenance, that is to be found in the hallowed surroundings of Augusta, Georgia?

Spring in the UK can be exceptionally cold and dry, or exceptionally cold and wet. Very occasionally we get a spring of the type remembered from our youth; a spring of mild weather, light rainfall and blooming greenness all around, but did this romantic vision of spring ever really exist? Many of the elder statesmen of greenkeeping will tell you not! So, more often than not, the start of the growing season tends to be a false start. Soil temperatures have to reach a consistent 5-6° C before grasses will grow uniformly and before they will respond effectively to fertiliser application. Bumpy greens are commonplace in the spring as the different grass species that make up any green respond with varying growth vigour. The level of moisture in the soil, high and low, influences the speed and uniformity of grass pick-up in the spring. Too wet and soil temperature is slow to rise, too low and early season wilt-stress will be seen. Bring into the equation the stress that the turf has been under through the winter, both from adverse weather and a continuation of play and compaction, and it is no wonder that many greenkeepers fear for their livelihood as March approaches! Greenkeepers have been known, on the odd occasion, to blame the weather for problems, or perceived problems, when minor adjustment of management could redress inadequacies in playing performance or presentation. Have no doubt however that blaming the weather for poor playing surfaces through the spring is often a legitimate excuse.

If we accept the vagaries of spring weather and the fact that golf greens in the UK are unlikely to play like the billiard tables of Augusta, is there anything that can be done to enhance the enjoyment of golf at this time of the year? The answer is yes, but all aspects of the maintenance programme must be addressed.

Bringing on Greens in the Spring

Coming out of the winter, golf greens are usually cold, wet and uneven. Promoting growth is the ideal but protecting what you have is often more practical. The following maintenance operations are probably the most important to bear in mind to bring the best out of putting surfaces through the difficult spring months:

Mowing: The temptation when faced with bumpy greens exhibiting uneven growth is to cut down to the slowest growing species. This is the worst thing you can do as it stresses every component of the turf and will slow down uniform growth. Be in no rush to bring the cutting height below 8 mm in the spring but there will be benefit from increasing the frequency of mowing to check the growth of the stronger grasses. Hand cutting can also help as the ironing action of the mower's roller will produce a smoother finish. Hand cutting when growth is slow can also reduce stress on green perimeters.

Scarification: A thorough scarification to lift organic debris may clean out the base of the turf and create a healthier environment for early growth but great care has to be taken not to damage young grasses emerging from their winter dormancy. Occasional, light verticutting can regulate the coarser grasses which grow more vigorously, and look so unsightly, at this time of year. Blades should only flick through the top growth and fortnightly treatment will be more than adequate, taking out minor surface blemishes, e.g. pitch marks, as well as straggly grass stems. Delay the onset of grooming until more even growth occurs.

Irrigation: Dry soils warm quicker than wet ones in the spring. Therefore, watering should be delayed as long as possible. Remember that the water from the irrigation source is going to be extremely cold and application could well retard growth. On the other hand, we often experience very dry weather in the spring, particularly down the eastern side of the country where cold easterly winds can severely check the first promising signs of life. Local hand watering to potential drought prone areas, combined with wetting agent, will help restore even coverage once warmer weather arrives. One of the longer lasting wetting agents might be preferred, provided it can be applied with enough water to avoid scorch. It is in the spring where dry patch is initiated as the top few inches of the soil dry out completely, eventually producing a water break which summer irrigation cannot bridge. Subsequently, irrigation only tends to moisten the surface layers of thatch and soil encouraging shallow rooting. If this situation is noted, treatment with the water injecting HydroJect could be beneficial come May/June to restore a uniform moisture gradient.

Fertiliser: The ability of the turf to respond to feed in the spring is directly related to soil temperature and moisture content. The soil must be warm enough for growth and there must be enough moisture to dissolve the fertiliser and to allow for absorption of the solution into the grass roots. The spring failing of slow release fertilisers is due to inappropriate environmental conditions for uptake. For early season growth, readily available nitrogen is what is required, hence the use of lawn sand and basic powder fertiliser over the years which contain sulphate of ammonia. Liquid feeds may give a reasonable response provided there is ample nitrogen in the analysis. Phosphate can give a boost to growth in the spring, provided soil analysis indicates a need. A little iron, say in lawn sand, will hit any moss and give colour but be wary of excessive iron in the spring as it induces the first stages of wilt. Organic conditioners may help stimulate root development, the spring being one of the main periods for root extension. "Gently does it" should be the way with feeding in the spring, avoiding lush growth which can be badly scarred by late frosts and cold, drying winds.

Top dressing: The application of a sand:soil mix will improve the smoothness of putting surfaces. Frequent dustings is the best means of dressing in the spring. 0.5 kg/m^2 applied up to once a fortnight as early as February/March if the weather allows through to the end of May would be ideal, ensuring that the preceding dressing is thoroughly absorbed by the turf before applying the next. Top dressing will not only perfect trueness but can also guard against rapid surface drying. Practically, it can be problematic getting onto the greens to carry out this work as the course gets busier. At the end of the day the answer lies with the golfer, greens can be smoother but at the cost of some disruption to play.

Aeration: Aeration should not cease with the last days of winter. Compaction from the winter's play must be relieved, perhaps with micro hollow tining backed up with top dressing. Continued deep slitting is not advisable as the drying winds associated with the first few months of the year can cause slit marks to gape. Intensive treatment, e.g. Verti-draining or jumbo coring, might also be an error as slow growth prevents the tine holes closing over until well into the summer. There will be milder parts of the country where such work is feasible but for most of us, spring is not the time to experiment. A turn to minimally disruptive pencil solid tining or shallow chisel tining must be considered, particularly to ground which sheds water and funnelled traffic routes.

Befriend the Golfer

Despite your best efforts, spring weather will always be the regulating factor to the condition of golf greens possibly affecting trueness and pace as late as June, especially to courses in the north, on the east coast and at high altitude. Explain the problems faced by the greenkeeper and the efforts being made on the golfers' behalf to the members, perhaps in a short bulletin or newsletter on the notice board. Golfers moan about the condition of the greens every spring, conveniently forgetting that they were no better the year before but were the best greens ever seen during the summer. Don't panic, the same will happen this year, next year and, unless the "Greenhouse Effect" becomes reality, probably every year that the golf clubs are dusted down after a winter's storage. Whatever happens, do not rush into rash measures as forcing growth on through watering and feeding, overly close cutting and severe grooming will backfire. Patience has to be part of the greenkeeper's make up, and spring is the time of the year when your patience, with the turf and the golfer, will be tested to the limit!

(SPI : B.189)

ON THE MOVE : HOLE CHANGING ON THE GREEN

What could be simpler than changing the hole position on a golf green? It demands no great physical strength or continuous effort, one-piece hole cutters make the business of plug extraction simplicity itself. Remove the cup from the old hole, place in the new one, tamping into position with the rim about 25 mm below putting green level. Replace the turf plug in the old hole and firm it in and off to the next green. To the lay golfer nothing could be easier except possibly selecting the site. First choice for them will always be centre of the green, preferably right at the base of any slight hollow or depression, what the golf architect Fred Hawtree always referred to as "armchair comfort". If your pitch was good enough to make the green there was every chance of getting down in two. There will certainly be no complaints from fellow golfers initially, but watch out for fireworks later on as the "best" positions become badly worn, weakened and uneven.

Have you every wondered why the central areas of so many greens are inundated with annual meadow-grass? One factor is certainly over use for the pin where a few selected positions are used in rotation – summer and often winter too, with no regard to weather or ground conditions. It is a frequent occurrence even through late autumn, winter and early spring to see the flags sited within a metre of badly worn thinned out turf at or near the centres of greens. These are the very places vital for hole positions during the main summer competitions, and many golfers still fail to appreciate that they cannot thrash such places unmercifully through the winter and still find them in perfect condition for the spring meeting.

Available Pin Positions

First look at what you now have in the way of pin positions on greens. There cannot be too many, and far too often there are too few areas that are satisfactory for use. Ideally we need an area between 0.6 and 1 m around the hole which should be level and it should not be within three or four paces of a severe slope or ridge. In an ideal world, and this should certainly apply on newly built putting greens, at least 80% of the available space should be capable of taking the flag at some time or other during the year.

On many older courses where surfaces often have exaggerated contours good pin placings, even for summer use, may be limited. In situations like that it is worth looking at the possibility of extending the greens, perhaps simply by working on the immediate apron and gradually incorporating it into the putting surface to allow a few extra pin positions, particularly for autumn and winter use. Otherwise the suitable places are likely to be over-used and never entirely satisfactory.

With so much golf played nowadays, it is equally important that golfers are aware that as much of the available putting surface on greens has to be used simply to spread wear and tear as evenly as possible. That inevitably means that on some greens more "adventurous" pin placings need to be chosen during the late autumn and winter if the better areas are to be given every change of recovering fully and being at their best for the main summer competition season.

Winter Strategy

Since our overall aim is to provide as near 365 days' play on the main putting greens as weather and ground conditions will permit, it follows that wear and tear must be spread evenly, particularly during autumn and winter. At that time of year ground conditions are the overriding factor so make as much use of the back and sides of the greens as possible during the drier days of autumn. As surfaces become wetter, gradually work forward down either side reserving the front edges for the late winter when it is always desirable to minimise golf traffic across turf.

Some greenkeepers adopt a rule of thumb in winter, taking pin positions to within 2 m of the edge of the putting surface. It can also be helpful to adopt a local rule that flags should not be attended in winter to minimise footprinting and wear and the potential for"crowning" around the hole. Nominating one player to retrieve balls from the cup, or the "gimmies" close to the hole can also reduce wear around it which is all important in the non-growing period.

Frequency of the hole changing is just as important as in summer because of the additional wear factor and far slower, if any recovery. At courses which insist on playing greens that are iron bound with frost it can often be useful to have two holes cut so that the pin can be swapped between them at need.

Summer Strategy

Once growth restarts there can be a gradual return to the more favourable summer pin placings. An old Scottish greenkeeper once reported that for the first spring meeting of the year he was always careful to choose hole positions that were as easy as possible, which is sound psychology since at that time of year weather and ground conditions are more than enough to contend with. Bear in mind the overall strategy in summer is still aimed at spreading wear evenly, at the same time avoiding areas reserved for more important club events and any tournaments which are scheduled that season. Some greenkeepers find it helpful to adopt a rough rule of thumb based on a clock face. If Monday's shift is placed at one o'clock the next change will be diagonally opposite at about seven o'clock and so on. With increasing amounts of play in summer, frequency of hole changes needs to be stepped up. As a minimum on Mondays and Fridays, but with additional changes Wednesday, if the course is busy, and for weekend competitions perhaps on Saturday as well.

Major Club Events/Tournaments

For major events in the club calendar it is worth going to that bit of extra trouble. Select likely areas for pin positions some six weeks in advance and try to keep general play away from those sites. One of the main aims in hole selection is that the good shot should be rewarded and the bad one penalised. The design of the hole and architect's intention as to how it should be played needs to be considered. Assess how length into the green might be affected by wind and rain and the holding quality of the surface. Always obtain a weather forecast and if rain is imminent avoid the low lying places which may gather water.

Allow sufficient space on the green for the anticipated shot, ie. towards the back for a long iron. As a rule the cup should be at least 4 m from the edge of the green. Positions of bunkers and slopes may require the hole to be further in from the edge. If possible the turf surface should be flat for 0.6-1 m around the hole and clear of severe gradients.

Aim for a balance of hole positions through the course between left and right, front, centre and rear. If the tournament continues over several days try to maintain the same degree of difficulty, ie. six relatively easy sites, six moderate and six that are fairly difficult for each day's hole positions. Use the pin placings which are closest to the places players walk off for the early rounds.

In Practice

It is taken as read that when selecting a hole position areas of coarser grasses such as creeping soft grass or perennial ryegrass will be avoided so as not to spread them further within the turf. The one-piece hole cutter has made the job of changing holes far easier now, given reasonably uniform soil. Consolidated soils, stones and a too shallow rootzone mix over drainage gravel as always bring their own problems. At the start of the season ensure the hole cutter is perfectly round and that the cups do not exceed 108 mm in outside diameter. If possible the cup should be set at least 25 mm below the putting green surface.

When the cup is in position it is worthwhile using a flat board over the hole and evenly firming down to avoid any suggestion of a raised "lip" or "crowning" around the hole. Trim around the edge with curved scissors to remove any grass leaves that are growing outwards. For special occasions, the exposed soil above the cup rim is often painted white using a non phytotoxic paint. Allow sufficient time for the paint to dry before play starts.

Take care when replacing plugs in the old holes to ensure a good fit, and especially that the surface of the plug is level with the turf around it. A plug left low upsets levels and restricts choice of pin positions later on. If it is high it will be liable to scalp. Before mowing on the day following a hole change and particularly if there has been rainfall or overnight irrigation, ensure that the old plug is refirmed into the hole. Thatchy turf plugs are liable to swell with moisture and are thus more prone to skinning.

It can be helpful to aid recovery if a handful of sandy top dressing material is rubbed into the joint around the old turf plug. In dry weather a soaking with dilute wetting agent solution can also ensure that the plug does not dry out and shrink, or worse still succumb to drought.

Even a brief article such as this illustrates there is more to changing hole positions than is immediately obvious. Like so many other jobs in greenkeeping a good deal of thought and care has to go into making the right decision and planning ahead if satisfactory results are to be achieved the year round.

(DFB : B.190)

FIRM VERSUS SOFT PUTTING GREENS

[1] The debate

This subject can still generate heated argument as the truths are often painful to accept by the golfer, who has limited or no understanding of the interaction of construction, turf composition, climate and management.

Pressures are often exerted by the rank and file (including committees) to create soft, so called "holding" greens during the summer. The corollery of spongy, pitch marked and disease ridden greens over the winter months are conveniently forgotten and either the climate or greenkeeper is blamed for the deterioration.

[2] Target versus traditional golf

There is a fundamental difference between 'target' golf developed in other countries (due to climatic factors) and the natural game played in this country on firm greens – epitomised by the links. The installation of watering systems during the 1960's and 1970's enabled the playing surface characteristics to be manipulated in an all too successful attempt to emulate the target greens typified by green, lush surfaces throughout the summer. With increasing play and compaction a downward spiral in the long-term performance of our greens, linked with annual meadow-grass dominance and thatch accumulation, was inevitable.

Links golf is still the closest to our natural game, which demands mastery of a wide range of shots including the 'pitch and run'. In the summer the playing surface can be lively in dry spells of weather, but the quality of winter golf on links courses is universally admired.

Usually the turf is formed of a significant proportion of bent and to a lesser extent fescue. Let us consider what happens when a golf ball pitches on a dry, firm surface of this type. At the first impact with the turf the surface deforms slightly but springs back, some of the initial backspin is scrubbed off, but on the second or third bounce residual backspin tends to check or even stop the ball, due to the frictional forces at the point of impact opposing the forward motion of the ball.

A typically soft annual meadow-grass and thatch playing surface performs very differently. The momentum of the ball is absorbed completely by the permanent deformation of the turf (pitch mark) and the backspin is killed. Sometimes the ball pops out of the pitchmark as backspin is converted to topspin after impact and rolls forward. Professionals may impart considerately more backspin, in which case the ball is momentarily at rest before friction takes over and the ball is drawn backwards, sometimes spectacular distances.

[3] Irrigation : the controlling factor

A turf based on *Festuca* and *Agrostis* will survive temporary periods of water shortage, but annual meadow-grass will tend to die unless kept well watered through the summer months. There are also annoying side effects when a policy of minimal watering is applied to annual meadow-grass. A dry fescue/ bent turf can be described as firm, but resilient, whereas an annual meadow-grass turf is truly hard when dry. Under these circumstances it can be observed that a number of bounces are needed before the ball is brought to rest, as backspin has little effect and energy or momentum of the golf ball is not lost due to deformation of the turf. No wonder the golfers call for more water!

Under our climatic restrictions it is not practical to have target golf in the summer and firm, uniform winter putting greens. The two are mutually exclusive. Water must only be applied to keep greens alive, not manipulate playing surface qualities. Too often, the irrigation system is used to mask the shortcomings of the golfer. This can be described as the 5-wood syndrome, i.e. the golfer expects the ball to stop dead regardless of where the shot has been struck from or how well.

Golfers need to be re-educated in how to approach and play the game. Before the advent of irrigation systems the receptiveness, i.e. degree of softness, of the putting green was variable and the golfer had to adapt his game to the conditions. If putting greens are allowed to become a little drier and firmer today (in response to sound

143

management policies) the golfer often expresses the view that playing conditions are unfair! The element of the 'luck of the bounce' has largely been eliminated from the game as the golfer can pitch straight at the flag with impunity from any part of the golf course.

Some golf courses still have the legacy of excessive thatch accumulation and annual meadow-grass domination. It would be unrealistic to expect a rapid transformation to pure fescue/bent turf which is sustainable, due to pressures of play and constructional limitations. Firmer greens and superior winter surfaces are usually possible by accepting the short-term consequences of exercising tight control over watering (as well as fertiliser input). Over a period of years it is possible to reduce meadow-grass and to gradually produce a more traditional type of green, but long-term consistant management is vital.

[4] The influence of golfing equipment

It is too simplistic to assume that the ball/turf interaction has been the only factor influencing the current attitude to the game and approach to management policies. Developments in club head design and golf ball technology must also shoulder a proportion of the blame. Increased length has been the main pre-occupation of the manufacturers, whilst control has tended to take a back seat. This has rendered many of our established courses 'too easy' and in an attempt to restore the equilibrium holes have been stretched and additional hazards added.

Surely a more logical solution would be to restore a greater element of control and placement to advantage on the fairway. There would be no need to introduce a surfeit of penal bunkers around greens or to hem-in fairways with trees if the challenge of playing on firm greens was re-introduced.

Perhaps some length could be sacrificed in the interests of control by modifying golf ball design. Tour pro's commonly use softer, more receptive golf balls specifically with this in mind – so what chance the amateur on firm greens with hard "bullets".

[5] Summary

There can be no doubt about the ecological and economic necessity of cultivating firm greens during the summer. In practice, there are many graduations between true links turf (fescue/bent) and exclusive annual meadow-grass (with associated thatch). The two extremes are most directly seen when supplanting a natural soil green with a free-draining construction – based on modern methods and materials. Golfers may well find it hard to adjust to the firm surface of the green and a re-ordering of golfing priorities may well be needed.

Remember that whether attempting to bring putting greens back from the brink of gross neglect or sustaining firm surfaces of admirable turf quality, the same influences and management policies apply. Water (both natural and applied) has an overriding influence on the immediate ability of the turf to "hold", but this should not overshadow the vital importance of the other complementary management practices aimed at bringing the best out of the turf long-term.

(JWT : B.187)

WINTER PLAY ON GOLF GREENS

The aim of management is to keep play on the main greens for as near 12 months in the year as possible. However, this ideal has to be matched with the drainage qualities, soil type, aspect and elevation of the greens in question as well as prevailing weather conditions. An indication of the type of damage arising from play under adverse conditions is given below and, whilst appreciating that golfers expect winter play, these requirements must be kept in perspective. Most competitive golf and important fixtures take place outside the winter period. Winter golf is normally less competitive and if the small inconvenience caused by playing to temporary greens of a satisfactory standard is accepted, when necessary, then the putting surfaces of the main greens are better preserved for when they are most required and expected to be at their best.

Wet conditions

In persistently wet conditions, the surface soil around the pin is likely to become severely compacted and the sward weakened and thinned out. Solid or slit tine aeration help minimise ill effects on drainage and the sward. Hole changes should be frequent, use being made of the outer regions of the greens as far as possible, although keeping towards the front in very wet spells. At short holes where plugging is severe under wet conditions, light applications of suitable sand can help.

Frosty conditions

Damage caused by play during frosty weather falls into two main categories.

[1] When frozen, plant tissues are easily bruised by players' feet. Following a thaw, it is often possible to see brown footmarks for several weeks, particularly around hole sites. The greater the weight of play in hard frost, obviously the greater becomes the extent of this damage. Affected areas remain thin for long periods, altering the trueness of the putting surface, and are more susceptible to disease in spring.

[2] Long term damage is caused when play takes place after a sudden thaw. In these conditions the top 13 mm or so becomes soft, whilst the underlying soil remains frozen. Root damage occurs from the shearing action as players' feet move the soft, unfrozen surface across the frozen sub-surface. This disrupts putting surfaces and creates weak areas that may not recover before the height of the competition season.

Temporary greens

The best way to overcome these problems is to mow out separate temporary greens of good quality, perhaps 100-200 m^2 well clear of the major putting surfaces, and prepared in advance. Many clubs do not wish to go to this trouble and put temporary holes on the approach, but damage may still be caused when retrieving balls which go through on to the actual green.

(IS No.9 Ref. 02/04)

THE SPEED OF GOLF GREENS

Some method of objectively assessing the speed of a golf green can be a valuable aid to maintenance. The relative speed of greens is a very important factor in summer course presentation, but it is something which can be very difficult to define. This is because an assessment of what is a fast, medium or slow green tends to be a subject-ive one, rather than something which is measured as routine, mainly because the recognised tool for the job, the Stimpmeter, has not been extensively marketed in the UK. Those which were first available here were imported by individuals from the USA, where it is distributed by the United States Golf Association and is in common use. The Stimpmeter is, however, now available for purchase from British sources.

The Stimpmeter was invented in the USA in 1935 by amateur golfer, E.S. Stimpson, "to achieve accurate, objective, statistically valid measurements of the speed of a putting surface" (USGA). It is a simple tool, which when used in a meaningful manner, gives a reflection of the rolling resistance of the turf surface, by rolling golf balls with a constant momentum over a level area in different directions and taking an average of the distance travelled.

It is an aluminium bar, 36 inches long with a V-shaped groove extending along its entire length. Thirty inches from one tapered end which rests on the ground is a notch which holds the ball. This notch is so designed that the ball will be released and roll down the groove when the bar is raised to an angle of about 20° from the horizontal. This ensures that the speed of the ball will always be the same when it reaches the lower end. To use the meter a level area of green must be selected, preferably at least 10 ft.sq. At least three balls are then rolled across the green using the meter and the distance that each travels should be measured. For accuracy, all three balls should come to rest not more than 8 inches apart. A further three balls should then be rolled across the green in the opposite direction. An average distance of travel should then be calculated. This distance can be compared with a series of figures produced by the USGA Green Section:–

Speeds for Regular Membership Play		Speeds for Tournament Play	
8' 6"	Fast	10' 6"	Fast
7' 6"	Medium-Fast	9' 6"	Medium-Fast
6' 6"	Medium	8' 6"	Medium
5' 6"	Medium-Slow	7' 6"	Medium-Slow
4' 6"	Slow	6' 6"	Slow

A set of figures should hence be obtained for each green and it should then be possible to produce more uniform conditions from green to green by management practices. Slow greens could perhaps be scarified or excessively hard greens watered.

As might be gathered, with this simple technology, once one has basic figures for greens at what is considered to be their best, it is then quite easy to see what effects are obtained by modifications to individual elements of the management programme, together with changing weather conditions, on the pace of putting surfaces. However, until Stimpmeters do come into more common use in the UK, we have to rely on the subjective judgement of individual club memberships. The usual request is for faster greens.

If golf greens are shown to be excessively slow, then maintenance can be modified to improve matters. A layer of spongy thatch immediately below the surface is a common cause and reducing this by scarification can be effective, although it is often also necessary to attack the cause of thatch formation too. This may involve improving surface drainage and soil conditions or reducing the annual meadow-grass content. Over-watering also produces soft, slow surfaces, as does the excessive use of fertiliser which gives unnecessarily lush growth, besides encouraging undesirable grass species. The use of soft or spongy top dressing materials like large quantities of peat may also encourage slow surfaces. Cutting too plays a part – greens cut too infrequently or at too high a level would tend to be slow, although the significance of mowing height is often exaggerated by golfers.

The particular treatment which is usually referred to as affecting the speed of greens is height of cut, and certainly shaving greens close can have a significant result in this respect. However, this approach is short-term and **short-sighted**, in that over-close mowing in the long-term leads at best to soft surfaces dominated by the weedgrass *Poa annua* and at worst to dead patches and thin turf. Fast, bumpy greens are no use to anyone. Cutting with mowers set at 5 mm ($^3/16$ in.) in the growing season and at 8 mm ($^5/16$ in.) in winter is normal and acceptable in most circumstances.

To achieve a balanced approach, it is necessary to tailor virtually all the elements of the maintenance programme to the end of promoting green speed, with the most important operations being:–

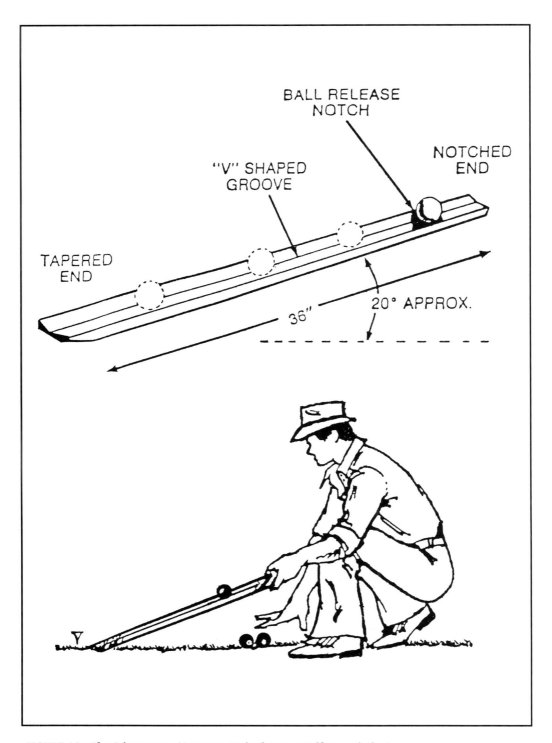

FIGURE 12: The Stimpmeter (Courtesy United States Golf Association).

- the frequency of mowing
- the frequency of verticutting/turf grooming
- control in the use of nitrogen
- a delicate management of watering during dry spells
- the approach to top dressing and the materials used
- producing good surface drainage and maintaining a good access for light and air flow over the green

Frequency of mowing is the key element. It does not necessarily mean that more grass is removed, but the more one cuts, the more polished the surface becomes and its rolling resistance falls. Similarly, verticutting or turf grooming to take out coarse, clumpy growth and eliminate any nap will also reduce rolling resistance. On the other hand, factors such as lush growth, soft surfaces, and a tendency to lie damp, all have a negative effect on the progress towards faster greens.

The whole object of treatment must be to produce firm, dry, very fine, slow-growing, uniform, and polished putting areas. Then greens will be fast. Even so, what is achieved ultimately will vary according to the turf type one is working with, changing weather conditions and with time. Fescue-dominated turf will always be faster than annual meadow-grass. Greens will be faster in a dry year than in a wet one, and there can generally be a trend for greens to become progressively faster between June and September.

A final point to bear in mind is that greens can be made too fast, a situation in which putting is totally uncontrollable. Indeed, there is a current fashion in America to work to produce greens for club members which are up to 25% quicker than a standard which is considered fast for professional golf, and this must be considered a move which is going over the top. In the search for control of pace, it is far, far more important to aim to achieve a **consistent** speed from green to green over the whole course, including the putting green.

(CGC 1 : 15)

SECTION 5
GREEN SURROUNDS & APPROACHES

❖❖❖

Green Collars & Aprons

Green-side Bunkers

*The Care of
the Golf Course*

GREEN SURROUNDS

To define to some extent what is meant by surrounds, these are areas with an intermediate height of cut between putting surface and fairway. The immediate surround is a collar, usually the width of one or two passes with a mower, which encircles the putting surface. In addition, features around the green such as mounds and banks are sometimes mown as surround. In front of a green, i.e. looking back towards the tee, the collar may be increased in width to form an apron or fore-green on the approach. Normal practice is to cut these areas as for tees.

No exact dimensions can be recommended for surrounds and aprons because the size and shape will vary according to the landform of the site, the positioning of bunkers, mounds, banks and water hazards, along with the length of the hole and how it is designed to be played. The size and quality of the machinery used, and time taken to cut and maintain these areas has also to be taken into consideration.

While surrounds help to provide a visual blend between putting surface and fairway, more important is their value in playing the game of golf. If carefully designed they can reward, be usefully employed in, or to some extent penalise the approach shot to the green as appropriate. For example, a reasonable shot which just trickles to the edge of the putting surface will be held on the collar and the player should still be able to take his putter. On the other hand, an over-hit shot into a bank behind a green should not be rewarded by the ball running back into the middle of the putting surface, and a well shaped surround at the toe of the bank could help to hold the ball at the margin. Similarly, an over-hit ball running through the green should not be held up by fairway length grass or mounds or a bank which falls away and could be allowed to run on, according to its momentum, across a wide surround area.

Hence, the design of the surrounds should be allied to the way each hole *should* be played.

The Right Surface?

To be useful in play, the turf and the surface developed on the surrounds has to be right. Much has been written in recent years about what is right for putting, that is a firm, fast surface composed primarily of fine grass species (bents and fescues). These criteria of species present, the texture of the turf, its density, the firmness underfoot and smoothness apply also to the surrounds. The only difference between the surrounds and the putting surface should be the length of cut. In general therefore, maintenance work on collars and aprons should be along similar lines to that applied on the actual putting surface.

Obtaining the ideal can often be a much simpler process on the surrounds than it is on the putting surface, as the former seems to get somewhat less abused. Frequently a soggy, thatch-ridden, annual meadow-grass green is surrounded by firm turf composed of fescues and bents.

Maintenance

All the major operations of greens maintenance should be applied to the surrounds. The need for regular mowing at a level intermediate to the putting surface and fairway is an obvious point, but cuttings must be boxed off to help keep the surface firm. It is usual to cut immediate collars and aprons at 8 mm in the summer, perhaps lifting to 12 mm for winter golf. Sit-on triple mowers are very useful for these areas. Also, this will help to keep down weeds and worms, and hence reduce expensive spraying.

On collar and apron, occasional light treatments with verticut units or a pedestrian-operated scarifier should be considered during the growing season.

But, of course, just keeping these areas trimmed is not the end of maintenance. As with all turf areas, fundamental and regular aeration must be carried out throughout the year to encourage strong, dense turf and as an aid to surface drainage. Particular attention must be paid to the apron, on to which traffic from the fairway will be funnelled, and the line of walk-offs to the next tee. However, watch out for sprinkler heads when spiking – a tine through a cap can cause expensive damage, especially to the gear-driven type.

Top dressing must not be neglected on collars and aprons which have to be smooth enough for putting, while no-one will be encouraged to pitch in front of a green if the ball kicks badly instead of running on. Compost applied to the putting surface can be dragged into the surrounds when matting in, allow for extra material on a green where the apron is wide.

As to fertiliser treatment, the emphasis should be on supplying nitrogen if needed and being cautious about frequency of application.

By watering during a dry spell the aim should be to maintain an evenly moist topsoil without over-watering. Watering systems should be well designed to apply water routinely to aprons, and can be adjusted to cover surrounds.

Traffic management is also a vital part of surround maintenance and appropriate guidance to players, such as hoops or white lines, have to be carefully positioned to spread wear (and that guidance must be enforced).

Drainage

The drainage qualities of the approach and surround must be good to maintain the right quality of turf and to provide a satisfactory surface for play. If the natural drainage through the subsoil is not good, then a drainage system to cover the whole area of the green site will be needed. The immediate surrounds should be incorporated within such a drainage system, extending this as appropriate to ensure the apron or approach is well covered. Trapping surface or sub-surface flow of ground water onto the surrounds by means of catchwater drains is often required on hillside courses.

In Conclusion

It can be seen from the above that a great deal of thought needs to be given to the design (construction) and maintenance of the surrounds to a golf green, but it is evident up and down the country that this attention to detail is lacking on many courses. So, why not stand back and look at your greens – could a bit of artistry in surrounds make yours a better golf course?

(CGC 1 : 35)

THE HISTORY OF BUNKER DESIGN AND CURRENT PROBLEMS RELATING TO CHANGING SHAPE AND CONTOURS OF BUNKERS THROUGH SAND ACCUMULATION/EROSION

Historians tell us that golf originated in Scotland following the adaption of an ice game from Holland, played amongst the grassy dunes alongside the sea. The ball was played from close to the previous hole, not more than one club's length, to clearings along the gorse and whins, and then on to the next hole. Bunkers as we know them today did not exist and any places where trees grew were avoided, "Nature was their architect and beast and man her contractor" (Guy Campbell). This type of links course prevailed for decades until the latter part of last century when many superb links courses were created on the machairs and sandy, natural sites, e.g. Troon 1878;

Formby 1884; Lytham 1886; St. Georges and Nairn 1887; Portrush 1888; County Down 1889; Deal 1892; and Portmarnock 1894. Sadly, and also around this time 1890-1900, a decade referred to as the dark ages of golf course construction, many courses were built in inland situations, whose features included plateau/flat greens, oblong fairways, central cross bunkers, greens surrounded by bunkers. The concept offered by such designers (not architects) was one to punish the bad shot, under the mistaken belief that the good player should have every possible advantage over his weaker counterpart. Thus, 'penal' golf was contrived.

During the early part of the century golf architects at last appeared on the scene. Such men pointing out that bunkers for instance should be used to encourage positional play. Both Braid and Vardon favoured the diagonal cross bunker rather than the horrid straight across the line of play bunkers which were a strong feature of the penal type of hole. Here we have then the first suggestions of strategic golf holes being formed as against the penal which gave the player only one route to the green.

The early 'strategic golf course' aimed to reflect the technical skills and mental agility required of the old links course site amongst the turf covered dunes where hazards consist of hollows and mounds so that the ball could be played where it lay with reasonable possibility of recovery if it had strayed from the proper line. In direct contrast 'penal' golf only compounded error with frustration.

How did early architects, and since then the true golf course architectural profession, set about design of golf holes to achieve necessary change as they saw it? It is quite obvious that the designers who produced such penal golf holes as we have referred to, considered that the only purpose of a hazard, in the form of a sand bunker, should be its penalty and this perception persists to this day in certain quarters. Certainly hazards are the source of great thrills in the game but when avoiding them is pure luck and recovery is well nigh impossible, except at the loss of many shots, the hazard ceases to be merely a hazard and becomes a source of legitimate annoyance and, possibly derived from that loss, of revenue to the club. So in the construction of sand bunkers, how important is strength as against strategy? Should bunkers be placed as traps or intimidators?

It is a small part of a bunker's function actually to catch the wayward shot and indeed it should be removed if this is its only purpose. The bunker should be there to provoke the player into some less obvious error and to repay the player who can manoeuvre the ball with the club head to negotiate the hazard. If it is subtly placed near enough to the side of the green or fairway it serves such a purpose admirably and it was this type of thinking which played a large part in the change in hole design in the early part of this century along with other developments, e.g. orientation of green to fairway, shape of fairway etc.

Frankly, the bunker should tease rather than offend on the basis that a shot played to avoid it may find trouble, but trouble of a more human kind. When introduced at an angle to the line of play the low handicap player can clear its furthest edge (when he/she is in the mood), whereas the high handicap player can with reasonable ease clear its nearest edge. Braid and Vardon introduced this diagonal type of fairway bunker with its furthest edge on the target line through the fairway, thus demanding from the golfer a decision as to whether or not he plays to carry the bunker.

As well as shape, thought was also given to the positioning of bunkers. The early architects were influenced by what they could see on the great classic links golf courses such as the old course at St. Andrews, North Berwick, Royal Dornoch etc.

On the old course at St. Andrews, for instance, a large number of the sand bunkers came into being around the very position where the ordinary golfer wanted to place his shots! It is this characteristic amongst others which makes the old course such a good test of golf. The obvious shot is continually a non-starter and the player has to think in order to find a better way round, viz the par 3, 172 yd, 11th. 'Strath' bunker is placed precisely where the ordinary player would wish his/her shot to pitch.

With significant improvements in club heads and balls, many fairway bunkers are now obsolete as they are out of focus from the tee. Position of bunkers then has a great part to play in the education of the player. The golfer should be compelled to use his head in determining how to play each shot. Bunkers are often sited where individual committees consider suitable. After a few years they are filled in by another committee and resited as they consider appropriate. Thus, we have unnecessary expenditure of capital and aggravation to members. The ideal course is one in which players, whatever their handicap, have equal pleasure, thrill and excitement. The club which does offer a course to its members which exercises their mental skill and gives good physical recreation comes closest to fulfilling the spirit in which the game was originally conceived. Variety is the key!

Inevitably, as the game of golf is played bunkers degenerate and change shape both as a result of climate erosion (especially on links sites), and as a result of play. Golfers contribute by causing both physical wear and by continually depositing sand on the tops of bunkers and the immediate area hole-side of the hazard. The problem is most acute on and around greenside hazards. The process of degeneration can create a number of problems:-

- *Visibility:* Over time sand deposition raises the area between the hazard and the green. This results in steeper, more acute banking that becomes difficult to maintain and retain a grass cover upon. As a result of this the hazard itself and its associated banking becomes more visible to the player, whilst the area behind the hazard becomes less visible. This can result in unintended strategic changes to the way a hole is played - this may in some instances be unfair.

- *Impact on play:* In addition to the factors mentioned above, steeper banks, downhill lies and overhanging lips all have an impact on play. They all make bunker play more difficult. The development of such symptoms may be minimised by good maintenance practices.

- *Maintenance:* Continual deposition of sand, particularly on closely cut turf on the aprons of greens and to a great extent on the greens themselves, results in the formation of a very sandy rootzone. This combined with the raising of the area in question can make it extremely difficult to retain a grass cover during warm summer conditions. Frequently, localised hand watering together with hollow coring, and the integration of organic amendments and wetting agents are required. In some instances, recultivation through depth, recontouring and returfing are required to restore these areas and ensure they meet the Architect's former intention.

The bunker has come a long way since its natural development on the links land during the latter part of the 19th Century. They now assume many shapes and forms but they still fulfil their fundamental aim of frustrating the golfer as well as dictating the way in which a particular hole should be played. In essence, they make the game of golf interesting and appropriate maintenance is very important if they are to retain their intended value.

(DDW & AJB : B.189)

PLATE 4: Overseeding, usually combined with aeration and top dressing, is an essential method of assisting the recovery of worn tees. Performed at the end of the playing period for both summer and winter tees, a surface seeding machine is a useful means of carrying out the work. (Courtesy SISIS Equipment (Macclesfield) Ltd.)

SECTION 6
GOLF TEEING AREAS
MAINTENANCE & CONSTRUCTION

—————— ✤✤✤ ——————

Tee Management

Winter & Summer Tees

Synthetic Tees

Construction of New Tees

*The Care of
the Golf Course*

MANAGEMENT OF GOLF TEES

Mowing

Tees should preferably always be cut with a cylinder type of mower which will give a finer finish. On average, twice weekly cutting is necessary during the growing season with perhaps more frequent mowing during intervals of spring and summer growth. The cutting level should be 6–13 mm as appropriate. As a general rule, clippings should always be boxed off as allowing them to fly always encourages worms and weeds and can lead to an accumulation of matted material which will not withstand wear. Such soft, spongy surfaces should be avoided. In view of this, it is not a good idea to cut tees using fairway gang mowers even if tees are large enough to make this possible. The time saved by such practices is appreciated, but it is only gained at the expense of the finish of the playing surface. For larger tees, speedy machines such as triple mowers are available which allow mowing to be carried out rapidly but with the added facility of clipping removal.

For banks and surrounding areas hand mowers of the hover type are frequently used, or strimmers which depend on a rotating nylon cord. Many steep, small banks can only be cut with these types of machine but it is an advantage to avoid such features during initial construction so that larger sit-on machines can be used, so saving valuable time.

Fertiliser

For the average tee, a spring fertiliser dressing giving balanced quantities of nitrogen, phosphate and potash can be sufficient to maintain good growth through the year. The application of phosphate and potash may not be necessary and should be based on chemical analysis. If growth slackens off during the summer or early autumn, a booster dressing of nitrogen can, however, be given in order to maintain sufficient levels of growth and help in the rapid regeneration of worn areas. Autumn top dressing can also be valuable, ideally supplemented by a spring application too.

Weeds, Pests and Diseases

Adequate weed control is essential to maintain an even and attractive playing surface on tees and when required this work should not be neglected. Weedkilling should be carried out during a period good growth, preferably in the early summer using a suitable selective weedkiller which should prove adequate for the usual spectrum of weeds encountered in such situations – daisies, dandelions, clover, etc. Worm control is another essential if good teeing surfaces are to be provided as worms can cause very muddy conditions, particularly during moist weather in the autumn and spring. It is at these times of year that control should be carried out when the worms are working actively near the surface. Only short-term wormkillers are now permitted by the pesticide regulations. Clearing worm casts makes for cleaner and neater mowing as well as improving the playing surface.

Turf diseases are seldom of great significance on tees which are not as intensively maintained as greens. Perhaps the most common disease is Corticium (red thread) which produces mottled patches during the summer. This disease is associated with low levels of nitrogen and nitrogenous fertiliser is generally sufficient to control the disease by improving the grass's ability to combat it. Occasionally, fusarium patch disease may also be troublesome on tees and needs treating with fungicide.

Renovation

Divot repair work should be regarded as a continuous process from spring to autumn, a weekly round of repair work by the greenkeeping staff being the ideal to aim for. Some Clubs opt for leaving a suitable supply of soil and seed mix at each tee for members to use as appropriate, but this approach seldom proves really successful. Again, non-ryegrass seed should be employed, mixed with a good quality soil. A 50/50 sand and soil mix can be usefully substituted where tees have heavy topsoil surfaces but very sandy divot filling mixes tend to blow out of place in dry or windy conditions. As with fairways, healthy tee swards composed of the desirable grasses show good natural recovery and minimise the problem of continuous repair.

Seeding after mid-September is rarely successful in the North, though may be worth risking up to the end of the month further South. Since seeding is far and away the easiest and cheapest method of renovation, clubs wishing to play off well-grassed tees during spring and summer should consider closing down damaged general tees in September to allow timely renovation and a recovery period from the wear and tear of hectic summer use. If the Medal tees are kept in play, then their damaged areas will have to be repaired by turfing later on during the winter. It is usually only links courses that have to resort to extensive turf patching in autumn and winter to repair damage.

Autumn Work

On most golf courses, summer tees come out of play at some point in the autumn, play being transferred to winter tees or tee mats. The main tees should then be renovated as promptly as possible in order to ensure complete recovery by the time they come into play next spring. Thorough spiking is frequently useful at this time to relieve any compaction caused by the season's play. The flat slitting type of tine is usually adequate, although deep hollow tine aeration may occasionally be required, and perhaps Verti-Draining. After spiking, surfaces should be trued up by top dressing, preferably using a light sandy compost, and reseeded or returfed. Returfing establishes the surface more quickly than reseeding but adequate supplies of good quality turf suitable for the purpose are obviously required. A turf nursery for tee renovation purposes is always a useful feature on golf courses, although at a pinch an area to the side of one fairway, adequately mown and receiving some attention such as weedkilling, etc. during the summer can serve for tee repair. In addition to the main annual top dressing, tees can benefit from supplementary sandy dressings during the rest of the year, aimed at maintaining firm, dry and level surfaces.

Although greens should be considered top priority on golf courses, it should not be forgotten that we are looking for similar conditions on tees, i.e. level, firm and free draining. Indeed, top dressing tees is a most important operation, especially those on par 3 holes which tend to receive most wear. The same materials that are used for top dressing greens should be used on tees, although somewhat cheaper commercial "rootzone mixes" are an acceptable alternative. Annual overall top dressing can be sufficient with regular divoting work through the main competition season.

As levels on tees are usually poorer than on greens at the end of the main competition season, then a valuable 'additional' source of dressing can be found by hollow tining tees and working the cores back on to the tee along with the sandy top dressing material that has been bought in.

After autumn renovation work, tees should be rested until fully established, play continuing on alternative winter locations. Similarly, winter tees, if used, should be renovated in the spring at the end of their period of use so that they will be once again ready for play the following autumn.

Another autumn job required is tree pruning as tees are often surrounded by trees and can become heavily shaded. Heavy shade is a common cause of wet teeing surfaces and poor grass growth, so trees should therefore be pruned regularly, all over-hanging branches being removed. Thinning surrounding shrubberies increases air flow and reduces surface dampness.

Tees Are Important

Given good initial construction, adequate size and regular attention, tees can be a credit to any golf course. Inevitably, they take second place to the greens in the greenkeeper's mind but one cannot claim to have a first-class golf course without first-class tees.

(CGC 1 : 39)

TEES – WINTER AND SUMMER

In the early days of golf there were never any formally-built teeing grounds – the rules merely stated that the ball should be teed within a certain number of club lengths of the previous hole. The first written record of purpose-built teeing areas appeared during the last years of the 19th Century. Their position, size, construction and use have been subjects for contention ever since. Clearly, where play is concentrated on to a strip of grass barely 16 m² at the start of each hole, there are the beginnings of a problem. Since tees were often the 'poor relation' in new constructions, constructed with existing soil having slow natural drainage qualities and often mishandled and compacted into the bargain, with inadequate provision for drainage and, above all, limitation in size, the seeds of today's disaster areas of many courses were sown right at the start.

Areas that could support 10,000 rounds per annum or less in the early years – when minimal winter play was of no consequence, have not the slightest chance of surviving the summer on today's thronged courses, busy from dawn till dusk and perhaps averaging 50,000 rounds per year, let alone take winter play as well.

The successful tee must be slightly elevated, allowing a view of the fairway at 200 metres, not overhung by trees nor with exaggerated slopes. Its surface should be firm, level and adequately drained at all seasons with a uniform cover of turf.

Size

To achieve this aim, the first requirement is adequate size for the amount of play that the course takes. If you are embarking on a new construction, make sure you build to cope with any projected increase in play. Many existing tees like Topsy "just growed", the original 5 x 5 had an extra piece stuck on the side one year with an extension on the rear the next, each piece with different soils and turf. Through differential settlement the whole aspect can become displeasing, to say nothing of vital areas being lost to use. Yet again there is the situation where a multiplicity of pocket handkerchief size tees have sprung up over the years, each with banks requiring tedious, labour-intensive 'hover' mowing and surfaces unfit for cutting with anything other than an 450 mm hand mower.

In these situations committees must develop a planned programme of tee construction to meet the needs of today's golf and spread over, say, five years with a clearly defined order of priorities. They must address the following aspects relating to each site: route to and from tee (including a separate route for winter tees wherever practicable); size; drainage; soil improvement; access to surface and banks for easy maintenance with modern triples and the need for irrigation.

At par 3 holes it is generally most satisfactory to have one large tee accommodating Ladies, General and Medal play. Aim for at least 400 m² with sufficient width for three or four shifts of the tee boxes. There may well be amalgamation of two or even three separate teeing areas to achieve this. At longer holes it is preferable to retain separate tees, aiming for, say, 350 m², possibly divided up as 50 m² Ladies, 200 m² Mens, 100 m² Medal.

158

Position

Tees will have been originally sited by the Architect to make best use of the immediate topography, to allow the drop from the tee shot to be seen and to suit natural or man-made fairway levels, features and bunkers, as well as green design. Changing the actual position of a tee should therefore never be made lightly – the usual need is for a greater surface area to accommodate increased play.

Aim to provide at least sufficient width to allow two shifts of the tee boxes, i.e. 14-20 metres, so that wear can be spread more evenly over the surface, minimising traffic over repaired places. This is especially important for medal tees where the measured length of a hole at the distance marker governs where tee boxes may be set. In general, go for width rather than length which also helps overcome problems of sight lines for landing zones. These are often obscured from the rear of long, narrow tees, especially where the ground in front falls away sharply.

Shape

Far too often tees stick out like sore thumbs – they may serve architectural and golfing requirements but by no stretch of the imagination can they be said to blend into the natural landscape. The elevated rectangular tee with sharply sloping banks has been the standard for many years. It looks unnatural, is difficult to maintain with modern-day equipment and often banks are so steep as to require expensive, laborious hand Flymo-ing.

On flat ground there is no need for excessive elevation, a mere 230 mm above surrounding level is ample for drainage purposes with banks eased out to gradients no more than 1 in 3, corners well rounded off for easy mowing of the surface with wider machines and no sharp angles along the edges that will scalp. Above all, the tees and their banks should blend into the natural ground contours around them.

At some sites, of course, elevation or the need for quantities of fill are dictated by the terrain and the chances of achieving a natural look are much reduced. On a descending slope, cut and fill minimises cost but always looks unnatural and certainly needs careful handling to create a durable and useful tee. Be particular to provide an adequate depth of soil on the 'cut' side, proper internal drainage and the essential catchwater drains at the rear and sides where slopes shed surface water towards the playing surfaces. Do not neglect the approach paths to such tees either, protecting these from excess water can be just as important as the tee itself. The use of additional imported fill will help to avoid excessive cut into a hillside and similarly a slight gradient of 1 in 80 back to front is imperceptible and helps drainage, as well as reducing the quantity of fill needed.

Tees sited on rising ground will benefit from an upward slope back to front and it is surprising how strong a slope can be acceptable to golfers on a sharp rise.

Layout

For years the standard tee has been of rectangular shape, very often with sharp edges that are frequently scalped, pointing roughly at the green or fairway landing zone. Although this type of tee allows maximum use of the maintained area, its angular corners are more easily kept with hand mowers than triples. The shape does not blend into any landscape and edges and corners must be well rounded off if they are not to be mangled by mowing. To save critical comment from golfers, its alignment to the hole or landing zone must be perfect.

The less formally shaped tee is something of a rarity, possibly less easy to execute well but it can blend far better into the natural landscape. The easy curves and gentle gradients look right as well as being easier to negotiate and cut tidily with a triple. However, do not over-emphasise softened edges otherwise too high a proportion of the flatter, useful area will be lost. Even the random informal tee shape should not be taken too far, golfers still require of their tees a sense of orientation and the more successful informal ones are those which do not blur the required sense of direction.

Winter Tees

There is no doubt that given a choice every golfer will opt for playing the year round off grass. There is equally no doubt that no municipal courses and very few private ones have such low levels of winter play that the standard summer tees can cope with 12 months' use. One could argue that if tees were made large enough this objection would be overcome, but this is rarely feasible and, in any case, routes between green and tee would be sadly over-used, requiring unsightly hard surface paths everywhere.

The best compromise is undoubtedly to provide separate winter tees on the opposite side of the green to the summer tees and with their own separate access. This takes wear off summer traffic routes for the worst part of the year, giving them chance to recover or to be repaired. The smaller winter tees and their access tracks can be repaired in April and have a full summer's growth to recover.

At short holes there may not be sufficient space to allow this strategy to be adopted, in which case an artificial tee, temporary or permanent, within the grass tee may have to be accepted as a last resort. Many clubs already adopt these tactics, moving off summer tees, preferably in early October, so that they have some chance of making recovery growth. Selected areas of fairway or carry are used in winter but too often length is a sacred cow that cannot be sacrificed and some of the potential of separate winter tees is lost by positioning them immediately in front of or, worse still, to one side of the summer areas. How much better to give their placing a little thought, selecting a flatter area of rough or semi-rough that must be reasonably free-draining and chosen to move traffic off routes so often disrupted by summer play. If you must have the same length, go forward a little at some holes, back at others – you may even attain greater benefit with different landing zones coming into play.

There are as yet no really satisfactory artificial tee surfaces although products are improving very rapidly. Those based on nylon or polypropylene bristle become clogged with mud, the pile abrades quickly or becomes severely flattened in use and difficult to get tee pegs into. Such tees must be large enough to provide a firm, dry standing area as well as the teeing surface which must, of course, be capable of taking and holding a tee peg firmly. The rubber link type of mat is, to some extent, self-cleaning and when set in a solid wooden base with a slatted base over a free draining area with a short section of artificial grass tee in either end (easily replaced when worn out), can be quite successful. Artificial tees must be set near a well-drained access path.

Presentation

The good Head Greenkeeper always has something of the showman in his make-up. Directed into the proper channels, this ability can set off a good course to perfection and will always enhance the mediocre. It does not encompass the provision of bedding out plants or exotic shrubs around tees or on their embankments – such unnatural excrescences should be confined to their proper place, in the environs of the club house.

Nowhere does presentation count for more than at the opening and closing holes of a course. Size of the 1st tee is vital – wear must be well distributed and divot repairs kept fully up-to-date so that the surface is irreproachable. Levels must be smooth and true, the soil sandy and free draining to provide a firm, dry stance in all weathers, and supporting the dwarf, hard-wearing, fine-leaved bent and fescue grasses that blend so well together. Near to the club house a permanent path will be in keeping with traffic, regulated further by a neat fence and all notices sited neatly and logically. Always strive to get the players off to a good start and in the right frame of mind to enjoy the game.

(CGC 1 : 40)

TEE CONSTRUCTION AND ENLARGEMENT
Think Long and Hard
Tee building should not be embarked upon without careful consideration of a number of factors. In the first place tees were never simply constructed at a set distance from a green, they form an essential part of the architect's design and strategy for play at a particular hole relating strongly to line, good landing area and hazards on fairway and approach. With the incessant search for greater length on golf courses these days, it is never simply a question of building a new tee x metres behind the existing ones. Some courses are littered with sites of tees built with considerable effort and at no little cost by the greenkeeping staff only to be abandoned within a year or two when the Green Chairman whose project they were retires. It is also a sad but true fact that increased traffic on the course leads to extra wear on areas unable to support it. Therefore, tee changes which tend to disperse traffic are preferable to those which concentrate it.

Site
New tees should be reasonably close to the preceding green, certainly no more than 50 metres away. Drainage must be at least adequate, not so much from the tee point of view, which are normally slightly elevated and should not suffer ill drainage, but in order to maintain satisfactory access for players. Alternative routes to a tee are also valuable in helping spread wear and aiding sward recovery.

Sloping sites present their own special problems and a cut and fill formation will generally be more economical and also more stable than one built up by filling. Guard against surface water run-off from higher slopes on to such tees and especially take care that the surface does not slope towards the rear cut bank which provides no escape route for heavy rain.

Tees in the Wood
This is a favourite ploy of Committees with little appreciation of the maintenance problems created by such sites. Fearful of criticism from conservationist members, they are too timid in removing enough of the trees surrounding the site. Thus the tee may look attractive for a spell in summer over a year or two but it will be pretty awful in autumn and winter. The best grasses for tees have their natural environment on windy, open moor or links not the moist, airless and dark woodland clearing. Little wonder that in such situations the best turf fails to thrive, deteriorating into a soft morass of spongy annual meadow-grass and moss during winter or a dry, thread-bare and imperfect surface in summer. Grass species are versatile and several have adapted to the woodland environment but avoid using so-called 'woodland' seed mixtures. These grasses cannot withstand normal fairway cutting height, let alone that adopted on tees. If there is no alternative to a tee in a woodland setting, be bold in its construction. Remove enough trees and branches to allow good light on to the tee surface and an adequate flow of air. Avoid long, narrow formation and ensure that the clearing fans away at the front to avoid play concentrating on the tee centre.

161

Building

Construction work must be carried out when soil conditions are reasonably dry if severe drainage problems are not to be created through soil compaction or loss of structure. Enlargement of existing tees should commence in early October and where new sites are developed away from general play it makes sense to get on with earth work during the drier summer months, i.e. importation of fill if this is needed. Remove and dispose of rank grass growth, scrub and especially tree roots, all of which eventually rot and decompose in time to cause settlement if merely pushed in as fill or buried. Strip all recoverable topsoil off the site and its surrounds and stack it close at hand.

Tees will normally be slightly elevated to give an adequate view of the target area and possible hazards from the back as well as the front, which must be borne in mind on longer tees. If not levelling by cut and fill, utilise clean subsoil fill from a convenient borrow area in the rough. The fill should be free of large stones, bricks, etc., which hinder good drainage and the completion of essential secondary drainage aids like subsoil cultivation. Build up the material in consecutive layers 230 mm deep, ensuring each layer is evenly firmed to avoid settlement. This point is most important – many a grand tee has subsequently become a liability through settlement destroying the surface levels and the blame must lie with poor or hasty preparation. This applies even more so to tee enlargement where simply filling to extend the area is often the easiest approach. Loads of subsoil tipped along the edge of a tee and pushed down will inevitably settle unevenly. The correct procedure is to tip small loads, level out and build up in evenly firmed layers. When all is done, replace the preserved topsoil to provide a minimum cover of 150 mm firmed depth on the tee surface, rather less on banks, say, 75 mm firmed.

Plan and Gradient

Since the end of the 19th century the rectangular tee with sides parallel to the line of play has been the norm, with much to commend it. Banks must not be too steep, a slope of 1 in 4 with edges well rounded off allows scope for maintenance with modern wide cut triple units or even at need the use of gang units, although the latter are not advised as clippings cannot be boxed as they should be.

It is desirable that the upper surface of a tee should have a slight gradient but no more than 1 in 80. This is scarcely visible to the player but still enough to allow surface water run-off. As a general guide, tees at uphill holes should slope upwards from back to front and those at downhill slopes, downwards.

Size

For ease of upkeep, reducing bank maintenance to a minimum and providing scope for modern, faster and wider aeration, top dressing and cutting equipment, it is better to have one large teeing area. However, site considerations and Par for the hole will determine the best approach and it may be necessary to have championship and medal tees separate. Also, separate teeing areas for ladies, men and medals allow for different lines of attack at any hole which helps variety. It is advisable to allow for 300-350 m² at Par 4 and 5's and 400-450 m² at Par 3's. Where separate tees are provided, ladies will only require a forward tee of about 50 m², the general tee should be at least 200 m² and the medal tee 100 m².

Drainage

Most tees on normal soils will not require special pipe drainage systems. They are slightly elevated which keeps them further removed from any water table problem in winter and also helps surface run-off. If they can be given a slight gradient, so much the better. It is, however, vital that compaction in fill material and topsoil is properly relieved so that any panned layers do not impede drainage away from the surface. After returning topsoil, use a tractor-mounted subsoiler, making at least two passes along the length and then across the width of the tee, pulling out at the sides and ends. The implement should be set to work at a depth of 460 mm and at 600 mm centres.

Pipe drainage will only normally be required as a catchwater drain or limited system around the foot of the bank at the rear and possibly the side of a cut and fill tee in order to trap run-off before it can affect the surface.

Preparation

Restore the tee surface following subsoiling using a tractor-mounted bar grader if necessary. Then complete rigid tine cultivation or use a power harrow to produce a workable, fairly fine soil tilth. If any sand amelioration is required it should be thoroughly worked in at this stage. Carry out hand raking and heeling at least twice to produce a fine and evenly firmed soil surface, removing stones 12 mm and over in the process. Corner and intermediate pegs should be set at the required level and with a tight line stretched across, these allow a check on surface levels as the work proceeds. Adequate firming of the topsoil by heeling without over-compaction is essential to locate and remove softer pockets of soil at this stage. If left, these will invariably settle to create unevenness. A roller will not do the same job since it tends to bridge softer spots.

Establishment

Apply and rake in any lime needed, usually only where the soil is very acid, and a light application of fine bone meal. Turfing is the best method of bringing the new tee into play and fits well with the normal autumn construction period on established courses. Bought in turf may be the easier option but ensure it contains the desirable bent and fescue grasses with no coarse ryegrass or no weedgrass – annual meadow-grass – and allow time for it to establish properly before use. The commonest and often least satisfactory method is to lift turf off the practice ground or fairway which may be full of weeds, certainly fibrous, and then chop it down to tee height. Not surprisingly, such turf establishes poorly and is hacked up the first summer. If using turf from the course, plan in advance and give the chosen area initial preparation including a light feed, spiking, summer scarification and weed control if needed, taking the height of cut down a little. Fibrous turf must be cut thinly for it to establish quickly and it should be laid working off boards placed on the turf surface not the carefully prepared and levelled soil bed. Give a fairly heavy top dressing of suitable sand or compost afterwards and lute this into the joints.

Seeded areas take longer to establish before they are fit for play – from an August sowing, perhaps 18 months; seeding in April, often two years and that with good management. Prepare as described for the turf bed, raking in a little pre-seeding granular fertiliser then sow with a bent/fescue seed mix, possibly including a proportion of a finer-leaved, hard-wearing cultivar of smooth-stalked meadow-grass.

Winter Tees

Where grass tees are small and subject to heavy play, there is no other practical alternative except to close early and renovate by seeding. During the winter period artificial teeing surfaces, which must include an appropriate hard-wearing stance area as well, can be used or alternatively, as many clubs do, a selected piece of fairway. It is important to site such winter tees with care so that traffic during this period from green to tee and tee to fairway is diverted away from routes that are heavily used all summer. The latter areas can then be rested; it may provide an opportunity for renovating them, and skilful siting of winter tees can bring alternative fairway landing zones into use, again saving wear and tear on areas affected by summer play.

(CGC 1 : 65)

GRASS IN SHADE

Turfgrass persistence in shade depends not only on the amount and quality of such light as there is, but on the height and frequency of cut, the available moisture (especially if there is competition from tree roots), and the microclimate of the shaded area, particularly insofar as it may encourage disease. Moderation is the watchword – in mowing, nitrogen application and wear.

The selection of grasses for shade usually implies the aim of producing something as near ordinary turf as possible in spite of adverse conditions. The need is not for shade grasses, but for turfgrasses that will tolerate shade. Typical shade grasses would be wavy hair-grass (*Deschampsia flexuosa*), wood meadow-grass (*Poa nemoralis*) or wood millet (*Milium effusum*). These are well adapted to tolerate stress in shaded habitats and would obviously be suitable for the creation of a woodland flora, but they will not form a turf or stand up to wear. Therefore, they are not recommended for golf tees or greens.

Philip Grime, in "Plant strategies and vegetation processes" states that "in response to shade, the majority of plants produce less dry matter, retain photosynthate in the shoot at the expense of root growth, develop longer internodes and petioles, and produce larger, thinner leaves." This is fairly widely known, but he goes on, "However, when the responses of different ecological groups of plants are compared, a paradox becomes apparent. This arises from the fact that the capacity to maximise dry matter production in shade through modification of the phenotype is most apparent in species characteristic of unshaded or lightly shaded environments whilst plants associated with deep shade tend to grow slowly and to show much less pronounced morphogenetic responses to shade treatment."

In other words, the natural shade grasses like wavy hair-grass are basically slow-growing plants, and nothing will alter this. So they have no potential to produce turf for normal use. Wood meadow-grass is likewise only suitable for areas to be mown very seldom, if at all. It should be thought of as the most readily available natural grass for shade, rather than as a turfgrass. Instead, for the dry and difficult conditions, one must look to the turfgrasses which have some ability to withstand stress; or, for conditions which are more favourable for growth, to the opportunistic species. Bakker & Vos in the Netherlands in 1976 explained well the two kinds of shade, for which the most appropriate grasses are indicated in the following Table.

GRASSES ADAPTED TO VARIOUS SHADE CONDITIONS

No mowing	------------------- Infrequent mowing -------------------	
	Dry shade	Moist shade
Red and fine fescues, esp. strong creeping red fescue. Wood meadow-grass. Wavy hair-grass.	Chewings fescue. Slender creeping red fescue. Strong creeping red fescue. Possibly other fine fescues in moderate shade.	Bentgrasses. Red fescues, as for dry shade. Rough-stalked meadow-grass.

For **dry shade** in UK conditions, typically under trees where there is competition from tree roots for moisture and nutrients, the most useful grasses are the various forms of red fescue (*F. rubra*), including Chewings fescue. They are suitable both for severe shade (5–10% of daylight) where mowing is best avoided altogether if possible, and moderate shade (20–30% of daylight) where infrequent mowing, say three to five times a year at about 50 mm, is reasonable.

In **moist shade**, where rain falls even though light is restricted, as for example against a wall or building, fine fescues are also valuable but in addition bentgrasses will grow well once they have come through their slow establishment phase and provided that disease is controlled. The most shade-tolerant bent is generally considered to be velvet bent, but there seems to be little difference between it and the other species of bent, and 'Highland' browntop or a creeping bent could be expected to establish and develop faster. Rough-stalked meadow-grass and annual meadow-grass are also well adapted to moist conditions. The fast establishment of rough-stalked meadow-grass is advantageous.

Even with the fescues and bents, the degree of wear which they will tolerate will depend on how vigorously they grow and how full a cover is maintained. The responses to shade described by Grime – less dry matter, reduced root development, and longer and weaker leaves – all diminish wear tolerance. The most wear-tolerant UK turfgrasses – smooth-stalked meadow-grass, perennial ryegrass and timothy – are not really suited to shade conditions, although it is possible for the two former to survive to some extent. In the USA there is considerable emphasis on testing for shade tolerance, and some cultivars of smooth-stalked meadow-grass in particular are advertised for shade tolerance. Nevertheless, smooth-stalked meadow-grass is generally less well adapted to UK conditions than perennial ryegrass, red fescue or bentgrasses, and therefore even the most shade-tolerant cultivar of smooth-stalked meadow-grass is not likely to do very well.

Some of the cultivar differences in shade tolerance are bound up with resistance to various diseases. For example, powdery mildew (*Erysiphe graminis*) has been shown to be very important on smooth-stalked meadow-grass, and leaf spots on fescues and rough-stalked meadow-grass. In UK conditions several diseases, particularly fusarium patch disease, are made worse by the absence of sunlight and the humid conditions of some shaded areas, and this is an additional factor to bear n mind with shaded situations, especially where bentgrasses and annual meadow-grass are growing.

(CGC 1 : 42)

WINTER TEES AND LINES OF PLAY

Why Winter Tees?

All golfers hate the idea of playing off anything other than purpose-built grass tees, even in the winter. Unfortunately, the reality on very many courses is that the size of teeing area available at the majority of holes has never increased in line with the soaring popularity of the game. Most tees are, in fact, too small to support the volume of summer play today, and their condition reflects this, especially late season and early spring. To stay on such tees all winter would be the utmost folly, and whilst golfers reluctantly accept this, they still insist on utilising summer tees well beyond the time when renovation and what little natural recovery there is in late autumn can combine to restore a satisfactory grass cover. That, of course, leads to discontent in the spring, blamed on the greenkeeping staff, of course.

Tradition

On many courses it is standard practice to move off summer tees late, and simply put winter play onto a relatively flat area of fairway in front, sometimes not even mown out beforehand. No wonder golfers are reluctant to move! The other obvious drawbacks are poor stance and sight line to landing areas, possibly ill-drainage as well and deteriorating conditions as winter progresses. Additionally, there is seldom much thought given to siting these areas so as to move traffic off summer routes.

Trends

Many Clubs recognising the problems with small tees have embarked on reconstruction and enlargement programmes. This naturally encourages golfers to expect the same tees to be used both summer and winter. With a large enough grassed area that may well be practicable, but fails to address the concomitant problems of damage to routes used across surrounds in order to reach tees, tracks alongside them and out to fairway, as well as damage to landing areas that never enjoy a rest.

Artificial Tees

In the short term, and at par 3 holes possibly longer term, it can be extremely useful to employ artificial tee surfaces. There are some good products available now which golfers find acceptable and that cope with wear and tear. Unfortunately, many manufacturers still persist in a penny-pinching attitude to size.

At least one type of tee is readily moved with adjustable legs to suit uneven ground. Its surfacing material is stretched over the base board and held by the metal frame and so can be turned and then replaced when it becomes worn. Many admittedly cheaper sorts of tee have surfacing bonded to the base and these have to be discarded after one or two seasons.

Artificial tees are and will remain expensive, and most golfers dislike them. There is certainly a place for them, principally at par 3 holes where space for enlarging the grass tees and altering traffic routes is often non-existent. In situations like this, ensure that the artificial tee is set at the front edge of the main summer tee with a good hard standing area, and access from adjacent hard-surfaced paths.

Aims

There are three main aims in providing winter tees. First and foremost to allow early enough closure of the summer tees for effective renovation and to preserve them over winter, to limit further damage to routes used during the summer and, wherever practicable, to provide alternative sight lines and a separate traffic route out to a different fairway landing zone.

With thought and careful planning, plus the understanding and co-operation of the majority of the playing membership, all these objectives should be achievable at most holes. It is clearly essential that Committees communicate and consult with members beforehand, explaining exactly what they have in mind and why such measures are necessary. After all, the object of the exercise is to preserve or improve playing conditions for everyone, especially through the main summer competition season.

Strategies

Not all Clubs are in the fortunate position of St Andrews where the Old Course can be played the wrong way round in winter, should the need arise. Here the design, with those big double greens, lends itself to such an approach. Far more could be achieved by Architects at the design stage if strategies for winter play were given more consideration.

Another approach which works well is that adopted at Royal Troon Golf Club.

There, the 2nd to 5th holes have winter tees on the left and summer tees nearer the sea on the right. This spreads wear and tear either side of the greens on surround areas, provides alternative walkouts to the fairways and, because of the different sight lines, landing zones never coincide exactly with those that are used during the summer. The Club has certainly appreciated the foresight of the Architect originally responsible for that part of the layout and it has proved so successful that they have sought to extend the principle at some of the other holes, wherever practicable. It works well, encompasses all our aims and one can commend it.

There are, of course, many layouts where such an approach could not work, and a variety of strategies have to be adopted. The accent has to be on variety, clubs will not persuade members to accept the all too common approach of simply putting winter tees forward and shortening holes. Where space is at a premium, there may be no option but to go forward, preferably on the side nearer the previous hole so that the winter traffic can be routed off summer tracks.

However, where you can do it, go back at some holes where extra length would not be unduly punishing in winter, i.e. where the prevailing wind will be with, rather than against, the line of play.

Where there is space, a wider summer tee with alternative winter and summer routes down either side, together with separate walks out to the fairway can often work very well.

To sum up, a combination of all these strategies with artificial tees at short holes, a construction programme to provide separate large winter tees, combined in some cases with enlarged summer tees, will provide a realistic and workable solution to the problems of teeing grounds in the winter. At the end of the day, the main summer tees should be in far better shape since it will be practicable to close them early enough for late summer renovation to be fully successful and, of course, the areas used throughout winter can be shut down completely in early spring to allow full renovation, and with a rest all summer they should be in good condition once again for a resumption of use in the autumn.

(DFB : B.180)

ARTIFICIAL (SYNTHETIC) TEE SURFACES

There can be no doubt that there are no substitutes for a properly constructed, natural turf tee and some clubs are proud of their tradition of never having an artificial tee mat on their course. At the STRI we constantly expound the merits of large summer tees and designated winter tees to cope with the demands of year-round play, without sacrificing playing surface standards. This is a worthy ideal but in practice there may be limits to tee expansion or placement of separate winter tees – particularly at par 3 holes where damage is more acute or space-restricted. Under these circumstances artificial teeing surfaces can be extremely useful, either used in conjunction with the natural tee or exclusively over the winter months.

Types of Mat

Mats in the "rubber link" category are the cheapest and still the most durable. They are comparatively easy to keep clean and accept a tee peg, but with iron play there is the risk of severe jarring and lack of "give" does little to inspire confidence. Unless they are placed on a firm, level, well-drained base or fitted in a heavy duty frame, the stance on rubber mats can be a little precarious and the "feel" underfoot is disconcerting to many golfers. The appearance of squares of black rubber also detracts from the aesthetics of the golf course.

There are a bewildering number of synthetic grass tees on the market which attempt to emulate the playing qualities of natural turf, but without the associated damage. Most are based on either a woven or tufted polypropylene or nylon yarn of varying pile length. The densely-woven surfaces generally have a shorter pile (9-15 mm) and either rubber tees, tee peg holders, simple drilled holes or occasionally slits are provided. A bonded resin backing or rubber shock pad helps to cushion the impact of the club head.

Loosely tufted carpets mainly rely on sand filling for support of the fibres (generally 25 mm in length) and equally to reduce the hardness of the playing surface. Tee pegs can be pushed through into the sand.

A combined coir (coconut) and polypropylene matting is available, which does not require sand filling but the dense 35 mm length fibres readily accept a tee peg.

There are hybrid mats which combine the durability of a rubber surface with the improved characteristics of a synthetic turf insert (for both right and left handed golfers). Some manufacturers also supply synthetic grass tee mats with a "brush" grass insert, so that these are replaced rather than the entire mat!

Direct comparisons between these different types of mat can be misleading as costs vary significantly (£85-400) as does life-expectancy. Sand-filled tees need to be topped up with a properly graded sand, but there is still a tendency for the fibres to flatten at the tips and as the sand becomes more solid, it is difficult to push in a tee peg. The dense, shorter pile of the woven mats can also abrade and with constant iron play there is a risk of delamination (separation of the woven fabric from the rubber base) and ripping of the synthetic turf.

Size of Tee and Installation

There is no standard size for synthetic tee mats, but the most common dimensions are nominally 1 x 1.5 m or 1.5 x 1.5 m. This provides a minimum area for a comfortable stance whilst keeping the cost of the product competitive. Larger, artificial tees are available (up to 4 x 4 m) but the advantages need to be carefully weighed against the greater investment/replacement cost and the cumbersome nature of the mat when installing or moving.

Security and evenness of stance is important with any tee and artificial tees are no exception. A stable foundation can be provided by placing the mat on concrete slabs proud of the surface. Less obtrusive is the method of inserting the turf so that it is flush with surrounding ground, excavating to a sufficient depth to accommodate a minimum 50 mm (2") depth of packed sand to ensure a level base. Some manufacturers specify a graded stone base as an alternative to sand to provide stability and assist drainage. It is desirable to be able to lift mats periodically so that they can be rotated and thereby spread wear and tear uniformly.

Maintenance

Compared with a conventional tee there is far less commitment to maintenance of a synthetic tee. One of the major problems is keeping the surface free from mud and debris, therefore regular brushing and occasionally hosing down are essential. Permanently positioned, artificial tees require a decent area of hard-standing along side, as well as a path serving the tee. Bear in mind that placement of a synthetic tee in the middle of an existing tee will poach a valuable area and it will prove difficult to prevent golfers tracking over the surrounding tee surface. A preferable location is either forward, back or to the side of the tee nearest to the previous green. Thoughtful positioning will also help to break established patterns of golf traffic flow from green to tee.

Movable Tees

One solution to mud development around synthetic tee mats is to regularly move the playing surface. Several commercial mats are supplied with frames for this purpose, enabling the tee to be lifted and moved to a fresh position before the surrounding ground turns into a quagmire. The most expensive, substantial models provide a good, firm surface for play but at the cheaper end of the market, thinner wooden bases are used, consequently the tee tends to resemble a spring board! A few frames are mounted on adjustable legs so that the tee can be levelled on uneven ground.

The woven polypropylene is either held firmly in a metal frame or stretched and fixed to a tanalised wooden frame. Cheaper versions are directly bonded to the base and therefore, have to be completely discarded when the surface is worn.

Summary

Many golfers regard the use of artificial tee mats as devaluing the game as they are synonymous with basic pay and play golf courses. This inherent aversion can be countered at least in part by investing in a good quality product, ensuring that it is properly located as well as properly maintained and installing a service path or hard standing around static mat positions to minimise mud development around the perimeters.

Selection of the type of artificial tee will depend on a consideration of the weight of play and ratio of iron to wood tee shots; as well as the emphasis placed on the following factors: durability, appearance, feel, ease of installation, maintenance and price.

Faced with a choice between a muddy, uneven, "natural" surface (which needs to be completely renovated each season) and a firm, even, resilient synthetic surface, only the most bloody-minded of golfers would choose the former in deference to tradition.

(JWT : B.185)

PLATE 5: Fairway scarifiers such as this hydraulically-operated Veemo machine remove matted and fibrous growth and can help provide more uniform fairway playing surfaces. (Courtesy SISIS Equipment (Macclesfield) Ltd.)

SECTION 7
GOLF FAIRWAYS, ROUGH & SEMI-ROUGH

✦✦✦

Maintenance Operations

Mowing & Aerating Equipment

Divot Repair

*The Care of
the Golf Course*

FAIRWAY, SEMI-ROUGH AND ROUGH MANAGEMENT

Fairways

The fairway is usually considered to be the turfed area between the tee and the putting green which is mown at a lower height of cut than the surrounding rough. To produce good quality fairways where golfers' judgement and control are tested to the full, certain criteria have to be met. The main desirable characteristics are smoothness, grass density, uniformity and being firm yet resilient. The management programme is therefore tailored to develop these qualities in the playing surfaces and goes hand in hand with favouring conditions that encourage the best grass species, namely bents and fescues.

Mowing

An important part of summer maintenance is to develop uniformity and the formation of a dense, upright turf which is firm yet resilient to the well--truck shot. Fairways are mown relatively closely to promote these qualities, but not cut so closely as to cause scalping. Indeed, height of cut is critical in achieving proper ball positioning on the turf and control in hitting the shots. The preferred height of cut is 13-19 mm, although deviations from this range will occur depending on the state of growth and prevailing weather conditions. Frequency of cut may well fluctuate between three times a week on lush, green fairway to once a fortnight – an average would be weekly during the growing season.

The delineation between fairway and semi-rough should be distinct and should never be mown in a straight line, mow in an undulating contour pattern that will give shape and character, especially on holes where all the fairway is visible from the tee.

Divots

Minimising the extent of divot damage by cultural means is the primary policy to adopt, followed by efficient repair work. A soft, lush, spongy turf is associated with larger divots; a situation that can be reversed with management practices, including improving drainage and root growth by aeration, verticutting to remove thatch accumulation and cutting out fertiliser applications. Smaller divots will then be produced on a firmer surface, assuming the same basic stroke type. Divot repair should be confined primarily to the growing season, employing a mixture of screened sandy compost and a suitable fescue/bent seeds mixture. Aim for a seeding rate in the order to 17-35 g/m^2. The best results will be achieved under good growing conditions during moist spells of weather.

A useful tip in the early spring before gang mowing starts is to sweep up all the dead turves and debris left from winter play and follow up with a divoting party. This leaves a clean surface and encourages recovery as growth starts to pick up.

Weed Control

The cultivation of a dense, healthy fescue/bent turf is one of the soundest means of preventing weed invasion. Other beneficial cultural practices include worm control and avoiding application of lime and too much fertiliser. Worms bring up dormant weed seed to the surface, and a smeared cast is an ideal seed bed for weedgrass invasion. Lime and fertiliser can encourage worm and weed activity, and excessively lush pasture-like growth which is not ideal for golf and which requires very frequent mowing.

If chemical weed control is warranted, use an appropriate selective herbicide and apply strictly at the manufacturer's recommended rate. Timing should ideally coincide with a calm, dry, overcast day during a period of good growth.

Fertiliser

Maintenance of a bent/fescue sward is dependent on low fertility, so fertiliser should not be warranted. In fact, fertiliser application will only increase coarse, unwanted grasses and mowing requirements, a distinct disadvantage when time is so important in the summer months. However, there are instances where compaction, poor drainage and soil poverty result in thinning of the sward, moss invasion and the formation of bare areas. Here, a combination of aeration and careful fertiliser treatment (based on nitrogen) is recommended on selected localised trouble spots.

Aeration

With the ever increasing levels of play on golf courses, particularly during the winter, soil compaction and impeded surface drainage are becoming real problems. This condition is highlighted on areas where traffic is funnelled into confined sections, such as the entrance to the fairway from the tee.

Aeration is vital in combating compaction and impeded surface drainage, but it also has numerous other benefits. These include encouraging root growth (deeper root means enhanced drought resistance), the natural breakdown of thatch and, in the long term, the finer grasses, fescue and bent. There is now certainly a need to increase the frequency and intensity of aeration treatments to combat compaction brought about through play. Regular deep slit tine aeration is therefore essential during autumn to spring on a two to three weekly basis. In fact, this work can be extended to any time when the ground is firm enough to take the tractor without rutting yet the soil is moist enough to gain good tine penetration. Aim to give all traffic routes and other concentrated areas of wear a double pass with the aerator whenever the fairways are slit.

Improvements in tractor-mounted aerators now allow deep penetrating tines to be fitted (225–300 mm) and with the facility of hydraulics for enhancing tine penetration. Verti-Drain machines are extensively used on fairways and, despite being an expensive unit to hire or buy for large-scale fairway aeration, there are real benefits to be gained by breaking up compaction to a depth of 400 mm and improving surface drainage. The use of Verti-Drain machines is most useful on traffic routes and compacted areas.

Drainage

On clay sites, aeration alone may not be sufficient to overcome compaction and poor drainage imposed by the nature of the soil profile. In these cases drainage in the form of ditches and/or a piped drainage scheme may be required to alleviate the problem. Mole ploughing has also proved to be a useful exercise in providing temporary drainage channels running into the drainage aggregate of a main drain or connecting laterals within a system.

Verticutting

One management treatment that has become more prevalent in recent years is verticutting. The practice is widely carried out on greens using verticut reels on the triple mower; it is simply a question of extending the work to approaches and fairways to gain the same benefits yet using different machinery. Time the operation for periods of good growth and, bearing in mind the limited time available to implement fairway work during the summer months, it is recommended a spring and autumn treatment be undertaken. A number of tractor-mounted or trailed units are available. All arisings should be picked up with a large tractor-mounted leaf sweeper or similar if the verticut unit does not possess a collecting facility.

Worm Casting

Worm casting can be particularly troublesome on parkland type courses where the casts create a messy, unsightly surface which is disruptive to winter play and efficient gang mowing. Casts also encourage moles, effect surface levels and smother turfgrasses which, in turn, provides a seed bed for weeds. Worm activity can be discouraged by avoiding creating limy conditions and by not using excessive amounts of fertiliser and organic materials. When cultural methods fail and casting is prolific, chemical control becomes a necessity.

A number of wormkillers are available on the market, although long-term products are now banned. Alternative wormkillers are available, e.g. those based on carbendazim and thiophanate-methyl, but these are not as long lasting. Strict adherence to the manufacturer's recommended rate is vital (and a statutory requirement) if successful control of large areas is to be achieved. Remember the cost of treating fairways will be expensive whatever the product chosen.

The Rough

The rough is not specifically defined in the Rules of Golf but is included in "through the green" as follows:

"Through the green is the whole area of the course except: (a) the teeing ground and putting green of the hole being played; and (b) all hazards on the course."

In terms of management, the rough is the area of the course surrounding the green, the tee and the fairway of each hole. Like many aspects of golf course maintenance, the management of the rough consists of achieving a balance. In this case, it involves striking a balance between virtually the whole course being mown at fairway height – the wide open prairie syndrome – to deep jungle-type rough extending right up to the fairway edge. The former creates a situation where the golfer can hook or slice a drive with little fear of stroke penalty, the latter extracts maximum stroke penalty, but creates the major problems of losing golf balls and slowing up play, a very pertinent point when considering high levels of play, e.g. public courses.

There is also variation in the types of rough encountered, from the semi-open with tall-growing grasses, e.g. links, to heather ling/grass mixtures, e.g. moorland or heathland, to pastureland, lush, dense, spongy, e.g. parkland. Since no hard and fast standards exist, it is up to those responsible for golf course management to balance the speed of play desired and the ease of finding golf balls with the degree of difficulty sought and the desirability for a low maintenance regime. This can be largely achieved by variation in cutting height and grading of the rough from deep rough to perimeter fairway.

Semi-Rough

Breaking up the rough into component parts, the semi-rough is that band of rough immediately surrounding a fairway and lying between the fairway and the most distant rough. If space permits, an intermediate band can be introduced between the semi-rough and fairway to extract different degrees of stroke penalty, as well as providing shot variety. In a similar fashion to developing definition between putting surfaces and fairway, by introducing a collar, the semi-rough fulfils the same function between fairway and deep rough, only in this instance is virtually created by mowing alone.

The mowing height, contouring, frequency and width of cut depend on the degree of difficulty and rapidity of play desired, but there are ground rules. Firstly, a common height of cut would be in the order of 37–63 mm with a typical mowing frequency of weekly or fortnightly, depending on the state of growth. An important point to stress here is that the semi-rough is mown with gang mowers on a regular basis to maintain a clear definition between fairway and deep rough.

There is still a distinct tendency for operatives to mow in straight lines because it is easier and quicker, but for presentation, the semi-rough and fairway should be contoured to the terrain of the land and graduated to provide more of a challenge to the better golfer, e.g. increase the semi-rough width to give fairways 30 m wide at the

230 m mark compared with 40 m at the 140 m mark. (A useful average to take for fairway width is 32–35 m.) The width of the semi-rough would generally be between 3–5 m, although on municipal courses this figure is often increased to speed up play.

On large acreage courses, a further refinement would involve introducing another band of semi-rough mown at an intermediate height between fairway and semi-rough height, i.e. 25–37 mm, and to a width of 1.5–2.5 m. This band of semi-rough would be mown more frequently, say every five to ten days.

Other Maintenance

Whilst maintenance of rough areas needs to be kept to a minimum, this does not mean neglect. Apart from mowing, slit tine aeration with a tractor-mounted aerator is recommended for the semi-rough, as well as verticutting or raking to remove dead growth that can often build up to form a mat.

Weed control may be necessary to prevent infection of the fairways, but as there is a movement towards conservation of the rough and promoting native flora and fauna, caution should be exercised before chemical control is implemented.

It is most unlikely that the semi-rough will have any fertiliser requirement.

Leatherjackets can cause considerable damage in the semi-rough where the turf is soft and spongy and, therefore, control using an appropriate insecticide is advisable. However, cultural practices should not be forgotten, the aim is to improve the uniformity and density of the turf and firmness of the surface, i.e. through aeration and verticutting.

On golf courses with deciduous trees it is essential in the autumn to pick up leaves and thereby keep play flowing and prevent unnecessary problems to turf growth. A large tractor-mounted leaf sweeper is the most common means of quick and efficient leaf removal.

Deep Rough

On parkland courses the rough adjacent to semi-rough is usually mown at a height of 100 mm for presentation and speeding up play. Depending on the height of cut, gang mowers, flail mowers or rotary mowers are employed, the latter two are useful for cutting heather on heathland or moorland courses. In the case of heather, a yearly late autumn mowing prevents heather becoming too 'leggy' and instead encourages the formation of young, new shoots.

In the sometimes obsessive quest for presentation, manicuring of courses has developed to such an extent that there are often few natural areas where the grass is allowed to grow in its natural state. Besides cutting down maintenance costs, there are advantages in allowing the deep rough to grow without mowing, especially where golf shots seldom stray. There is a good case for bringing grassy mounds in the semi-rough into this category of rough, as well as carry areas from tee to fairway.

Desirable grasses will be allowed to seed, leading to colonisation of adjacent areas. Existing or sown wild flowers provide colour and the deep rough can be a cover and food source for wildlife. These all enhance the aesthetic value and interest of the golf course to golfers.

A word of caution, natural areas require careful planning and effort as there is a thin dividing line between a natural setting and an unkempt one which appears to have been forgotten. In this respect, a yearly mowing regime would be appropriate, as well as grubbing out saplings, e.g. hawthorn, to prevent scrub forming.

Some Other Factors

Moles

It is worth mentioning that mole problems can coincide with a large worm population, as worms from a major part of the mole's diet. If the mole infestation is severe, then some form of trapping, poisoning or gassing will be necessary. Various mechanical mole traps are available. They are carefully placed in the mole runs and have to be checked daily. Toxic baits have also been used to poison the pests but may only be available to licenced specialists. Gassing can be carried out using gas or smoke generators which fill the mole tunnels with cyanide or hydrogen phosphide gas. Once the moles have been eliminated it is worthwhile carrying out worm control to deter further re-invasion by moles from neighbouring land.

Trees

Apart from on some links courses, trees are an important feature on the golf course and they do require attention from time to time. The majority of trees on the golf course are found around the tees, greens and between the fairways. Group plantings on the fairways are not often found but individual specimen trees are sometimes used to create additional interest. An annual inspection will usually show which trees require attention and if any major branches need lopping due to disease or some other hazard, then it is wise to employ the services of a competent tree surgeon. A planting programme is needed to maintain an even distribution of younger and mature trees. Deciduous trees can be planted from October to March, but evergreens are usually most successful if planted in autumn or early spring. With these, you should avoid planting in the winter months of December, January and February. There are many possible pitfalls when it comes to buying and planting trees and it pays to thoroughly read up on the subject or seek the advice of an arboriculturist before going ahead.

Spreading the Wear

The practice of only allowing wide-wheel trolleys on the course is common at many clubs – particularly during the winter. This sort of restriction will help to reduce wheel-marking on wet fairways. Muddy tracks can often be seen on regularly used areas whatever type of trolley is being used and it is a good idea to try and spread the wear evenly. This can be achieved by means of temporarily fencing or roping areas off to guide the traffic in a particular direction away from tees, etc. The fence or rope guides should be moved every week or two to ensure that maximum use is made of the space available. Without this sort of friendly persuasion the golfers are likely to continue using the same old paths and boggy conditions can soon result.

It is clear from the above that the fairways should not just be neglected through the winter. Regular aeration work to help relieve compaction is perhaps the most important operation, but it must be emphasised that the tractor should only be used when ground conditions are suitable.

(CGC 1 : 44)

FAIRWAY MAINTENANCE

The underlying objective of fairway maintenance on any golf course must be to produce an acceptable playing surface on a year-round basis. Ideally, the surface should be firm, tight and uniformly grassed so that clean contact can be made with the back of the ball. Seaside links turf tends to provide the above characteristics naturally when well maintained, as do many heathland and moorland courses. However, on courses frequently situated on heavier, less free-draining soils, there is a tendency for a coarser, denser turf to predominate. The maintenance regime must be directed towards discouraging this and encouraging the more desirable, finer-leaved grasses which provide better golfing conditions.

Increasingly, problems are being experienced on golf course fairways due to increased levels of play. For example, some links courses are experiencing erosion of the turf surface on heavily played areas, exposing the native sand beneath. On parkland courses, compaction of a clay based soil may lead to drainage problems during the wetter, winter months.

Like any management regime, a fairway programme must be flexible and it must be accepted that demands will vary from course to course dependent upon terrain, level of play, architecture and design, and a natural soil drainage characteristics. Nevertheless, the following operations form the backbone of most management programmes, but their intensity and frequency must be adjusted according to need:

[1] Mowing

Demands on mowing equipment vary dramatically from course to course. For example, on fast-growing, fertile parkland courses it is often necessary to mow the fairways at least twice per week. In contrast, during a dry summer many links fairways may only require mowing once a fortnight. Essentially, the aim must be to provide a fast running surface and this is usually achieved by mowing at a height of between 12-18 mm ($^1/_2$ -$^3/_4$ in.) through the growing season.

In order to improve presentation, some clubs are now cutting their fairways with ride-on hydraulic mowers as opposed to the more conventional trailed gang units used in the past. These do undoubtedly provide an improved cut and presentation in the short-term as well as reducing scalping which is a problem frequently encountered on some undulating links land. At the end of the day, the type of implement used and its frequency of use will depend upon the course in question.

[2] Scarification

This is an often forgotten treatment on golf fairways. Greenkeepers think nothing of regularly verticutting greens to prevent lateral growth and thatch accumulation, but often do not have the time or the equipment to carry out a similar type of work on the fairways.

Thatch accumulation, exacerbated by poor drainage and compaction, will reduce the quality of surface in the long-term. It will encourage shallow rooting grasses such as annual meadow-grass (*Poa annua*) which will then be susceptible to drought during the drier summer months. In addition, the thatch accumulation will impede surface drainage when conditions are wet.

Frequency of veemo-ing again depends upon site conditions, which in turn will affect the rate of build up of fibre. Most parkland, moorland or heathland courses will, however, benefit from veemo-ing or similar scarification work at least once per year during the spring or early autumn to check fibre build up and fine down the texture of the sward. Do, however, also be aware of the need to pick up debris after the operation is complete – this can be excessive in certain instances, especially if it is some time since the operation was last carried out.

[3] Weed and worm control

Weed control measures remain fairly standard, although new selective herbicides continually come onto the market. Many of the chemicals now available are broad spectrum and therefore make weed control relatively straightforward. Provided spraying conditions are appropriate, manufacturer's directions are adhered to and the most suitable product chosen, most broad-leaved weed problems can be controlled.

The situation with worms has, however, changed somewhat with the revocation of chlordane in recent times. The alternative lumbricides only have a short-lived effect and many clubs are beginning to notice an increase in worm activity on fairways. This may become a more serious problem in the future.

Acidification of the surface is known to be effective against worm activity and this can be achieved in the short-term by the application of sulphur or more gradually by regular application of sulphate of iron. These options will certainly be cheaper than lumbricides available commercially and will in all likelihood spear head future control measures.

[4] Fertilisers

As a general rule it is unwise to drift into a regimented programme of applying fertiliser to fairways on a regular basis. In theory, mature fairway areas should retain good growing characteristics without the need for fertiliser application, although there are weak and impoverished areas of fairway on most courses that would benefit from an occasional application of fertiliser or organic-type soil. In contrast, newly sown fairways will often require fertiliser for the first few years to thicken and encourage the swards, which they should then be gradually weaned off once this has been achieved.

With the return of clippings after mowing, fertilisation of fairways should generally be avoided. Over-use of fertiliser will encourage annual meadow-grass and coarser-leaved grass species and ultimately reduce the quality of the surface. Once this folly is realised, a decline is often seen before improvements can be generated.

[5] Divoting

Fairway landing zones, particularly on short par-4 holes and collection areas, are always susceptible to surface damage. Often, autumn renovation and resting are required at the end of the season, but during the season there is a requirement for regular divoting to encourage recovery and to maintain reasonable surface levels and therefore reasonable lies. A mixture of top dressing compost, together with a little fescue/bent seed should suffice, but do ensure that a ryegrass-free mixture is used.

[6] Autumn and winter work

Keeping fairways in good condition during the main competition season is the priority. Come the autumn, all necessary measures must be taken to ensure that these conditions are again achieved the following year – in many cases this will require compromises from the membership.

[a] Badly worn and damaged areas should be roped off and should undergo renovation. This may involve, for example, hollow coring or Verti-Draining, to be followed by overseeding and top dressing. This work must be completed whilst there is still plenty of growing weather left to allow seed to germinate and establish. All renovated areas should ideally be rested throughout the winter period and if this means closure of whole sections of fairway, then so be it – the benefits will be seen the following spring.

[b] Initiate trolley restrictions if appropriate. If the use of trolleys through the winter is to be permitted, then ensure summer routes are changed and when practical, areas of rough and semi-rough are used to protect the fairways.

[c] Routine slit tine aeration work on fairways should be continued throughout the winter months unless the surfaces become unduly wet or frozen. Regular aeration work is essential for encouraging root structure and depth, enhancing aerobic microbial activity and promoting better, natural drainage.

[d] Perpetually wet areas should be investigated and drainage improvements commenced when weather conditions are appropriate.

(AJB : B.187)

MOWING EQUIPMENT FOR FAIRWAYS AND ROUGH

To appreciate the advances in fairway mowing equipment, particularly in recent years, we must take a historical perspective. It was not too long ago that many courses relied on sheep and rabbits to preserve a close cropped turf. The poor quality grazing land incorporated into the first links were already inhabited by these woolly and furry mowers. Of greater significance, was the movement of golf course developments inland to more productive terrain, where sheep grazing became an impractical method of checking growth.

Budding's invention of the lawn mower in the 1830's was not capitalised on for larger areas until later in the century. The pony mower, a cylinder unit drawn by quadruped, was quickly superseded by the first gang mowers trailed behind a tractor. The structure of trailed gangs has changed little since 1921 when they were first used in this country, essentially a frame housing 3 or 5 cutting cylinders. Larger units are available, up to 9 cylinders, but these tend to be too wide for golf course use, restricting manoeuvrability. Three-gang units are capable of coping with a 9-hole course or for cutting the narrow band of semi-rough on 18 holes. For the greater expanse of fairway found on an 18-hole course the greater width of the 5-gang is needed. The performance of trailed cylinder gang mowers if often criticised but this is usually as much to do with the operator as the machine. Well maintained and adjusted trailed gangs will perform well if travelling speed is regulated, a decent pace can be accommodated on stretches of level ground but a much slower speed is essential to obtain anything like a quality cut on undulating turf. Trailed gangs have a gear drive mechanism so that the same number of cuts per metre can be obtained at different forward speeds. More often than not travelling too quickly is the reason for poor performance from a set of trailed gangs and a panic reaction is to up-grade the mower. Speed of forward movement will also regulate the ground-hugging capability of trailed gangs and there is a degree of flex on the frame, to facilitate the mowing of more highly contoured land. The gang mower is supported by pneumatic or steel wheels, the latter giving better grip on contoured ground or in wet conditions. Burn marks or scuffing of the turf can result if the mower slips on unsafe ground, again a basic fault of the operator taking the mower out in unsuitable conditions or turning too quickly on greasy turf. The outer units on trailed gangs can be raised manually or by hydraulic lift on the more advanced models, to reduce the width of the mower and expedite movement around the course, but when the units are grounded they cut all the time necessitating a constant flow of mown paths around the course on the navigational route of the equipment. The greenkeeper must plan the mowing route carefully to avoid carving out unsightly paths across the course. Paths are usually cut from tee to fairway and then green to tee, so there is always a danger of the tractor-mounted mower having to pass close to the putting surface. The beauty of trailed gang mowers is that little can go wrong with the cutter itself, there are many golf clubs cutting fairways with gang sets of 30 years age and over. Apart from grinding the cutting cylinder and fitting a new bottom blade prior to each growing season, the major maintenance is hammering out dents in the frame!

Trailed gangs do have problems in providing a truly uniform quality of cut as the cutting rate is controlled, to a great degree, by forward speed. Grip is also a problem, particularly when the grass is wet. Ideally, mowing would only be done in dry conditions, but the playing demands on golf courses mean that grass often has to be cut when wet, either during periods of rainy weather or early in the morning when there is a dew on the ground. Speed of operation is also a consideration and the need to cut a complete circuit around the course does add extra time to the operation. The introduction of gang mowers with cutting cylinders driven at a constant rate by the tractor's hydraulics was seen as the means of overcoming the deficiencies of the trailed mower. Each reel is driven by a hydraulic motor so the cuts per metre are constant whatever the forward travelling speed. Hydraulic connection also provides the ability to raise the cutting units from the isolation of the tractor cab. The degree of sophistication of the gang set determines whether all units are driven by a single lever or under split control. This relates to the number of spool valves required for mounting, operating all 5 units or the 3 central and 2 outer units independently. The spool valves operate the cutting mode, in motion or static and whether the units are raised or grounded. Forward, neutral and reverse drives provide hydraulically driven gangs with more cutting options than trailed units. With neutral drive it is not necessary to cut ground which is being travelled over, nor do the cutting cylinders have to be raised to avoid cutting a section of ground. With the outer gangs raised the cutting width is reduced allowing greater manoeuvrability into tight areas. In the raised position the reels will not operate, this is an important safety feature. Reverse drive can virtually double the life of the cutting edge and, in some models, provides back-lapping facility. Extra adaptability comes with the option of fixed or floating heads with a choice of number of blades to the reel. Fixed heads and/or a reduction in blades allows speedier mowing, although to a lower quality, and the versatility to cut semi-rough. On the down side, having switched to a hydraulically driven gang mower, some greenkeepers found the model they chose followed the tractor too closely, or that there was inadequate movement in the frame mounting to flow over severely undulating ground and in some instances have changed back to trailed gangs. On ridge and furrow terrain, or similar undulating ground, neither type of gang mower guarantees a perfect finish, scalping of ridges and riding over the furrow leaving lush grass is common and until recently, the only means of cutting such ground may well have involved the use of triple machines, usually employed for green surround and tee work.

All tractor-mounted mowers have a basic problem when it comes to cutting golf fairways, the tractor itself. There is a definite potential for damage where employing a unit with linkage. The mower does not always follow the line of the tractor. Manoeuvrability is restricted by the large turning circle, overcome on some models by having the hydraulic pump attached directly to the tractor's PTO rather than a PTO drive shaft. The length of tractor and gangs reduces the options on direction of cut, basically to straight up and down the fairway and this may mean turning the whole assembly on green approaches. The latest development in gang mowing is the dedicated fairway mower. These are 5 unit ride-on machines which are basically an extension of the greens triple idea or originally developed for estate mowing, theoretically giving greater manoeuvrability, contour hugging and lower ground pressure. More cynical observers may see this evolution as purely the result of televised golf, i.e. striped, informally shaped fairways of carpet-like appearance which bear little relation to everyday golf in this country. There is more to a dedicated system than that, but is the considerable cost of such a unit justified?

(SPI : B.185)

LARGE-SCALE MECHANICAL AERATION

Aeration machines can be usefully employed on golf fairways. This article deals with the above as distinct from relatively small areas of intensively managed turf such as golf greens. On the latter area relatively small mechanised aerators are most often used, occasionally supplemented by hand forking on localised problem areas. The use of such small aerators on larger fairways is limited because of the time factor, though they can be useful for alleviating the effects of concentrated wear, puddling, etc. in major trouble spots when ground conditions do not permit tractor work.

Reasons for Aeration

In fertile soils with open structure permitting free passage of water and air, surface drainage can be satisfactory and where root development is not unduly impeded, the growth of a vigorous, healthy turf is possible. Under playing conditions, however, particularly in winter when the soil is soft and wet, the topsoil surface becomes smeared and destructured, often with a compacted layer in the top 50 or 75 mm causing impeded surface drainage. Play under these conditions rapidly makes matters worse, compaction increases, the affected places become even more smeared and puddled, with the muddy areas increasing in size. There is deterioration in the grass cover and playing surface, and ill effects can also persist into the summer, affecting root growth, vigour and recovery.

On many courses with sound comprehensive underground drainage, surface drainage can still be affected due to the above factors. The compacted, destructured soil layer prevents quick water movement away from the top into more open soil underneath. The rate at which soil becomes destructured depends on the soil itself, the amount and timing of play, and the weight of machinery such as mowers used in maintenance.

Regular thorough use of machines capable of piercing through the compacted surface layer helps alleviate these problems. Frequent use helps preserve a vigorous turf with good root development, and maintains some soil structure to produce the quick draining surface so vital for sports turf.

On very fibrous turf such as exists on some fairways, regular aeration helps water to penetrate the fibrous layer, improves aeration which, in turn, helps breakdown the fibre to some degree. Drought resistance can also be encouraged through improvements in root growth.

Aeration units are also of value for other special purposes. On new grounds with very infertile soil or on sandy, drought-prone fairways, additional organic matter such as dried sewage or fenpeat can be helped to integrate with the soil through loosening or opening up the surface with aeration prior to application. Similar effects can be achieved following sand applications on heavier soils. Aerators are also useful for loosening the surface soil prior to renovation. Hard pans existing below the immediate surface may also be broken up to some extent by deeper piercing or sub-aeration units.

Machinery Available

The following main types of aerator are available:–
(a) tractor-mounted units and trailed versions hauled by tractors
(b) tractor-mounted Verti-Drain type machines
(c) tractor-mounted units that cut continuous slits or relieve compaction with a shallow vibrating mole attachment.

In most cases, tines of different design are available to meet various requirements, e.g. diamond-shaped slitting, chisel or solid for routine aeration and deep piercing, hollow or spoon tines for use where severe compaction exists or to help the incorporation of amendments into soil. The tines are mounted and, in some cases, spring-loaded so as to minimise turf tearing in use. Penetration from 100–150 mm is the normal range, though some heavy duty units achieve 230 mm. Various competing Verti-Drain machines are available penetrating up to 450 mm which also feature tine movement in the soil to obtain positive compaction relief.

When to Aerate

Fairways need regular aeration, and treatment at least once a month, or preferably every two weeks, during the autumn and winter should be the aim but only when ground and weather conditions are suitable. After a dry summer these areas often require more intensive spiking once showery weather develops in autumn to open up the turf, allowing better penetration of moisture to aid recovery growth and to encourage deep rooting in the turfgrasses. On severely compacted traffic routes and walk-offs from greens and tees, it may be necessary to Verti-Drain the area in the autumn to relieve the compaction.

After Aeration

Depending on ground conditions, slight turf tearing or lifting may arise where the tines penetrate. Whilst growth is still occurring, normal gang mowing will often suffice to correct this. Heavy rolling nullifies any benefit from aeration.

(CGC 1 : 47)

DEALING WITH DIVOTS

Scarred areas of fairway, strewn with divots, are not only unsightly but also provide unsatisfactory and unfair playing surfaces, often giving a player a poor lie after a good previous shot. Even in cases where most fairway areas provide perfectly acceptable surfaces, concentrated divoting can occur on areas where most tee shots tend to land and the layout of some holes unfortunately tends to encourage the development of such localised problem patches.

The problem of divots on fairways can be approached in two ways – prevention by minimising the chance of serious scarring developing, and cure by efficient repair work. As with most other problems, prevention is undoubtedly better than cure.

Preventative Treatments

In the case of some holes, the widening of a particular section of fairway, the elimination of surplus bunkers or mounds, or more frequent changing of tee markers can do much to prevent the deterioration of small areas where concentrated play has occurred. Spreading wear over larger areas helps considerably.

The correct basic maintenance of fairways is also of importance. In the past there has unfortunately been a tendency to try to reduce the divot problem by encouraging lush and vigorous grass growth with the idea that strongly growing swards will recover from scarring more rapidly. Such mistaken attempts to improve grass growth by the liberal use of fertilisers and by liming can be disastrous in the long term. Such treatment encourages perennial ryegrass and other coarse grasses which, although it is certainly strong growing and wear-resistant, has no useful role as a fairway grass. Most golf courses (particularly parkland courses) unfortunately have some ryegrass in their fairways which, although it is the most desirable species for rugby or soccer pitches, does not produce good golfing surfaces. Ryegrass swards are lush and require very frequent cutting, using time and labour better expended in other vital tasks. The ball tends to sink into such a sward instead of being set-up in the way which is mandatory for a good fairway surface. Encouraging ryegrass by fertiliser and lime is therefore definitely not the right way to minimise the divot problem as this approach creates a situation which is worse than the problem it purports to solve.

No, the best fairway surfaces are predominantly made up of finer grasses, particularly bentgrasses, which if well maintained provide enough growth to allow good natural recovery of divot-scarred areas. Such swards can be maintained under moderately acidic soil conditions and where a controlled degree of soil poverty prevails. The ability of such swards to recover from the effects of play can be increased by reducing excessive fibre or thatch accumulation (by spring harrowing or rotary scarification work) and by maintaining good surface drainage and root development (by aeration work, mainly in spring and autumn). Of course, there are situations where soil poverty becomes extreme and even the desirable finer grasses start to suffer, with thin growth, bare soil patches and moss invasion. Here, judicious and circumspect fertiliser treatment (usually with nitrogen and certainly not with large quantities of phosphate) may be useful on chosen localised areas.

In situations where large numbers of divots are lying scattered on a fairway area, a cleaner playing surface may be obtained simply by running over with the gang mower to chop up and dispense the debris. Ideally, of course, all players should replace divots on all occasions but it sadly seems impossible to persuade all members of the average club to act thoughtfully in this respect. Even where members do conscientiously replace the majority of divots, surfaces can remain scarred particularly in dry weather or in the winter when replaced divots are slow to heal. Bird activity can be a nuisance too, with seagulls, crows or starlings picking up and scattering carefully replaced divots. Here, the problem can sometimes be minimised by eliminating insects like leatherjackets, or by controlling earthworms as birds are often looking for food.

On most heavily played courses some reseeding work proves necessary at times even where the necessity has been minimised by attention to the points covered above.

Repair Work

Divot repair is best carried out in the growing season, when labour can be spared, using a good screened topsoil into which a suitable non-ryegrass seeds mixture has been mixed. The seeding rate should be about 17–35 g/m^2, although it is obviously difficult to achieve any great exactitude in such circumstances. The seeds mix used should match the prevailing composition of the existing fairway sward as far as possible with the limitation that the egregious perennial ryegrass should not be included. Repair work should theoretically be carried out when there is good growth and no danger of drought but in practice it tends to be one of those jobs carried out simply when time can be spared from other greenkeeping operations.

(CGC 1 : 45)

GROWTH RETARDANTS

There is nothing new in the idea of using chemicals to retard the growth of grass. Maleic hydrazide, the original grass growth retarder, was introduced in 1948 and has been used regularly, but has never really made a big impact on the management of amenity grass. Mowing, costly and labour intensive though it is, still remains our main method of management, even for relatively low grade grass areas.

What are Grass Growth Retardants?

Grass growth retardants are part of a group of chemicals described as plant growth regulators. They enter the grass plant via the leaves or roots and are translocated through the plant to their sites of action. Here they begin to affect the growth rate of the plant, slowing down leaf development and in some cases halting the production of flowering stems. Used at higher doses they will quite efficiently kill plants just like conventional herbicides, but at the correct doses the retarding effect wears off in eight to twelve weeks and normal growth resumes.

What Growth Retardants are Available?

There are three growth retardants currently available for use on grass, maleic hydrazide, mefluidide and paclobutrazol. Maleic hydrazide was tested by local authorities in the 1950's for retarding grass growth on road verges, parks and cemeteries and also for retarding hedges and shrubs. Unfortunately, the early formulations of maleic hydrazide were not rainfast, and in Britain's rapidly changeable weather many users found that the compound was washed out by the rain before it had a chance to enter the grass. Yet, other users found that the rather narrow range of safe application rates could result in accidental scorching of swards when the chemical was applied by unskilled operators. Much of the early enthusiasm for the product lapsed in the light of these experiences. However, some authorities still use maleic hydrazide for road verges with great success. The more recent formulations of maleic hydrazide include stickers that help to make them rainfast so that more reliable results can be obtained.

Following the discovery of maleic hydrazide a number of other growth regulator compounds for use in agriculture and horticulture appeared but it was not until 1975 that a new grass retarder, mefluidide was produced. Mefluidide has a number of advantages over maleic hydrazide that should make it easier to use and more effective and reliable. Like maleic hydrazide it enters the grass plant via the leaves and is translocated through the plant to the growing points. Mefluidide checks the grass growth faster than maleic hydrazide and in mixed grass swards it is better at preventing the formation of flowering heads. Mefluidide produces a very tidy looking sward and its effects last up to twelve weeks. Mefluidide has a relatively wide dose range and the danger of discolouration and damage to the sward is consequently less than with maleic hydrazide. Mefluidide can also be used on closer mown swards than maleic hydrazide with less risk of phytotoxicity.

The third growth retarder, paclobutrazol, differs from maleic hydrazide and mefluidide in that it is taken into the plants via the roots. Uptake is therefore dependent upon the soil being moist enough to allow transport of the chemical to the rootzone of the grasses. In years with very dry spring weather this could be somewhat of a disadvantage with chemical retardation delayed, though in drought situations grass growth is naturally retarded to an extent. A rather more serious disadvantage is that paclobutrazol acts predominantly on the shallower rooting finer grasses. Coarse grasses with deeper root systems are not adequately retarded so that the sward can appear untidy and coarse in appearance. In addition, paclobutrazol has little or no effect upon the production of flowering heads, again making treated swards untidy. In its favour it has a longer period of suppression, with effects sometimes carrying over to the following year.

Table 1 compares the three available grass growth retardants.

Cost Effectiveness

Whether or not the new generation of grass growth retarders make an impact on amenity grass management depends to a large extent upon their cost effectiveness. The greenkeeper may expect between eight and twelve weeks control of grass growth following application. The usual alternative is regular mowing which is labour intensive and for which costs vary according to the situation. A second alternative is to sow new grass areas with low growing cultivars, a range of which are now available. Only the greenkeeper can decide which alternative is most cost effective in his circumstances. A second factor that cannot be costed in monetary terms is the improvement in sward composition that repeated use of maleic hydrazide or mefluidide can produce. Finer grasses are encouraged at the expense of coarser species, leading to a more pleasing appearance and reduced cutting requirements.

Should You Consider Using Grass Growth Retardants?

If you deal exclusively with fine turf the answer is definitely not. None of the currently available retardants are suitable for golf surfaces, whether greens, tees or fairways. They are however sometimes used on awkward areas – around trees, on steep banks and perhaps other odd corners of the rough. Rarely, growth retardants might be used on bunker edges or for helping control particularly heavy rough, but their suitability for such purposes depends on individual circumstances. Difficult to maintain areas are the places where growth retardants can be very cost-effective and where they will find increasing use.

TABLE 1
Comparison of Growth Retarders

FACTOR	MALEIC HYDRAZIDE	MEFLUIDIDE (M.H.)	PACLOBUTRAZOL
Mode of Uptake	Foliar	Foliar	Roots
Typical reduction in dry matter yield from a single application under 'best' conditions	Up to 25%	Up to 45% (*Festuca/Poa* spp.) Up to 60% (*Agrostis* spp.)	Up to 45%
Duration of effects	Up to 8 weeks	Up to 12 weeks	Up to 14 weeks, occasionally carry over to following season
Effects on sward composition	Tends to favour finer species of grass – in particular *Festuca rubra*. There is some suppression of flowering and seedhead production. Some increase in	Encourages finer grasses at the expense of coarser species. Very good seedhead suppression. Tends to produce a finer and much tidier sward broad-leaved weeds than M.H.	Poor suppression of some deeper rooted coarse species. No seedhead suppression. Long term use where coarse species are present may lead to untidy appearance
Discolouration	The rate of use is critical otherwise there can be severe scorching, browning and death of more susceptible species	Tends to make the sward greener and more lush in appearance. Some discolouration in drought conditions with high dose rates	Occasional browning of sward
Reliability	Unpredictable results due to climatic effects – dose rate critical. Rainfast formulation essential	Very reliable in use with a relatively wide dose tolerance by most species	Relatively inactive in dry conditions but acts reliably when soil moisture is high and therefore during periods of growth
Flexibility of application	Fairly critical – rainfall after application can negate effects	Rainfall shortly after application can somewhat reduce effectiveness	Considerable flexibility in timing and season. Leached slowly

Remember always to follow the manufacturer's instructions on the label when applying growth retardants.

(CGC 1 : 88)

PLATE 6: In the right circumstances mole ploughing can be an effective and economical method of improving golf course drainage. (Courtesy SISIS Equipment (Macclesfield) Ltd.)

SECTION 8
SAND BUNKERS

Bunker Maintenance

Bunker Construction

Choice of Sand

*The Care of
the Golf Course*

BUNKER CONSTRUCTION & MAINTENANCE

The game of golf evolved on the barren and windswept links of Scotland due to the unsuitability of the terrain for any other purpose. The courses and the hazards they incorporated developed naturally, with grazing animals playing a significant role. Certain areas of the land would be grazed bare, particularly where sheep took shelter from the elements in hollows or on the leeward side of dunes. These areas then became unstable and collapsed into pits, exposing the native sandy soil beneath. These sandy pits, or bunkers as they became known, dotted the landscape and menaced many a golf shot. These bunkers acted as natural hazards, and as the interest in the game increased and inland sites were developed as golf courses, these hazards had to be created artificially. Architects then began to design golf courses involving the strategic placement of bunkers to punish the errant or mis-hit stroke, and to this day these "portable hazards" dictate the way a golf course should be played.

Although there are two main types of bunker, the fairway and greenside, they are essentially of the same design, albeit in certain instances greenside bunkers tend to be deeper and more penal. However, although the construction and maintenance of bunkers is essentially standard on any given links course, the situation changes somewhat as we move inland from the sea.

Construction

There are a number of important factors to be considered when bunkers are being constructed. The location is usually dictated by an Architect in order to provide strategy and playability, and to add visual impact to a hole. However, other factors such as soil type, degree of exposure to the elements and natural land contours must be considered if the hazard is to fulfil its envisaged potential.

On links courses where the inherent conditions are free draining, there is no need to install additional drainage in the base of the bunker, although it is advisable to check the natural winter water table, and keep above this if possible. It is usually sufficient to excavate the area to the desired shape, remembering that depth is important on exposed sites in order to prevent wind blowing sand from the bunker. At this stage, the steepness of the face should be considered so that subsequent revetting with turf can follow the excavation contours. The degree of severity can be varied, but should mirror difficulty found in similar bunkers around the course. Links bunkers are usually narrower than their inland counterparts, but they should be sufficiently wide not to be unfair. They should be free from overhangs and should permit easy entry and exit, as well as allowing a full back-swing to facilitate extrication, especially from pot bunkers.

The faces of both fairway and greenside bunkers on links courses are traditionally comprised of a turf banking which provides stability along with a steep face (see Figure 13). Upon a flat, firm and level foundation, which should be at least 300 mm below the final sand level at the base of the bunker, a wall of old thatchy turf is constructed against the excavated face. Ideally, the turf should be cut into sods approximately 600 x 300 x 50 mm and be laid down. Each level of turf should be set back slightly from the one below it and as the face takes shape, sand should be packed behind the wall. The turf wall should be continuous to the rim, with the final layer of turf marrying in with existing contours. A final light top dressing will help to promote uniformity of the surface surround areas. Such a technique is the only way stability can be achieved on exposed links sites and, if carried out correctly and diligently, will last for a number of years before the turves gradually break down. For the establishment of surround turf around the bunker, a minimum of 150 mm firmed depth of sandy soil should be present.

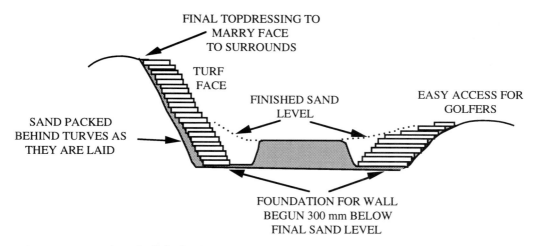

FIGURE 13: Revetting of a links bunker.

On inland sites where free draining soils are the exception rather than the rule, problems with drainage can develop if the construction is inadequate. Because of the impermeable clay subsoil that often exists on parkland sites, inland bunkers must be built up rather than excavated as they are on links land. In addition, it is usually necessary to install drainage in the base of the bunker to prevent ponding during wetter periods of weather, and to ensure that external ground contours shed rather than gather water. Because of these factors, inland bunkers tend to be flatter, larger and more visible than their links counterparts (see Figure 14).

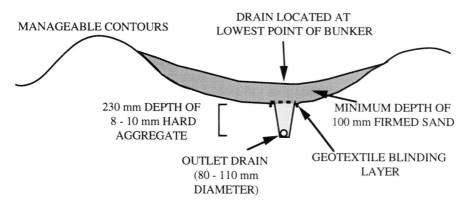

FIGURE 14: Cross section of an inland bunker.

The base should be no more than 150 mm below ground level and should be shaped according to the Architect's design. The drainage requirements will depend upon the nature of the bunker. Smaller bunkers can be drained by shaping the bunker floor to provide a uniform fall to a drain running the width of the bunker, or to one low sump point or soakaway from which an outlet drain can be provided. Larger expanses of sand may require a herringbone type system to drain them adequately. Drain lines (clayware or perforated PVC) should be installed centrally in a drain trench formed 230 mm below the bunker floor, and having a uniform fall of at least 1 in 200 to connect with a suitable outlet drain. This trench should then be backfilled with clean, hard aggregate of 8–10 mm diameter to the base of the bunker, and made evenly firm. In order to prevent sand from filtering into the gravel below and rendering it ineffective, and to prevent gravel contaminating the sand, it is necessary to cover the gravel with a blinding material. Traditional methods involved using upturned sods of turf or sacking material, but these techniques have now been superseded by geotextile membranes such as Terram, Lotrak, etc. A correctly graded material should be used to cover the gravel drain trenches or sumps. If the subsoil is particularly stony or problems have been experienced in the past with stones working up into the bunker sand, then it is advisable to cover the whole of the base of the bunker with this type of material. Over trenches it should be cut to overlap the sides by 150 mm and then be firmly fixed into the subsoil base. Where the geotextile membrane is used over the whole base of the bunker, the surrounding turf should be lifted and the material firmly pinned into position prior to replacing the turf. Again, allow 150 mm firmed depth of topsoil on new constructions and on surrounds and banks in order to ensure satisfactory grass growth.

All greenside bunkers should be constructed to allow for a definite 'collar' to the green which can be cut at an intermediate height, making the sward less susceptible to drought effects as sand splash builds up. Banks and surrounds should be finished with smooth, easy contours that permit maintenance with modern triple-head surround mowers.

Bunker Sands

Bunkers on links courses are normally filled with the free and abundant native sand on site, with a compact depth being raked to provide a "fluffy" top. The sand surface should be raked to form a central depression so that all shots are played from the centre of the bunker, giving the golfer a reasonable chance of recovery.

On most inland courses, Clubs must look to purchase a suitable sand to meet aesthetic and playing requirements. The material chosen must have a suitable particle size distribution, colour and be free from lime, which can cause turf disease problems where it splashes out onto turf areas. Our current recommendations for a bunker sand on an inland course are to select a material that has all particles between 0.125 and 1.0 mm diameter, with the majority of those being between 0.25 and 0.5 mm. In addition, there should be no more than 2% fine gravel, less than 2% silt and clay, and the particles should be angular for stability and of a hard nature so that no further breakdown occurs. A lime-free sand fulfilling the above criteria and having a light colour, such as white or light tan, will provide the best option for inland courses. When the sand is added to the bunkers, a firmed depth of 100 mm over the base will be necessary in order to create the correct characteristics, with the surface being raked to form acceptable playing conditions.

Bunker Maintenance

Raking – Ideally, bunkers should be raked on a daily basis by greenkeeping staff in order to supplement raking carried out by golfers. The aim should be to provide a uniform and consistent surface from which to play shots, with the sand shaped to form a slight central hollow in order to collect balls. Raking by golfers can result in an accumulation of sand towards the rear of the bunker, which ultimately results in a slope of sand forming which accentuates the difficulty of the hazard. A correct raking procedure can always avoid this problem and prevent golfers complaining that the hazards are unfair. On links courses, regular raking is vital if deposits of fine sand that have accumulated at edges of bunkers during windy weather are to be redistributed and provide for uniform conditions for play.

Mowing and Strimming – Surround contours and banks should be gentle in order to permit mowing with triple machines. However, strimming will be necessary to control unsightly growth on bunker lips, surrounds and faces in order to preserve the definition of the hazards.

Sand Splash – When golf shots are played from a greenside bunker, a proportion of sand is removed each time and this usually begins to accumulate on the apron/banking between the bunker and the green. If neglected, this area becomes particularly prone to drought damage and a thin and weak sward develops. If, on the other hand, this material is brushed back into the bunkers each time they are raked, then we can prevent this problem from developing.

Weed Control – Regular raking will prevent weed species from developing on the base of the bunkers, but occasionally problems with creeping weeds and grasses will develop, and chemical control is an option to consider. Non-persistent total herbicides such as paraquat or glyphosate should be used which are rapidly inactivated in the sand.

Replacement of Sand – Sand levels in bunkers should be constantly 'topped up' in order to replace that which is lost by play and adverse weather conditions. Periodically, it will be necessary to excavate bunkers and replace old sand with new in order to prevent the build up of debris and to ensure that consistent surfaces are maintained. Sometimes this work can be combined with the upgrading of bunker faces which tend to break down in time due to the effects of play and erosion.

(AJB : B.177)

BUNKER CONSTRUCTION

Bunker design must relate to the architect's concept of their strategic and visual impact at a hole. If contemplating changes to the layout of bunkers to a hole, or more extensive alterations to bunkering through the course, then it would be wise to employ a qualified golf course architect to ensure that the original concept is retained. STRI can provide this service to clients. The design of bunkers must also take into account soil type, degree of exposure, natural contours of the surrounding land, as well as future maintenance and costs.

Inland sites

On inland sites, especially where impermeable clay subsoil exists, drainage must have priority. Ensure that external ground contours are shaped so as to shed surface water run-off around the bunker. This will vary according to site from a gentle rise to the bunker lip of some 25 mm to a carefully shaped shallow grass swale around the front and sides most affected by run-off.

On poorly drained subsoils, build up rather than excavating deeply into the ground. The base need be no more than 150 mm below general ground level to minimise difficulties achieving a suitable drain outlet. Shape the bunker floor to provide a uniform fall to a drain running the length of a larger bunker, or to one low sump point from which an outlet drain can be provided.

Pipe drains – clayware or perforated PVC – should be laid centrally in a drain trench some 230 mm below the bunker floor, and with a uniform fall of not less than 1:200 to connect with a convenient outlet drain. Backfill the trench with clean, hard stone aggregate, 8-12 mm gauge to subsoil formation level, and make evenly firm.

It is essential to stop finer particles from the bunker sand filtering through to rapidly block up the pipe drains. In the past, upturned fibrous sods or old sacking were used to cover the gravel. Nowadays the trend is to use a geotextile membrane, taking care to choose one of a suitable grade. The fabric should be cut to overlap each side of the trench by 150 mm and then firmly fixed into the subsoil, pushing the free edges into a 75 mm slit and firming in.

At sites where the bunker floor is gravelly, or is the type of subsoil which works into and quickly contaminates the sand, it is worth using the geotextile membrane over the whole base of the bunker.

Provide 150 mm firm depth of topsoil over surrounds and bunker banks to ensure satisfactory grass growth. Allow for a definite 'surround' to a putting green, the contrasting heights of cut set off the close mown putting surface to advantage, and the intermediate height of surround turf is much less susceptible to drought effects (inevitable as sand splash builds up).

Ensure that slopes to banks and surrounds near bunkers are graded and finished with smooth, easy contours that allow maintenance with modern triple-cut surround mowers.

Bunker sand

There is no perfect formula for bunker sand, final choice being a compromise between material having suitable particle size, colour, freedom from lime, and cost in descending order of priority. Current recommendations for an inland course are to select a sand with at least 95% of the particles in the size range 0.125 to 1.0 mm, and the vast majority between 0.25 and 0.5 mm. There should be no more than 2% fine gravel and less than 2% silt and clay. The choice of sand used is very important and a laboratory analysis is useful. The STRI can carry out the appropriate tests.

Avoid angular sand which will abrade turf and damage mowers when splashed out of the bunker, or round, uniform sand in which it is difficult to achieve a firm stance and into which balls will plug. Select a sub-angular, lime-free sand which is not liable to break down to a finer material.

The lighter coloured sands, white or light tan, are preferred, contrasting well with the green of the putting surfaces.

Allow for providing 75–100 mm firmed depth.

Links

On seaside or naturally sandy soils, drainage will usually be satisfactory and, within reason, depth can help minimise wind blow of the finer dune sand commonly used for filling. However, check the natural winter water table of the chosen site, and keep well above this if possible. Such bunkers need to be narrow to check wind erosion, though they should always allow a full back swing, and this requirement must be taken into account when raking and maintaining such bunkers.

Depth helps limit the height of greenside bunker mounds, the faces of which are still often stabilised in the traditional, expensive, though very satisfactory way by building a turf wall.

The rear line of the bunker, against the green, is established and a flat, firm and level foundation is prepared. Build up a wall of old, fibrous turf (weed and weedgrass-free, links-type grass) cut 600 mm x 300 mm x 50 mm thick, laid (grass side up) in courses with bonded joints. Each course of turf should be set back slightly from the edge of the previous course to form a stable, 'revetted' face, 1:1 or steeper to suit the design. As the building proceeds, pack sand firmly and solidly behind the 'wall', finishing at the surface with a minimum 150 mm firmed depth of sandy soil for establishing surround turf.

The above is a very satisfactory method of construction for bunkers facing south east around to the south west; exposed to both sun and wind. Bunkers with a more northerly aspect may be more satisfactory with the face covered with 150 mm of sandy loam topsoil and turf 'rolled over' the top and brought part way down the face.

Further reading
Sands for Sports Turf Construction and Maintenance available from the STRI.

(IS No.14 Ref. 02/04)

BUNKER SANDS

The selection of a good bunker sand is one of the more difficult tasks facing a Head Greenkeeper and one which requires a good deal of thought and attention. First of all, we must decide on the criteria which are required of this sand. From a golfer's view, the sand is required to be of a light colour such as white, light grey or tan to provide a sharp contrast with the surrounding turf and should be visible from a distance. If the bunker is to provide a fair hazard, it is important that when a ball lands in the sand, the surface is neither so hard that the ball bounces out of the hazard, nor too soft that the ball plugs to an excessive depth. The sand should be stable underfoot and, ideally, stacked to a high angle on the bunker face.

Specifications to meet the above requirements for golf bunkers have been developed in the United States. The recommendations state that sands are required with 95% of their particles within the 0.125 mm–1.0 mm diameter range, with the majority of these particles falling between 0.25–0.5 mm diameter. These sands are said to provide the best all-round conditions in terms of ball lie, firmness of footing, minimum surface crusting, internal water drainage and ease of bunker maintenance. However, this does not say that any sand which falls within this range will be an excellent bunker sand. What it does suggest is that a sand falling within this range will have a better chance of being a good bunker sand, rather than one which falls outside this range. Particles greater than 1.0 mm in diameter should be avoided as the particles tend to lie on the green surface which could lead to slow play due to golfers removing visible grains from the putting line. Large sand grains also have the potential to blunt mowers and damage bottom blades. Particles smaller than 0.25 mm are prone to wind blow; can cause a reduction in drainage of water and, where sand has a significant proportion of silt and clay, the sand is likely to set hard and form a surface crust.

On links courses, where bunkers are generally deeper and smaller than on inland courses, dune sand materials with particles in the range 0.125–0.5 mm are often used as they are generally cost-free and maintain the characteristics of this type of course.

Ideally, bunker sand should have slightly angular particles which provide a good lie and a firm surface. Round particle sands, especially of a single size, provide a soft, fluffy surface in which balls can become buried and on which it is difficult to achieve a firm stance for the recovery shot. Recent studies at Bingley have confirmed that very uniform materials, particularly those with spherical grains, should be avoided because of their instability and susceptibility to ball plugging. Stability will be improved if sands with greater than 60% of grains in the rounded or well-rounded shape categories or highly spherical grains are avoided, though the main specification should be based on particle size distribution.

On any golf course it is essential to retain consistent playing characteristics between the bunkers, which can only be achieved by using the same sand both in each bunker and for topping up purposes. Avoid at all costs placing a good bunker sand over a poor bunker sand – it is always best to empty the sand from the bunker and replace it completely with clean material. Where different sand is used to top up, this leads to variable characteristics between individual bunkers on a course and consistency is lost. Fresh sand should be introduced whenever the sand depth has decreased below a minimum of 4–6 in. on the bunker floor or 2 in. on the face. Redistributing the sand from low areas to high areas will often suffice and actual topping up will be required only every three to five years.

For as long as there are bunkers on a golf course there will always be controversy over the size and shape, placement, need, type of sand used and depth. Low handicap golfers prefer one type of sand; higher handicappers another and, depending on local supply, the quality of bunker sand may not be good from the start. This article has aimed to qualify the criteria which are set out for bunker sands to provide the standards expected.

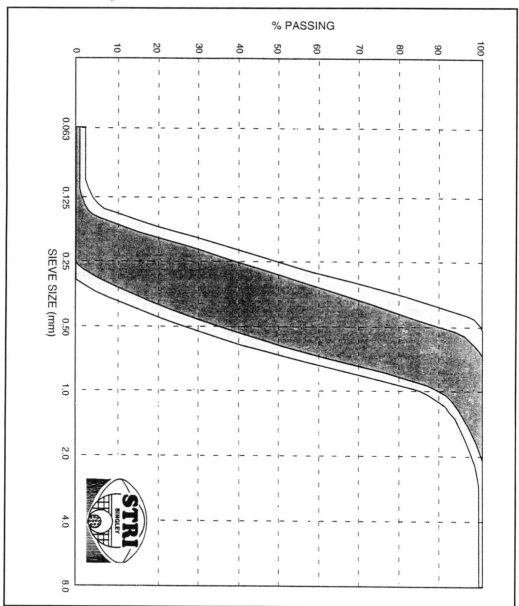

FIGURE 15: Grading curve defining recommended and acceptable limits of sand size for golf bunkers on inland courses.

(GCG 1 : 59)

194

SECTION 9
DISEASES OF TURFGRASSES

❖❖❖

Disease Management

Turf Fungicides

Descriptions of the Commoner Diseases

Fairy Rings

Dry Patch

STRI
BINGLEY

The Care of
the Golf Course

INTEGRATED DISEASE MANAGEMENT

Integrated disease management has been defined as the complementary use of cultural, biological and chemical control to maintain disease at an acceptable level. In response to an increasing concern for the environment and "green" issues becoming of greater public interest, attention has been focused on non-pesticide methods, ie. cultural and biological means, of preventing disease outbreaks. Whilst integrated disease management programmes have been devised for many agricultural situations and, to a lesser extent, for sports turf in the USA, to date this concept is virtually unknown to Greenkeepers and Groundsmen in the UK. This article describes the basic principles of integrated disease management for fine turf.

(a) Identification

In order to inhibit disease development it is essential to be able to recognise the problem as a disease and to correctly recognise which disease it is from the symptoms to be seen. In turfgrass, diseases are almost always caused by fungi. If the problem has been misdiagnosed, eg. the damage is due to scorch and not disease and the symptoms confused, then a non-appropriate control method may be implemented. This could lead to the wasteful (and costly) application of fungicide, which would have no effect on a non-disease problem whatsoever. Guidance on disease identification may be found in *Turfgrass Pests and Diseases* published by the STRI, price £7.50 plus 50p postage and packing.

(b) Disease Management

Disease management, ie. maintaining disease at an acceptable level, is preferred to disease control as the word 'control' implies disease eradication which is almost impossible to achieve in practice. In fine turf, standards of disease management are set very high (due to the disfiguring effect of disease on the turf surface) and consequently are difficult to maintain. It is probably these high standards that we set which make disease problems relatively important in overall turf maintenance.

Integrated disease management may be divided into the following:

Cultural Methods – Cultural methods are the effect of various turf maintenance practices on disease development. Diseases are affected by the prevalent environmental conditions – temperature, fertility, moisture, etc., some of which are under the influence of the Greenkeeper. For example, fusarium patch disease, as it is favoured by humid atmospheric conditions and a moist turf surface, will be inhibited by promoting good surface drainage and moisture removal by switching; also anthracnose disease, which affects annual meadow-grass only, will be inhibited by reducing annual meadow-grass in the sward through good turf maintenance. It must be remembered that everything done to the turf by way of maintenance has an implication with respect to disease development.

Biological Methods – Biological control is usually thought of as the use of one organism to either push or out-compete another (ie. the pest or disease), as it is in this way that the technique has been developed successfully for several horticultural situations. However, for turfgrass there are few biological methods employing predators or antagonists currently available, although research is currently underway in this area, both here and the USA and some commercial products are now on the market. The use of turfgrass cultivars resistant to disease attack is another way in which biological control methods may be implemented. The STRI produces the *Turfgrass Seed* booklet annually which lists each turfgrass species and cultivar according to their disease resistance. For example, fescue cultivars are ranked according to their susceptibility to red thread and dollar spot diseases. Thus, when planning a new turf area or overseeding existing facilities, disease resistance may be considered.

Chemical Methods – Good turf management utilising cultural and biological methods will help keep disease problems to a minimum. However, due mainly to our cool temperate climate, applications of pesticides will be necessary in many situations to achieve the required standards. It must be explained, however, that pesticides are only part of an integrated disease management programme and their ready availability must not reduce the attention paid to the cultural and biological methods which reduce the risk of disease attack. Thus, the careful and judicious use of pesticides has a key role to play as part of an integrated disease management programme.

(NAB : B.178)

COMMON DISEASES FOUND ON THE GREEN

Numerous fungi are capable of causing disease on amenity turf, but there are a few common diseases which occur more frequently and can be more damaging than others. Perhaps the most important disease that occurs on the highly-maintained turf of golf and bowling greens is fusarium patch. This disease, which can be highly disfiguring, is caused by the fungus *Microdochium nivale*; the same fungus being responsible for the disease pink snow mould which is evident after snow melt. Fusarium patch generally occurs during the late autumn to spring but may occur at any time of the year under conditions of cool, wet weather. The disease first appears as small orange-brown patches approximately 2-5 cm in diameter, but may rapidly increase in size under moist, cool conditions. As the disease progresses, the patches enlarge and the turf at the centre becomes pale and water-soaked. The leaves of the turfgrasses become matted together and may become slightly slimy to the touch. The edges of the diseased areas generally show an orange-brown border as the plants around the edge of the patch become infected. White or pale pink aerial mycelium which resembles cobwebs, may be seen on the affected turf and this aids matting of the diseased leaf tissue.

All turfgrasses are susceptible to attack by *Microdochium nivale* but *Poa annua* (annual meadow-grass) is probably the most readily susceptible grass species. This may be due to its rapid response to applications of nitrogenous fertiliser which can cause weak, forced growth if applied too heavily or at the wrong time of the year.

Turf is most likely to be attacked by *Microdochium nivale* under low temperature conditions accompanied by free moisture in the form of rain, dew, fog etc. The severity of fusarium patch is related to the pH of the top 2.5 cm of soil. With increasing pH, the severity of the infection increases, and the disease is generally considered most likely on alkaline turf.

With regard to control of fusarium patch, several cultural practices can be employed to minimise the incidence and severity of the disease. Switching and increasing surface drainage through spiking keep the moisture levels lower on the sward thereby reducing the likelihood of disease occurrence and development. Ensuring that top dressing is not applied too heavily and that clippings and fallen leaves are removed from the turf surface will also help in reducing the incidence of fusarium patch. Maintaining appropriate turf vigour and avoiding inappropriate late fertiliser applications will lessen the risk of disease attack.

Numerous contact and system fungicides are currently available with approval for use against fusarium patch on amenity turf. When the turf is actively growing, systemic fungicides offer lasting disease control through being translocated around the plant tissue. These are less effective during periods of slow growth/dormancy when contact fungicides may prove more effective. The continuous use of one fungicide is not recommended due to the possible development of fungicide resistance within the fungal population. Regular changes between products with different active ingredients and mode of action is the most suitable way of controlling turfgrass diseases.

Another disease commonly found on both golf greens and bowling greens is superficial fairy rings (thatch fungi). Numerous fungi are capable of causing the symptoms of superficial fairy rings but most belong to the group of fungi known as basidiomycetes. The fungi that cause the readily identifiable symptoms live in the thatch and the mineral soil just below it. The common symptoms that characterise superficial fairy rings include the presence of fungal mycelium around the shoot bases and within the thatch layer, frequently producing a characteristic musty smell. Other possible symptoms are patches of slightly stimulated grass growth or conversely patches of yellowing turf which show slight surface depressions within the affected areas.

Since the fungi associated with the development of superficial fairy rings are thatch inhibitors, the thatch depth and condition will affect the severity of the symptoms produced by the fungi presence. The fungi cause the decomposition of the organic material of the thatch layer and utilise the compounds produced for their growth and development. If the thatch layer is allowed to build up, a greater amount of material is available for the fungi to decompose. The result of the decomposition of the thatch layer is not only the increased presence of the fungi but in many cases, the development of unsightly surface depressions. The occurrence of stimulated grass in areas affected by superficial fairy rings is a result of increased nutrient availability for plant uptake following the fungal breakdown of the thatch. In certain cases, slight yellowing of the sward can be seen in affected areas. This occurs as a stress response of the plant to low moisture availability. The mycelium of fungi causing superficial fairy rings is naturally water-repellent and if present in large amounts, the mycelium forms a barrier to water and prevents it from reaching the root system.

Removal of clippings to prevent rapid thatch build up and the use of maintenance practices to reduce or dilute the thatch layer, will decrease the incidence and severity of superficial fairy rings. If fungicides are considered necessary to control a severe outbreak of superficial fairy rings, it is advantageous to spike the area prior to treatment and to apply a wetting agent before the fungicide. The wetting agent will allow the infected thatch to be wetted and ensure greater coverage of the thatch with the fungicide thereby increasing the likelihood of control.

An ever increasing disease problem on areas of fine turf appears to be take-all patch. This disease is caused by the fungus *Gaeumannomyces graminis* and is occurring more and more frequently on recently constructed golf greens. The fungus is soil-borne and only causes disease on bentgrasses. The symptoms of take-all patch generally become evident during late summer and persist into autumn and even winter if the conditions are mild. Infected bentgrass is first seen as bronzing of the leaf tissue. The bentgrass within the affected patch dies but the border of the area remains bronzed during the period when the fungus is active. The patches increase in size and may coalesce to allow disease development across much of the sward. Within the affected area, the turf becomes colonised by resistant grasses is *Festuca* spp., *Poa* spp. and possibly broad-leaved weeds. The result of this disease attack on areas of fine turf is reduced visual and playing quality of the sward.

The fungus responsible for causing take-all patch is generally restricted from doing so by the presence of certain other fungi and bacteria in the soil which limit the growth and development of *Gaeumannomyces graminis*. However *Gaeumannomyces graminis* is better suited to growing under alkaline soil conditions than these so-called antagonistic fungi and bacteria. Because of this, if the soil pH becomes too high or increases by a small amount but rapidly, the pathogen is able to attack the bentgrass roots before the population of antagonists has been able to respond to the change in soil chemistry.

Once take-all patch has developed, it can take up to five years before the natural antagonists in the soil are able to effect the decline of the disease. Certain maintenance practices can be employed to minimise the detrimental effects in the sward. Applications of acidifying fertilisers will serve to reduce the pH of the soil thereby producing conditions which favour the growth of the antagonists. The pathogen responsible for take-all patch disease lives and over-winters in the thatch layer, and thus keeping the thatch to a minimum reduces the amount of dead plant material available to the fungus.

At present there are no fungicides available which have approval for use against *Gaeumannomyces graminis* and indeed current recommendations suggest that fungicide applications should only be made on turf affected with take-all patch if fusarium patch develops on the same area. It is believed that fungicides may adversely affect the natural build up of antagonists to take-all within the soil but research is being completed to identify possible control of take-all patch using specific fungicides at different times and rates of application.

(CAY : B.191)

TURF FUNGICIDES

In turf, pathogenic fungi are often present in the thatch and soil, but disease will only occur under suitable environmental conditions. Therefore, good cultural and management practices can do much to prevent disease by providing conditions unfavourable to disease development. However, the weather is unpredictable and errors of judgement may be made, resulting in a disease outbreak. Then, an application of fungicide may be necessary to limit disease severity and to produce a high quality turf surface. Applying fungicides involves many considerations such as choice of material, application method, application rate and timing to achieve effective disease control. This leaflet is a brief guide to the efficient and judicious use of fungicides.

Disease Identification

When disease appears the first step is correct identification from the symptoms observed. If in doubt reference may be made to the STRI publication "Turfgrass Pests and Diseases" or a turf sample may be sent to STRI for disease diagnosis and our recommendations for control.

Fungicides currently available for use on turf can be divided into two groups. Systemic fungicides, so called as they can be absorbed by the grass leaves and roots and redistributed to protect all plant parts, are most effective when the grass is **growing actively** i.e. between spring and autumn. Also, if applied in late autumn as a preventative treatment they may protect the grass from disease through the winter months. The most common systemics are those belonging to the benzimidazole group, mainly used for control of fusarium patch and red thread diseases. Contact fungicides, so called as they can only protect plant parts or eradicate disease from areas which the chemical touches, are most effective when grass growth is slow i.e. during the winter. If a disease has become established contact fungicides have the best 'knock down' effect. However, as contact fungicides are not absorbed into plant tissues they may be washed off more easily than systemic fungicides during rainfall or removed when mowing, and consequently give reduced disease control.

Application of Fungicides

Generally, fungicides should be applied at the first signs of the disease rather than routine preventative spraying. Regular inspection of turf areas is essential as disease outbreaks may occur rapidly under favourable conditions. Usually it is best to treat the whole turf area to minimise disease spread, although spot treatment of active disease using a knapsack sprayer may also prove beneficial. To avoid problems of fungicide resistance (strains of the pathogen developing which are resistant to the fungicide) it is best to alternate fungicides from different groups of active ingredients.

Fungicide Groups		
Benzimidazoles (Systemic)	*Dicarboximides (Contact)*	*Others (Contact)*
carbendazim fenarimol (some contact effect also) thiophanate-methyl thiabendazole	iprodione vinclozolin (for use through tractor sprayers only)	chlorothalonil quintozene

For example, a fungicide spray programme designed to minimise the possibility of resistance occurring in fusarium patch disease would be a benzimidazole in spring, followed by a dicarboximide or either chemical under the 'Others' heading during the winter. When using fungicides the manufacturers' instructions found on the product label should be followed carefully – many of them are now legally binding. Products based on a mix of systemic and contact fungicides are also now available – a chlorothalonil-carbendazim mixture and an iprodione-carbendazim product. For the specialised treatment of fairy rings, fungicides based on triforine or oxycarboxin have approval for turf usage.

Choice of Chemical

In our experience, the best fungicide to use against the more common turf diseases is shown in the following table. All fungicide/disease combinations are approved by MAFF under the Control of Pesticides Regulations 1986.

Pesticides Regulations 1986

All concerned with pesticides should make themselves aware of legislation and obligations under the Pesticides Regulations 1986 by consulting the publications "Amenity Pesticides" and "Pesticides : guide to the new controls".

ACTIVE INGREDIENT OF FUNGICIDE (PRODUCT NAME)	FORMULATION	ACTION	GREY SNOW MOULD	FUSARIUM PATCH	FAIRY RINGS	LEAF SPOT/ MELTING OUT	RED THREAD	DOLLAR SPOT	BROWN PATCH	ANTHRACNOSE
Carbendazim + iprodione (Vitesse)	SC	H		✓			✓			✓
Chlorothalonil (Daconil Turf)	SC	D	✓	✓		✓			✓	✓
Iprodione (Rovral Green)	SC	A	✓	✓		✓	✓	✓	✓	
Carbendazim (Fisons Turfclear, Mascot Systemic, Turfclear WDG)	SC	B		✓			✓	✓		
Fenarimol (Rimidin)	SC	C		✓			✓	✓		
Quintozene (Quintozene WP)	WP	I		✓			✓	✓		
Thiabendazole (Tecto)	LI	B		✓			✓	✓		
Thiophanate-methyl (Mildothane Turf Liquid)	SC	B		✓			✓	✓		
Vinclozolin (Mascot Contact)	LI	F		✓		✓	✓	✓		
Dichlorophen (Super Mosstox)	SL	G					✓			
Chlorothalonil + carbendazim (Greenshield)	SC	H	✓	✓			✓	✓	✓	✓
Oxycarboxin (Ringmaster)	LI	E			✓					
Triforine (Fairy Ring Destroyer)	LI	B			✓					

Formulation : SC = Suspension concentrate, WP = Wettable powder, LI = Liquid, SL = Soluble concentrate.

Action : A = Contact fungicide with protective and curative action, B = Systemic fungicide with protective and curative action, C = Systemic fungicide with protective, curative and eradicant action, D = Contact fungicide with protective action, E = Systemic fungicide with curative action, F = Non-systemic fungicide with protective action, G = Contact fungicide, H = Systemic and contact fungicide, I = Protectant fungicide.

(CGC 1 : 82)

FUSARIUM PATCH DISEASE

Fusarium patch disease, caused by the fungus *Microdochium nivale* (formerly *Fusarium nivale*), was first recorded on golf greens in 1931 and described as being the commonest, most disfiguring and damaging disease of turf known at that time. Nearly 60 years later, despite the development of effective fungicides, this statement is still true today. Throughout the year requests for information on fusarium patch disease are received by the STRI. The cultural and environmental conditions that favour the disease and the most effective prevention and control methods available are described below.

Recognition
Great care must be taken in identification as chemical or fertiliser scorch may appear surprisingly similar. Remember, samples of turf may be sent to the STRI for examination. An incorrect diagnosis may lead to wasteful (and expensive!) applications of fungicides.

Fusarium patch usually usually first appears as small (up to 50 mm diameter) orange/ brown, water-soaked circular spots which, under favourable conditions, may increase rapidly and coalesce together to form large circular patches. Correct diagnosis of these early signs is important as the best possible control will be achieved if the disease is treated at this early stage. Under prolonged humid conditions, sparse white or pink mycelium may be seen around the edges of each patch which tends to mat the green leaves together. A pale straw colour at this time indicates that the disease has become less active, perhaps due to a drier climate. Eventually scars are formed which, particularly in the winter months, heal up slowly and are consequently prone to invasion by moss, undesirable grass species and weeds. If treatment is delayed until these later stages of disease development, poor control only will be achieved.

Conditions that Favour the Disease
Fusarium patch is favoured by cool, wet weather and is consequently most troublesome during the winter and spring months. The disease is found generally damaging fine turf, e.g. golf greens, especially where the sward contains a large proportion of annual meadow-grass (*Poa annua*), as this grass is highly susceptible to attack. High fertility conditions often created by late-season top dressing or fertiliser application also favour fusarium patch. Fine turf that is shaded from the sun or in a sheltered location, e.g. due to the close proximity of tall trees or buildings, will dry slowly and is therefore susceptible. Fusarium patch is also favoured by the presence of a deep thatch layer, as thatch is often moisture-retentive and its constituent dead plant material is a natural substrate for the disease. Also, the disease is most active in alkaline turf, created perhaps by ill-advised applications of lime or top dressing sands with a lime content.

Recommendations for Control
The ready availability of fungicides must not reduce the attention paid to those practices that reduce the risk of disease. Any management practice that helps to keep the turf surface dry, such as switching, spiking or slitting, will reduce the likelihood of fusarium patch occurring. If necessary, reduce the moisture-holding thatch layer, e.g. by scarification, as this will again help to keep the turf surface dry. Surface drainage may also be improved by aeration and top dressing with a sandy compost. It is also a good idea to promote air circulation over and evaporation from the greens by not siting trees, shrubs or tall buildings too close as this will inhibit the removal of surface moisture by the wind and sun.

Effects of Disease
During cool wet weather, fusarium patch disease may cause serious damage to fine turf. The fungal pathogen which causes fusarium patch, *M. nivale* is most active under neutral or alkaline conditions at the turf surface where the fungus is active. Consequently, sulphate of iron by acidifying plant tissues and thatch to which it comes into contact will help control the disease. Although not as effective as a fungicide spray, regular use of sulphate of iron will help minimise incidence and severity of fusarium patch and thus reduce the need for fungicide application. As well as fusarium

patch another disease namely take-all patch is favoured by an alkaline turf surface. Re-acidifying the turf surface with sulphate of iron may limit the spread of take-all patch disease.

Annual meadow-grass is very susceptible to fusarium patch and consequently a sward containing a large percentage of this grass could suffer severe damage. Good turf management, in its aim of promoting a healthy, vigorous sward of fescue/bent, both of which are much more resistant to the disease, will consequently discourage fusarium patch. Great care must be taken when applying fertilisers as excessive nitrogen, especially the organic types such as dried blood, applied during cool, wet weather can lead to severe disease outbreaks. The use of lime on golf greens is only recommended under exceptional circumstances and is best avoided as, as well as encouraging fusarium patch and other diseases, it leads to invasion of annual meadow-grass, weeds and worms.

In situations of prolonged cool and wet weather, despite all cultural control measures being implemented, fusarium patch disease is still likely to attack on many courses. Fortunately, if the need arises, then the disease can be controlled with fungicides, providing they are used wisely and according to the manufacturer's instructions.

(CGC 1 : 75)

RED THREAD

Until recently, red thread (Corticium disease) was believed to be caused by *Corticium fuciforme* but recent studies have revealed two different fungi are involved. This discovery has resulted in a major taxonomic revision of the causal fungi and two separate diseases being recognised. The new names are red thread when *Laestisaria fuciformis* is the causal fungus and pink patch (rarely seen on fine turf) when *Limnomyces roseipellis* is the causal fungus. From the practical viewpoint, however, both diseases cause similar symptoms, may occur together, are generally indistinguishable and can be prevented or controlled in the same way. Although both diseases have been reported in the UK, little is known about their relative distribution and importance.

Red thread is most often seen during the summer and autumn but may persist into winter if conditions remain mild. Any type of turf may be attacked but red fescue and perennial ryegrass are most often affected. The diseases are most likely to occur under conditions of low fertility, particularly insufficient nitrogen, during cool, moist weather.

Recognition

The intensity of red thread attack can vary from withering of a few leaves only, in which case it is often overlooked or ignored, to large-scale damage resulting in death of infected plants. Look out for patches of damaged grass initially 20–30 mm in diameter with a pink colouring. The patches may spread to 0.35 metres across and develop an irregular outline when grass growth is slow and favourable conditions for disease development exist.

Unique to red thread is the production of red needles (stroma) from the tips of infected grass leaves which have a survival role in the life cycle of *L. fuciformis*. Under conditions of high humidity infected plants may be bound together by a webbed mycelium and cottony flocs of mycelium may also be found in the sward. Pink patch first becomes evident along the margins of leaf blades as small blotches of pink mycelium. This pink mycelium never becomes as pronounced as the stroma of the red thread fungus.

Recommendations for Control

Pay particular attention to choice of cultivar, therefore consult the annual STRI booklet "Turfgrass Seed" especially if red fescue is being considered as this can help prevent red thread and pink patch. Generally, slow-growing, low-maintenance cultivars are more susceptible to attack. Adequate fertiliser, particularly nitrogen, during the growing season will also prevent severe attacks. However, care is needed as extreme nitrogen can favour other problems such as fusarium patch disease. All things considered, it may be better to rely on the timely and judicious use of fungicides. When the grass is growing actively, fungicide containing carbendazim will give good control of red thread but this fungicide is much less efficient against pink patch disease. As both diseases often become most severe when grass growth is slow, a systemic fungicide like carbendazim may not be very effective, as such materials act through the growth process. When applied as a preventative spray, reliable control may be achieved with fungicides containing iprodione, vinclozolin or chlorothalonil.

(CGC 1 : 81)

TAKE-ALL PATCH DISEASE

Take-all patch is caused by the fungus *Gaeumannomyces graminis* which was until recently named *Ophiobolus graminis*, hence the old common name for the disease, Ophiobolus patch. Take-all patch was relatively unknown in turfgrass until the 1950's when it was the practice to correct extremely acidic turf with applications of lime. As liming encourages take-all, many severe outbreaks were recorded. In recent years, take-all patch has been a relatively uncommon disease but when it does occur it can be very disfiguring and damaging. Due to the very destructive nature of take-all patch, its persistence and the absence of an effective chemical control measure, it is regarded as potentially a serious problem in turf management.

Symptoms of take-all patch usually appear in late summer or autumn. On fine turf, the disease often appears initially as saucer shaped, slightly depressed bare areas consisting mainly of dying bentgrasses, which are very susceptible to the disease. A photograph of take-all patch may be found in the STRI's booklet "Turfgrass Pests & Diseases" (£7.50 + 50p p + p from STRI). These small patches may then enlarge into a ring, measuring up to 30cm in diameter, of bleached or bronzed **bentgrasses**, the centre of each ring being occupied by plants resistant to the disease such as fescues, annual meadow-grass and broad-leaved weeds. Eventually, adjacent rings may coalesce together resulting in large irregular patches on greens and fairways. Dying bentgrasses can be easily removed from the turf, due to their rotted root systems. Affected bentgrass roots and rhizomes are blackened due to extensive colonisation by the take-all fungus.

Once the disease has become established, there is no effective control measure. All efforts must be aimed at **preventing** outbreaks of take-all. Firstly, recognise the situation in which take-all patch is likely to occur. Sand construction greens are particularly vulnerable, as are situations where seed bed, construction or topdressing materials have been sterilised. By far the best prevention of take -all patch can be achieved by avoiding the application of alkaline materials. Avoid applying lime unless it is absolutely necessary. Have all sand used for construction or topdressing analysed for its lime content. Irrigation water, if taken from a borehole source could be quite hard i.e. contain lime.

If take-all patch does occur then a long term solution to the disease is offered by a phenomenon known as take-all decline, in which, given the right condition, the disease will become less severe and eventually disappear . This decline is due to the build up of antagonists in the turf whose activities inhibit the take-all patch; it is extremely rare for take-all patch to re-occur once the decline process has been completed. Consequently, the best strategy for the long term control of take-all is to provide the conditions which favour take-all decline. This can be done as follows:-

Identify the possible sources of alkalinity responsible for the disease. Try to eliminate them e.g. by changing to a lime-free sand. Take-all patch rarely causes extensive damage in acidic turf. Have pH readings made of infected greens and if necessary, acidify the turf surface with a fertilizer programme based on acidifying fertilisers such as ammonium sulphate. Light applications of sulphate of iron may also be made at 3-4 week intervals to promote further acidification of the turf surface. Keep the application of fungicides to an absolute minimum. However, do not delay fungicide application if fusarium patch disease occurs. Maintain good turf vigour by supplying adequate nutrition. Most soils have sufficient phosphate and potassium but if in doubt have a soil analysis done. Appropriate fertilisers can then be applied after discussion with your advisory agonomist. Ensure the turf surface is free-draining by regular slitting, spiking etc. Remember, take-all patch spreads rapidly in wet, water retentive turf. If necessary, deploy thatch reduction operations such as scarification and hollow tining to reduce the amount of dead plant material available for the take-all patch to live on. Badly scarred areas can be renovated by oversowing disease scars with fescue which is highly resistant to take-all patch.

(NAB : B.180)

ANTHRACNOSE – CAUSING BASAL ROT/FOLIAR BLIGHT

Anthracnose is the common name for the disease which causes basal rot on annual meadow-grass (*Poa annua*) during the autumn and winter months. This has become an increasingly common disease over recent years, particularly on golf greens with a high percentage of *P. annua* in the sward.

It is perhaps less well known that the fungus responsible for this disease (*Colletotrichum graminicola*) can cause a foliar blight on other turfgrass species, including bentgrass and perennial ryegrass, although the symptoms which it causes on these grasses are markedly different from the basal rot of *P. annua*. The general symptoms of an affected bentgrass or ryegrass sward is a darkening of the lower leaves and the slight thinning of the sward, which gives an almost mottled appearance to the turf. The effect is quite subtle and without a complete investigation of the turf to identify the presence of the fungus, it would be possible to overlook it as a disease problem. Occasionally, areas of the sward may be killed, but generally its effect is seen only as superficial. The leaves do not become water-soaked but appear almost burnt, turning very dark brown and in most cases, quite dry. The growing point of the plants is generally not affected and the plants will almost invariably recover from the attack.

Basal rot on the other hand can be quite serious on amenity turf. Affected areas tend to become yellow/red (the oldest leaves discolouring first). In stressed turf the problem can spread, forming a very irregular, patchy mosaic of colour. Closer inspection will reveal the characteristic dark brown, slimy lesions within the base of the individual tillers. This rot will allow the shoot to separate from the roots quite readily when pulled.

Microscopic examination may reveal small structes or acervuli (a mat of hyphae) on affected lower leaves from each of which protrude several short, black needle-like structures, which under cool, moist conditions are released and are carried through the surface film of water to other potential hosts. If the conditions suitable for the growth of this fungus continue into the winter months, the high concentration of this inoculum on the plant material may cause more severe outbreaks.

Cultural control of foliar blight on bentgrass and ryegrass swards and basal rot on *P. annua* can often be achieved by light fertiliser applications to encourage the plants to grow more vigorously and show less susceptibility to the fungus. Maintaining a free-draining soil is also an aid to controlling the severity of this problem since this will minimise the spread of the inoculum to new infection sites. The use of certain chemicals (i.e. chlorothalonil) may control the fungus. It is always worth remembering that the disease is a biological indicator and is therefore more common when the sward is stressed, either through low nutrient, increased soil compaction, lack of drainage, the increasing traffic over a particular area or through problems within the turf, such as thatch.

(CAY : B.183)

BROWN PATCH

For many years brown patch (caused by the fungus *Rhizoctonia solani*) has been considered an important turfgrass disease in the USA but it is only in recent years that the disease has been seen on fine turf in the UK. Brown patch is now recognised as a serious disease of turf that occurs occasionally in the summer months.

Recognition

The symptoms of brown patch vary greatly depending on the prevailing weather conditions. The disease is only damaging during warm, humid weather that gives prolonged periods of the leaf wetness which is necessary for plant infection. If these weather conditions prevail, watch out for light brown circles of blighted grass up to 15 cm in diameter, which may develop extremely rapidly. All species of turfgrasses may be affected, although there is some evidence to suggest that the bents (*Agrostis* spp.) are more susceptible.

Recommendations for Control

Brown patch can be prevented from occurring by regular scarification, if necessary, to reduce water-holding thatch and also by switching to remove dew each morning to remove the conditions of prolonged leaf wetness that favour the disease. As brown patch is also favoured by high nitrogen fertilization, applications should be light and frequent rather than one large application. Fungicides, in particular chlorothalonil and iprodione, are effective against brown patch but, as the disease can spread rapidly, they must be applied promptly at the first signs of the disease.

(CGC 1 : 76)

FAIRY RINGS

The biology and control of fairy rings was the subject of a four year research programme at STRI, sponsored by the Royal & Ancient Golf Club of St. Andrews. Fairy rings are very common on amenity turf in the UK and consequently most greenkeepers will have experienced them on the turf under their supervision. For instance, they are particularly common on golf course fairways – few courses do not have one or more rings. However, the damage that these rings cause depends very much on the type of ring, their location and abundance.

Type 1 rings are defined as those that actually kill the grass, e.g. as caused by the fungus *Marasmius oreades*. If a Type 1 ring is examined closely three distinct zones can be detected. The most noticeable feature is a ring of dead grass (usually 10-30 cm in diameter) in which mushrooms may be found during early summer and autumn. This dead zone is surrounded by inner and outer rings of stimulated lush-green grass. These rings are a direct result of the activities of *M. oreades* in the soil. Excavation of Type 1 rings has shown that under the dead zone the fairy ring mycelium is at its highest density. As this mycelium is extremely water-repellent (hydrophobic) and the mycelium can extend to a depth of up to 1 metre in the soil, any water applied by natural rainfall or irrigation will not percolate through the soil to the grass roots but will be shed away from this area. Consequently the grass is water-stressed and dies to leave the characteristic ring of bare ground. The zones of lush grass growth adjacent to the dead zone are due to the feeding activities of the fairy ring fungus in the turf. Experiments conducted as early as 1917 revealed that *M. oreades* (along with other fairy ring fungi) is primarily a decomposer, i.e. it can release nitrogen from the organic matter in the thatch and soil below. Consequently, grass over these areas can utilise this nitrogen and lush growth is produced. On turf intensively managed for its appearance, e.g. golf greens, Type 1 rings may be disfiguring and further problems can be caused by the invasion of moss and weeds into the bare part of the ring. On lighter soils, e.g. on links courses, and in dry summers bare areas can become very conspicuous and consequently detract from the visual attractiveness of the area. If Type 1 rings occur on an area of fine turf, such as a golf green, then, due to the areas of dead turf produced, the playing quality of the area can also be significantly reduced.

Type 2 rings are those that produce a stimulated ring of grass only and do not cause any direct damage to the turf. Often, they are caused by the puff-ball fungi such as *Scleroderma* and *Lycoperdon* spp. These fungi do not produce extensive mycelium in the turf but are usually confined mainly to the thatch layer. Lush grass growth is produced in the same way as in Type 1 rings – uptake of nitrogen released by the fairy ring fungus through thatch decomposition. Type 2 rings are important as they have a marked effect on the visual quality of an affected area but, as they do not harm the grass directly, the playing quality of the turf is usually not really diminished.

Type 3 rings are those where a ring of mushrooms or toadstools is formed with no apparent effect on the grass, i.e. no lush or dead zone. To date over 60 species of fungi have been recorded as forming Type 3 rings on turf. In general, Type 3 rings are often ignored but they can present a nuisance value if the production of fruiting bodies is extensive.

Recommendations for Control

A solution to fairy rings has been sought for about 60 years and several traditional control methods have been developed. For example, the continuous drenching of rings or fertilizing with manure has been met with some success, but these methods have not proved reliable. Removing fairy rings by excavating all soil and turf containing mycelium has proved effective, particularly if combined with a soil-sterilant such as formaldehyde. However, this technique is very laborious and, as recent work has indicated that formaldehyde may be harmful to humans, the use of this technique has been discouraged.

From early research in the 1950's where drenches of sulphate of iron and potassium permanganate were tried for fairy ring control, it was realised how difficult it was to apply chemicals effectively due to the water-repellent properties of soil containing fairy ring mycelium. If a fungicide was applied it would be shed to areas not containing the fairy ring mycelium and consequently not be able to exert its toxic effects. These water-repellent properties have been alleviated by using wetting agents applied with the fungicide and also by combining the fungicide with special organic solvents. However, even with these methods, control has often been unsatisfactory.

Initial research at the STRI concentrated on how this water-repellent nature of fairy rings can be alleviated. As the fairy ring can make the thatch water-repellent, removal by scarification will enable fungicides to penetrate the ring. Hollow tining (shown to be preferable to spiking) provides channels down which the fungicide can flow into the fairy ring. Both scarification and hollow tining are thus recommended prior to fungicide drenching. If the fairy ring mycelium has penetrated deeply into the soil, then addition-al spiking may also be necessary. The water-repellency factor can then be alleviated by pre-soaking the ring with wetting agent. Experiments at STRI are under way to evaluate chemicals such as strong alkalis and organic solvents which will attack the water-repellent mycelium directly and thus promote the effectiveness of fungicides sub-sequently applied. Mechanical means of placing fungicide solutions in fairy rings are also under test – particularly the effectiveness of applying chemicals after treatment with the Verti-Drain and soil injection equipment such as the Terralift.

There have also been developments in the testing of more effective fungicides. Since the introduction of benodanil (now no longer available), oxycarboxin and triforine for fairy ring control, several new chemicals which may be possible candidates for toxicity against fairy rings have become available. Laboratory screening techniques have revealed that several chemicals, apart from those mentioned above, are highly effective against the mycelium of fairy rings and, as these chemicals may also persist in the soil, they may give more long-lasting control than those currently available. Full-scale field trials at sites in North East England are now under way with this material and preliminary results suggest that these fungicides could give effective and long-lasting control of fairy rings.

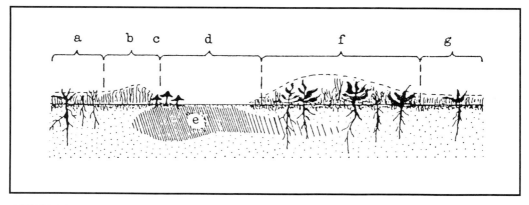

FIGURE 16: Cross-section through a Grade 1 fairy ring caused by *Marasmius oreades*. (a) outside the ring; (b) outer stimulated zone; (c) fruiting bodies of the fungus; (d) bare zone; (e) mycelium (hatched) in the soil (dotted); (f) inner stimulates zone; (g) inside the ring.

(CGC 1 : 79)

SUPERFICIAL FAIRY RINGS

In recent years, superficial fairy rings have caused widespread problems on golf greens.

Recognition

Some superficial fairy ring fungi produce only sparse mycelium in turf and consequently have little apparent effect on the sward. The most common type are not aggressive pathogens, but are able to cause some plant stress resulting in a ring of yellowing turf. Situations in which annual meadow-grass predominates are particularly prone to invasion by this type of superficial fairy ring. If a core of turf is taken from an affected area, fine white or cream-coloured mycelium may be seen in the thatch or around plant bases, and the core will have a faint or sometimes in severe cases, a strong musty smell resembling that produced by dry rot. It is these two diagnostic features, the presence of mycelium and the musty smell, which are highly characteristic of superficial fairy rings.

Other superficial fairy ring fungi may produce areas of stimulated grass growth, either in saucer-shaped patches or distinct rings. This is due to the fungi decomposing the thatch, releasing nitrogen in a form available for uptake by the grass, resulting in dark green lush growth. Thatch decomposition may take place to such an extent that surface depressions are formed which may have a marked effect on the playing qualities of the surface, especially on golf greens.

Occasionally, superficial fairy rings may form small arcs or circles of bleached grass where the grass plant has been attacked and killed. Affected turf has a very strong musty smell.

Conditions which Favour Superficial Fairy Rings

Superficial fairy rings are caused by a large and varied group of fungi known as basidiomycetes of which only a few in turf have been identified. As little is known about the basic biology of these fungi in the turfgrass situation, there is correspondingly little information on the cultural and environmental conditions which favour their development. In most cases, superficial fairy rings are apparent between early-summer and late-autumn when soil temperatures are high enough to enable fungal growth and associated thatch decomposition to occur. However, there are other superficial fairy ring fungi which are active at low temperatures and may cause problems in the winter months. Dry weather also promotes superficial fairy ring activity as air may penetrate deeper into the turf profile, thus allowing aerobic fungi to thrive. This is possibly the reason for the many reported cases of superficial fairy rings during the dry 1989, 1990 and 1995 summers. Also, mycelium of superficial fairy ring fungi may sometimes be seen following deep rooting in hollow tine or Verti-Drain holes – further evidence that these fungi require aerobic conditions.

Superficial fairy ring fungi have water-repellent hyphae – an effect that is most apparent in the early morning as dew will not settle on affected areas. Consequently in certain cases their activities may lead to the formation of dry patch (see later article).

In general, the activities of superficial fairy rings are confined to the litter and thatch layers of the turf and as such are sometimes referred to as 'thatch fungi'. This term is misleading as any fungi in the thatch (and there are many present) both beneficial or detrimental would be included and therefore the term is best avoided. Also, whilst the damage done by superficial fairy rings is often most severe in situations with a thatch problem, they have also been recorded in situations with no appreciable thatch, e.g. newly established all-sand construction golf greens.

It is interesting to note that superficial fairy rings were relatively uncommon 20 years ago, and speculation on the reasons for their increase and spread since that time has implicated changes during the same period in the fungicides available for control of turfgrass diseases. It is thought that the use in the past of persistent broad-spectrum organo-mercurial compounds for control of fusarium patch disease were also inadvertently inhibiting superficial fairy rings, which were consequently not noticed. Also, it is suggested that the recent use of systemic fungicides has led to this problem by possibly eliminating antagonistic and competitive fungi in the thatch, leaving superficial fairy rings to thrive. Whilst there is a scientific paper published in the 1970's to support this argument, a recent study has shown no association between systemic fungicides and superficial fairy rings.

Recommendations for control

In situations where there is excessive thatch, the reasons for this should be identified and the most appropriate control methods implemented. Thatch reduction is essentially removing the food supply for the superficial fairy ring fungi and will thus help to limit their activities. It must be emphasised that there is no evidence that the aeration techniques used in turf management are making the problems worse, they just allow the fungus to move deeper into the soil profile.

Any shallow depressions in the turf surface may be levelled by selective top dressing. The appearance of superficial fairy rings may also be marked by light applications of sulphate of iron or a liquid iron formulation. If dry patch is apparent then treatment with a non-ionic wetting agent to improve water infiltration into affected areas will be beneficial.

In cases of severe superficial fairy ring activity where appreciable surface disruption is being caused, treatment with an appropriate fungicide is probably justified. Some suppression of superficial fairy ring fungi can be achieved with fungicide based on triforine, which has approval for the purpose under the pesticide regulations, but results are somewhat variable in practice.

(CGC 1 : 80)

DRY PATCH AND WETTING AGENTS

With the summer of 1995 being the driest on record for many years, it is perhaps not surprising that dry patch is a major problem on many golf courses. Recent independent market surveys have indicated 84% of UK golf courses are affected by dry patch to some degree. These courses regularly use wetting agents, accumulating a financial cost to golf estimated between £1.5–2 million annually, which is further compounded by the high labour requirements for application. This section reflects on the experience of using wetting agents for the alleviation of severe dry patch, and recommends the most effective application strategies.

Dry patch, or localised dry spot as it is sometimes known, is where areas of turf dry out and become water-repellent (hydrophobic). Dry patch may be due to a physical cause such as high spots which selectively dry out, uneven watering systems or root-breaks where shallow-rooted turf easily becomes drought-stressed. Also prone are sites where there is an excessive fibrous thatch layer. Of increasing concern is dry patch caused by fairy ring fungi which excrete waxy substances onto the surface of sand particles thus rendering the turf hydrophobic. Physical causes of dry patch may be avoided or prevented, e.g. by improving the turf coverage achieved by the irrigation system. In most cases, however, a programme of wetting agent applications to re-wet and keep moist turf affected by dry patch is necessary.

The choice of wetting agent, made according to its chemical structure, for use on turf is all-important. In the 1930's soft soap solutions were used and in the 1950s mild detergents such as Teepol and ordinary washing-up liquid were employed. In many cases these chemicals had adverse effects on both soil structure and grass tissue and consequently are no longer recommended. Fortunately, the wetting agents currently available are 'non-ionic', i.e. neutral in charge, which means they are able to persist in the soil and are the least phytotoxic type of wetting agent.

Currently, there are a number of products available for use on turf. Whatever wetting agent is chosen it is important to apply the product as detailed below to achieve the greatest alleviation of dry patch. When applying wetting agents, prevention is much more effective than cure. On greens prone to the development of dry patch, the routine use of wetting agents between late March (before the turf has dried out) and October is recommended. Curative applications of wetting agents are generally problematical as the dry patch is extremely difficult to re-wet even with efficient wetting agents. However, if this situation has been allowed to develop then spot treatment will achieve initial re-wetting of water-repellent turf. After the initial application of wetting agent in the early spring, further applications should be made at 4-6 week intervals according to the severity of dry patch and climatic conditions. As well as blanket treatments to the entire green, more localised spot treatment of the worst areas using an injector attachment on a hand-held hose is beneficial.

A dry 'spreadable' formulation of some products is available which is well suited to spot application, especially when applied following hollow tining. Spreadable formulations may also be applied after hollow tining to place the wetting agent in the most hydrophobic zone. In all cases wetting agent applications should be tied in with the routine or local aeration using slit or preferably chisel tines. Also, wetting agents should be thoroughly watered into the turf shortly after application to minimise the possibility of phytotoxicity.

To summarise, dry patch should be treated with wetting agents in the early season when the turf is still moist, and the application repeated as necessary through the growing season. Spot treatment of severe dry patch areas with a spreadable dry formulation or liquid followed by selective irrigation is also beneficial. A regular aeration programme will assist penetration of wetting agent through the turf surface and watering in after application is essential.

(CGC 1 : 21)

DRY PATCHES ON GREENS

Most greenkeepers will have come across the condition known as 'dry patch' at some time during their working life. The typical symptoms occur as frequently on less intensively maintained areas like fairways as they do on the finer turf of golf greens, though perhaps not with the same dramatic effect on play and the sward.

Where management, particularly for greens, aims at uniformity of sward, a smooth, true surface and consistent speed, the occurrence of variably sized drier patches with a weakened turf cover can be a great inconvenience. Causes of dry patch are many and varied and some of them are considered below along with suggestions for tackling them or at least reducing their worst effects.

Induced Dry Patch

Drought created by compaction will cause weak, drier areas to develop on a green just as easily and quickly as they form on main traffic routes. On a golf green such areas develop at the edges often at the nearest convenient point where players walk off to collect their caddy carts en route for the next tee. There are two factors involved; the sheer weight of foot traffic moving on and off the playing surface and the effects of mowing. It is common mowing practice to make a final 'clean up' cut around the perimeter of a green and these areas then receive twice the mower traffic than other places. When using triple mowers on golf greens this can occur every day of the week at the height of the growing season. Naturally, the result is local compaction which lowers the infiltration rate of water into the soil and unless it is relieved by thorough and regular aeration, dry areas will develop. The type of aeration carried out is important and during autumn and winter thorough hollow tining of these areas, perhaps on a local basis, followed up by regular slitting can be satisfactory. During the summer solid tine aeration is often more appropriate despite the soil compaction that occurs around the tine hole as it is formed. Solid tine holes remain open to permit moisture penetration much longer than slits will on a traffic route and under a low watering regime they are much less likely to open up and so disfigure the turf and playing surface. Excessive irrigation to counter the latter problem or that of dry patches will always create more difficulties than it solves.

The formation of a surface mat of fibre can also be a factor in dry patch development. This is not quite the same as the thatch often seen as an excessive development of undecomposed organic remains below the sward, forming a soggy, yellowish layer that accepts and retains moisture, creating an entirely different surface problem. All turf will produce some mat or fibre and indeed a small amount is necessary to provide a degree of resilience at the playing surface. This acceptable type of fibre is often a brownish material showing decomposition and merging with the upper layers of soil. However, when such fibre becomes dried out it is extremely difficult to re-wet – very much like peat – and these places then show up locally as very dry areas. Prevention is always easier than specific curative treatment and regular aeration to keep the mat open and receptive to moisture helps considerably. If such patches do form, individual hand solid tining to supplement machine work followed up with an application of wetting agent solution and normal irrigation can correct matters. In severe cases it may be necessary to apply supplementary water to individual dry areas by hand sprinkler/hoses in order to re-wet them.

Development of dry patches on the lines described above could be hastened by the practice of treating individual mossy areas in turf with either a lawn sand dressing or frequently just calcined sulphate of iron and sand. Moss often invades turf that is weakened during summer droughts and controlling it with these types of mosskiller will lower the soil pH in the areas, creating more acid conditions that inhibit fibre breakdown and so the cycle continues.

Finally under this heading one must consider the higher mounds and sloping features within putting greens that nearly always cause this type of problem at some time. Fortunately nowadays the more acute featuring that is seen on older courses is less favoured by modern golf architects and with good reasons. Even slight discrepancies in height and slope can lead to surface run-off and thus create differential wetting and drying which no irrigation system can cope with properly. Excessive watering is highly detrimental to the production of good putting surfaces and to the desirable bents and fescue grasses which form the best type of turf. It is counter-productive to irrigate featured greens, especially using automatic watering systems to cater for the water requirements of higher features when inevitable surface run-off will result in gross overwatering of local hollows and flatter areas where most play occurs.

The best approach in this situation is to apply water to suit the needs of lower areas and ensure as far as possible that features are kept well aerated to aid moisture penetration using a wetting agent if necessary. Judicious supplementary watering of these features may also be helpful in a severe drought and, of course, with older manual watering systems the water can be applied only to features, leaving run-off to cater for low areas. Clearly, there is no easy answer to this problem and it is likely that some degree of droughting and discolouration will have to be accepted. In this situation, green is definitely not great.

Dry Patch of Fungal Origin

The classic example here is the dry bare patch or ring created by Type 1 fairy rings during the development of the fungus *Marasmius oreades*. This soil inhabiting fungus produces abundant mycelium which spreads through the soil beneath the turf making it impervious to the penetration of water. The grass dies out through drought and the characteristic bare zone of soil forms between a slowly advancing outer and inner ring of stimulated growth. The extent of the bare zone varies somewhat during the year with a little recovery of the turf around its edges in wetter months. The fungus can persist for many years very slowly extending outwards whilst the inner zone recovers as old mycelium decomposes and allows normal water penetration through the soil to support grass.

For many years excavation and soil sterilising was the only control method, but since this is laborious, disruptive and time-consuming, requiring meticulous attention to detail, it never found real favour. A simple method of control, after first spiking to open up the surface and treating with a wetting agent solution, is repeated soakings of the ring with water. Whilst in some instances this has proved effective where a number of rings occur, it can be as laborious as excavation.

Chemical control using fungicides based on oxycarboxin and triforine can be recommended. The great difficulty with any underground mycelium that is also hydrophobic is in getting sufficient of the chemical into contact with the fungus. Control treatment should be carried out when the fungus is active after intensively spiking the affected zones including inner and outer rings, an application of wetting agent solution and thorough watering. This initial treatment is essential to moisten the affected soil properly before the use of the proprietary fungicide. Other forms of dry patch, often with a yellowish or bronzy ring though without any distinct zoning or bare soil areas, may also be associated with the development of hydrophobic fungi in the soil, preventing moisture penetration. In these instances treatment on the lines discussed above could be appropriate.

Hydrophobic Soil and Sands

Past reports from New Zealand and the USA discuss hydrophobic or water repelling soils, particularly in relation to greens that are being modified by a sand top dressing programme. This treatment aims to improve surface drainage, sward and playing qualities of greens by very frequent light top dressings of a carefully chosen sand throughout the growing season. Various problems have been encountered, e.g. drainage and aeration at the interface where the sand lies over the original and usually heavy soil. Also as sand depth builds up, turf nutrition requires very close attention. In time, dry spots and patches appear where the sand has become hydrophobic.

The organic product which causes hydrophobic sand patches may be produced by the grass itself or by fungi which decay the grass. It has been found that the zone of maximum non-wettability in such patches is immediately below the fibre layer in the top inch of soil. No precise identification of the substances which produce the 'waxy' coating on the soil or sand particles from a dry patch area has been obtained. Photographs of sand particles from a dry patch area have been obtained at high magnification using an electron microscope and these clearly show the organic coating. It has been suggested that the substance is produced in limited amounts but that there is enough to coat the vast number of particles of clay or silt which collectively have a very large surface area in most normal soils. However, on sand there is enough present to coat a thin layer of sand grains which causes water to move over the repellent layer and enter cracks or pores where it channels down without wetting the surface soil. Hydrophobic dry spots occur commonly on sand top dressed greens and also on the naturally very sandy soil or links courses. It seems that when such a soil becomes dry, the molecules of the hydrophobic material align themselves on the surface of the sand grain so that water is repelled. In other words, if sand is not allowed to dry out completely it will not become water repellent. When dry spots do occur the best approach is to open up the immediate surface by spiking at close centres and shallow depth, following this with an application of wetting agent solution and thorough localised watering of the dry patches. There are a number of commercial wetting agents for turf on the market.

A three year research project on the subject of dry patch, funded by the R&A, has recently been completed at the STRI and will be reported in future issues of the STRI Journal.

(CGC 1 : 20)

SEEDLING DISEASES

Seedling diseases may cause significant losses during the establishment of turfgrass areas from seed. This article briefly describes the conditions which favour seedling diseases and gives recommendations for their control.

Although the term seedling diseases is generally used to describe this problem, disease may occur at three distinct stages in the germination, growth and establishment of grass seedlings. Firstly, there is seed rot where the seed fails to germinate and rots in the soil. Secondly, there is pre-emergence damping-off which is when the seed germinates but fails to emerge and lastly, there is post-emergence damping-off where the seedling emerges but fails to establish. There are over 60 different fungi recorded as able to attack seedlings, but *Fusarium, Pythium* and *Rhizoctona* are the most common and damaging.

The symptoms of seed rot are a thin stand and ungerminated seed which may be found in the seedbed will be rotten. Pre-emergence damping-off exhibits as a thin, patchy sward and very young seedlings may be found rotting beneath the surface. Post-emergence damping-off is the most severe type affecting large areas, seedlings often appearing crimson red or sickly yellow in colour.

In the turfgrass situation seedling diseases are favoured by cold, wet conditions. Severe problems were observed in, for example, the 1992 late autumn-early winter, a period of prolonged heavy rainfall in most areas. Other important factors which lead to outbreaks of seedling diseases are inadequate or excessive seedbed fertiliser, a poorly prepared seedbed and early spring or late autumn seedings are also severely attacked.

As with other turfgrass diseases, a programme of integrated disease management should be deployed to maintain losses due to seedling diseases at a minimal level. Much can be done culturally to prevent seedling diseases. The seedbed should be generally well-prepared, have good drainage and receive appropriate fertiliser, as determined by chemical soil analysis. Seed should be sown evenly and at the correct rate for the seed mixture used. Ideally, sowings should be made only in good growing conditions, i.e. not too early in the spring before soil temperatures rise, or too late in the autumn, i.e. not in wet, cold conditions. Once an outbreak of disease has occurred, it is difficult in practice to achieve control using fungicides. In the past, sprays or drenches of broad spectrum fungicides have been used albeit with limited success. This may be due to the fact that as seedlings are very small, so much of the applied chemical is wasted.

Recent research at the STRI has evaluated fungicide seed coatings for control of seedling diseases. Seed coatings are designed to be absorbed by the seedling as it grows, thus offering protection from disease. An effective material which is currently available is based on a mixture of thiabendazole and metalaxyl, active ingredients which inhibit *Fusarium* and *Pythium* respectively, the two most important fungi responsible for seedling disease. In ideal sowing conditions the chances of seedling diseases occurring are relatively slight and the expense of a fungicide coating may not be justified. However, in high risk situations, for example, wet seedbeds or early spring/late autumn sowings, then the "insurance" of having a seed coating may be rewarded.

(NAB : B.182)

SECTION 10
TURF PESTS

--- ❖❖❖ ---

Pest Management

Earthworms

Insect Pests

Moles and Other Animals

*The Care of
the Golf Course*

INTEGRATED PEST MANAGEMENT

The intensive management completed on areas of fine amenity turf serves not only to produce a desired playing surface, but more importantly, to promote a healthy sward. The health of the sward is a reflection of its management and a combination of many factors including sward composition, mowing height, nutrient levels, moisture availability, soil structure and soil composition. All factors associated with healthy turfgrass growth must be managed such that they are all at or near their optimum requirement. Adjusting one of these factors can affect one or more others and produce an imbalance within the turfgrass system. If turfgrass is stressed due to the action of any one or several contributory factors, the grass will be more susceptible to attack or damage by pests and less able to respond rapidly for recovery.

Turfgrass pests include living organisms that have the capacity to adversely affect the growth and/or function of the turf. These include plant pathogens (invariably fungi), insects, earthworms, weeds and nematodes but undoubtedly the most important pests of turf that occurs across the UK are fungi and insects.

The level at which a given pest becomes intolerable depends on the type of pest present, its numbers and the use for which the turf is maintained. For example, a leatherjacket population present on a golf fairway may pose less of a problem than on a golf green. The total eradication of a given pest problem from any area is not economically viable. It is necessary to manage the turf such that the potential of a pest outbreak in minimised and that levels of certain pest organisms are maintained below injurious levels.

Integrated Pest Management (IPM) is an ecologically based system which includes several management approaches including cultural, physical, genetic, biological and chemical controls. Organisms which are capable of causing problems on amenity turf are generally present at non-damaging levels. Only when there is a change of conditions that favours the growth and development of the pest population will the detrimental effects be expressed. For a successful IPM programme, it is imperative that the person implementing the programme be fully informed regarding the factors that lead to the outbreak of any given pest problem. Without a sound knowledge of these conditions, the IPM programme is unlikely to succeed. Early identification of certain problems will undoubtedly produce benefits to the maintenance team in reducing the cost of control measures.

With regard to cultural control measures, certain practices will reduce the susceptibility of the turfgrass to attack by given pests and also assist recovery from attack or injury. Many pests can be maintained at levels that cause no problems to the turf quality if conditions favour the grass rather than the growth of either the insect or the pathogen. If fine turf is not carefully maintained the sward can rapidly deteriorate to a weak sward which is more vulnerable to pest attack.

Disease development is closely associated with the level of available moisture both in the soil profile and on the turf surface. Correct watering of areas of fine turf is essential to promote healthy grass growth and to discourage disease occurrence and development. Insect damage is difficult to identify under conditions of drought stress and indeed there is some evidence that suggests insect damage is only a problem in dry soils. To promote a healthy sward, watering should be completed so as to wet the soil to depth but not so frequently as to cause a situation of waterlogged soil. Removing dew from the turf will decrease the chance of disease development across the turf surface.

Adequate but not excessive levels of nutrient availability are imperative for the health of the sward. Both a weak, undernourished sward and an over-fertilised sward can render the turf susceptible to disease attack.

The depth of thatch that can build up though management practices and the sward composition can severely affect disease occurrence. Thatch is a suitable environment in which certain pathogens can both live and survive adverse environmental conditions. If allowed to dry out, thatch will act as a barrier to water penetration resulting in a drought-stressed sward which will be more susceptible to attack. The thatch has a high water holding capacity which will aid movement of the pathogens through the sward and allow suitable conditions for disease development.

The use of biological control measures is receiving increased interest as an additional tool in the prevention of pest problems. The theory behind this approach relies on the fact that all pest organisms, be they fungi or insects, have natural enemies which if present in the same environment as the pest will prevent the development of the pest population and limit the potential problem. There is interest in developing a biological control method to limit diseases such as take-all patch which cause severe damage to the sward, but which at present have no effective approved chemical control. To date however, limited success has been achieve through this control method.

Arguably pesticides are the most important tool in the control of turfgrass pests. A range of pesticides are currently available which are effective at controlling pest outbreaks. It is important not to rely on pesticides as the sole management tool in combating pest problems since fungi in particular, have the capacity to develop degrees of resistance to fungicides if offered regular exposure. It is advisable to alternate both the active ingredients and mode of action of applied fungicides throughout the period when disease control is necessary.

The ultimate goal of an integrated pest management system is to maintain an all year round healthy sward using all of the means available to achieve this and not to rely solely on any one specific tactic too heavily. It is important to remember that total eradication of any pest organism from an area of amenity turf is not a viable option. All that is required is to minimise the pest population below that which has the potential to cause damage.

(CAY : B.189)

EARTHWORMS : PAST, PRESENT AND FUTURE

Earthworms play a vital role in the soil system as a nutrient cycling mechanism, mixing surface litter with the soil, breaking down organic matter and providing channels for infiltration and movement of both liquids and gases through the soil profile. Agricultural practices tend to automatically encourage this desirable earthworm activity which is of great benefit in sustaining long-term crop production. However, in some circumstances earthworm activity in soil under fine turf is not so welcome because of surface casting by some species of earthworm. It is these casts which have provided greenkeepers with major problems in the past, continue to do so at present and probably will do in the future management of sports turf. The aim of greenkeepers is to reduce surface casting rates to preserve turf and playing quality of grass whilst at the same time maintaining soil quality. Where earthworms are eradicated in sports turf by whatever method, it is important to counteract the reduced earthworm activity in the soil with mechanical means, maintaining aeration, hydraulic conductivity, infiltration rates, structure and litter incorporation.

Casts result in an uneven playing surface which reduces the playing quality of fine turf, particularly golf greens. Casts provide ideal seedbed conditions for seeds to germinate, having a higher level of available nutrients than the local soil. Undesirable seeds such as those of *Poa annua,* which are brought to the surface by the earthworms, stand a greater chance of establishing themselves in the sward in the exposed earth of an earthworm cast than when the surface has a cover of established grasses. The smeared soil casts can seal the surface, reducing water infiltration rate as well as interfering with mowing management and playing quality.

In British soils there are 25 species of earthworms and some research has shown that 8 of these species can produce surface casts in the slightly compacted soil conditions found under sports turf. The main surface casters include *Apporectodea longa* and *Lumbricus terrestris.* Earthworms feed on dead and decaying plant and animal remains and on free-living microflora and fauna. The type and amount of food supply determines the size of populations, growth rate and fecundity. Therefore boxing-off clippings and reducing thatch by aeration and scarification will reduce the available food supply and reduce the earthworm population. This is a method of control which has been employed in the past and should continue to be employed as a method for controlling casting.

Between the 1920's and 1960's control methods for the reduction of surface casting to an acceptable level in sports and recreational turf tended to rely on expellant methods. Materials were applied which would irritate the earthworms making them emerge onto the soil surface where they could be manually swept up and disposed of. These methods included applying potassium permanganate at the rate of $1/2$ oz. in 1 gallon of water/yd^2. Mowrah meal was a popular method whereby the fine red powder was watered in. Derris powder was used as it was known to be a contact and stomach poison to most invertebrates. Other materials were applied to the soil which killed the earthworms underground. Mercuric chloride was used as a control method, but banned as it proved extremely toxic to humans. Lead arsenate was quite commonly applied to soils and was extremely persistent in the soil system providing long-lasting control for between 5 and 6 years with an application rate of 2 oz/yd^2. Once lead was found to be an extremely toxic heavy metal, applications for earthworm control were banned.

The chemical chlordane was introduced to British golf courses and sports grounds as a worm control in 1961. From then until its ban in 1992 chlordane was the most popular lumbricide. Trials commenced at the STRI in 1961 to determine the effectiveness and persistency of two commercially available chlordane formulations compared with other methods used for controlling casting. Chlordane performed well on most sports grounds and golf courses but occasionally failed on soils low in organic matter. Chlordane was a very effective earthworm killer and much of its commercial success was due to its cheapness and the duration of control (between 5 and 7 years) which could be gained by one application. It is the persistence of this organochlorine compound in the soil system that has led to its recent ban, applications having been banned since December 1992. The result is that only carbaryl, carbendazim and gamma HCH + thiophanate methyl are presently available for earthworm control. Ironically it is the short persistence of these chemicals that has enabled them to stay on the market. Even so, with the ever-changing legislation covering pesticides it is possible that in the future these chemicals will also be banned because of concerns about the effects on the soil system and the environment. A ban on carbaryl is currently pending.

The Royal and Ancient Golf Club of St. Andrews is presently supporting a research programme into methods for controlling earthworm casting on golf courses. One trial is investigating the effects of soil acidification on casting rates with applications of aluminium sulphate and sulphur. Earthworms have been shown to dislike acidic soil conditions and applications of these soil-acidifying chemicals may control casting to an acceptable level. Claims have been made that it is possible to prevent earthworms casting by rolling a thin layer of iron filings into the turf surface. It is possible that this is effective as the iron filings may release iron into the soil thereby acidifying the soil.

Other claims for controlling casting include spreading ground glass on the turf surface. There is no documented research available to support these theories, but they may be worth investigating under future research at the Institute.

For many years various electrical methods for expelling earthworms have been suggested but it appears that all have been used with only minimal success. Methods can only be used over a small area, they are very time-consuming and there are safety implications. Conductivity is related to moisture content but if the surface is dry the electric current may drive the worms deeper into the ground. pH was found to be important to the success of the method, soils with low pH readings having higher expulsion rates. Golf courses are increasingly being built on less suitable land on heavier soils as the game continues to increase in popularity. Moisture-retaining clay-based soils more liable to compaction will provide difficulties for greenkeepers trying to control casting with the presently available methods.

So, what does the future hold for the control of earthworm casting? An ideal scenario would be the development of a species specific "safe" short-persistence lumbricide. This would mean that surface casting species could be removed from an area leaving the non surface casting species to benefit the soil. Until this happens, control methods will have to include all species. Future research to be completed under the R&A research programme will include expellant trials and investigations of biological and chemical control. The toxic effects of some fungicides are well documented and it may be possible that in the future son ? will be approved for earthworm control on turf. Soil acidification may be shown to be a useful tool for greenkeepers to employ, especially as the desirable bents and fescues prefer acidic soil conditions. Boxing-off clippings and keeping thatch down will also help prevent casting. It may be possible to minimise casting by building underground mesh barriers surrounding new or existing greens to prevent earthworms infiltrating the area.

It is imperative that an effective and acceptable method is found for earthworm casting control if golf courses are to maintain the quality of turf which people have come to expect.

(ECK : B.186)

POST CHLORDANE EARTHWORM CONTROL

For many years chlordane provided a reliable and long-lasting treatment for earthworm casting. The use of chlordane on turf is now banned under the control of pesticide regulations. This article examines the cultural and chemical options available to greenkeepers/groundsmen to maintain casting at a minimal level on the turf areas under their care.

Firstly, it must be remembered that there are several cultural advantages to maintaining earthworms away from the turf surface. Sub-surface populations of earthworms may thrive and confer advantages to the turf, e.g. improve aeration and drainage, but only if they do not produce casts.

In the absence of chlordane, the alternative chemical methods of inhibiting earthworm casting are as follows:

[1] The use of calcined sulphate of iron has been standard practice in turf maintenance for many years. The acidifying effect of sulphate of iron discourages the surface activity of earthworms and thus helps to keep casting to a minimum.

[2] The pesticide carbaryl is currently Approved for inhibition of earthworm casting, although it can only be used through tractor-mounted sprayers and a total ban is a future possibility. Whilst carbaryl works quickly, it does not have much persistency in the soil and consequently, duration of control is short. During a typical winter two or

three applications may be necessary.

[3] Alternatively, a pesticide based on a fungicide/insecticide combination (thiophanate-methyl/gamma-HCH) is available. In general, this product appears to be similar in its effectiveness to carbaryl, i.e. it works quickly, but only in the short-term. An additional property of this product is that it is also Approved for control of leatherjackets.

[4] One fungicide, based on the active ingredient carbendazim, currently carries label instructions for earthworm casting suppression. Fungicides such as carbendazim, based on the active ingredient termed "MBC", have been shown to discourage earthworms, as well as of course being effective against diseases such as red thread and fusarium patch. Thus, it may be possible to gain a very short-term suppression of earthworm casting using this material.

[5] Worm expellents, i.e. chemicals which do not kill the earthworm but make them rise to the surface, have also been used in the past. Materials such as mowrah meal and potassium permanganate fall into this category. Whilst mowrah meal is no longer available, research at STRI will concentrate on how to use expellents to their maximum effect. In the past brushing up of earthworms after an expellent has been applied has been messy and labour intensive. However, with the introduction of mechanical brushing equipment, this option has become more feasible.

In conclusion, the persistent long-term control of earthworm casting offered by chlordane is now a thing of the past and the likelihood of a similar material becoming available for use on turf is slight. In the future, cultural methods will be hopefully developed and we foresee these becoming increasingly important. In the meantime, the only practical treatment offered is by chemicals such as carbaryl and thiophanate-methyl/gamma-HCH which are effective in the short-term only, making their repeated use extremely time consuming and costly.

(NAB : B.182)

OTHER TURF PESTS

Possibly the worst pest of all, especially in fine turf, is the earthworm because of the harm done by the surface casts, but worm control is a subject on its own and merits separate treatment. Second in importance is the leatherjacket – the larval stage of various species of *Tipula* (the crane fly or 'daddy-longlegs') – which feeds on the turf and its roots. The adult crane flies are on the wing in late summer and autumn; they mate immediately after emerging from the pupal cases and lay about 200–300 eggs per female insect. The eggs hatch out into larvae in about 14 days, and these larvae remain in the soil and turf for about 9 months, feeding on the turf and its roots. They are very susceptible to drought in the early stages and this is just one of the reasons why myriads of crane flies observed in August or September do not necessarily imply a plague of leatherjackets the following year. Eventually the larvae change into the pupal stage where they remain for 9–10 days and then when the pupa is ready it works its front end above ground, and it is common to see the brown sheaths of the empty pupal cases sticking up out of the turf after an emergence of a flight of crane fly.

Fibrous Turf Favoured

Leatherjackets most commonly cause trouble in turf growing in sandy soils and they particularly like a fibrous turf such as is often found on golf fairways. They have tended not to be so common in the more intensively managed fine turf of golf greens because of the recent widespread use of chlordane for wormkilling – the chlordane killed the leatherjackets too. (Use of this chemical is now prohibited.)

Control in November

By spring leatherjackets have increased considerably in size and if large numbers are present they will be causing considerable damage, eating away at the roots to such an extent that the turf dies right back, especially if the weather is dry. Secondary damage results from birds like starlings and rooks searching for the larvae; in fact quite often the birds act as an early warning system, alerting the attention of the green-keeper to the presence of the leatherjackets. A tarpaulin or damp sack left overnight on the turf will usually give some idea of the numbers present, and if these exceed 20 per square yard on a golf fairway it is advisable to apply a suitable insecticide. In fine turf like greens there should really be no leatherjackets at all. About November is the best time to apply an insecticide, before the year's generation of grubs has grown sufficiently large to do any appreciable harm, and for large-scale work insecticides based on gamma-HCH are relatively cheap and effective.

Fever Fly Larvae Also Damage Turf

The larvae of the fever fly (*Dilophus febrilis*) and two species of *Bibio* (St Mark's and St John's flies) are sometimes mistaken for leatherjackets, but they are smaller and have a distinct brown head. The eggs are laid in clusters, and therefore the larvae tend to create local damage rather than affecting a wide area like the leatherjackets. There are two broods a year, the flies (rather like house-flies in appearance) emerging in May and September. The grubs cause similar damage to the turf to that produced by leatherjackets, though usually on a smaller scale. Control measures are the same as for leatherjackets.

Some Minor Insect Pests

Chafer larvae (the larvae of the cock-chafer, the garden chafer, the summer chafer and the rose chafer beetles) cause a good deal of damage on golf course turf on the Continent, but in this country the pest is less common. Nevertheless, cases of damage, mainly to golf course fairways, do occur from time to time, and the usual culprit turns out to be the garden chafer. Control is not easy but gamma-HCH may be tried, preferably after a thorough spiking of the turf, and the younger the grubs are the more successful the control is likely to be. Mining bees (about 60 British species but *Andrena fulva* perhaps the most common in turf) sometimes cause the little mounds of soil which appear on turf grown in sandy soils, these solitary bees excavating vertical burrows (which may go down as deep as 600 mm) in which they lay their eggs. The harm done by these rather attractive insects is minimal really and they can hardly be accused of causing appreciable amounts of damage. Nor can ants, frit flies, dung, dor and oil beetles, cutworms and mole crickets which occasionally occur on the British turf scene, though some of them, like the cutworms, are a sore trial to the managers of fine turf on the Continent, especially in the South. In a hot, dry summer the longer grass in the rough of the golf course – particularly the fescue grasses – will assume a red colouration which is rather puzzling to the inexperienced eye, but the phenomenon is due to the action of certain species of leaf-sucking aphid.

Rabbits

Rabbits are once again causing considerable damage, particularly on golf courses, having gained some measure of immunity against myxomatosis. On fairways and tees, especially where the soil is light and sandy, they will enlarge by their scratching and burrowing any areas which have been damaged initially by play – divot holes for instance. In a bunker they can create absolute havoc. Nor are the greens immune, and rabbits will crop the grass right down to ground level, causing uneven putting surfaces and light coloured patches in the turf. Trapping, gassing and shooting at night in the headlights of a Land Rover or similar form of transport are the most effective means of control, but the position is difficult where there is abundant cover available to the animals. Foxes are on the increase too, and though they help to keep the rabbits down they can be responsible, by scratching and urinating, for a certain amount of damage to the turf themselves.

Moles

The harm caused by these creatures on a golf course can be horrific. Trapping or gassing are also effective against moles, whilst worm baits dipped in strychnine and inserted in the runs at strategic points provide a method which is popular with the professionals. Strychnine is, of course, a very dangerous poison; permits are only available from the Ministry of Agriculture, Fisheries and Food and issued only to suitable applicants. An indirect method of keeping moles out of golf turf is to get rid of the worms and thus the attraction for the moles.

Really, thanks largely to our cool climate, turf in Britain escapes relatively lightly with regard to numbers of pests, particularly insect pests, compared with turf in tropical or semi-tropical countries, and if we consult the appropriate American literature for example we find we have much to be grateful for in this respect.

(CGC 1 : 84)

CONTROL OF ANIMAL PESTS

Introduction

Animal pests such as moles, rabbits, foxes and even geese can cause a considerable amount of damage to amenity turf areas and the following discussion will hopefully clarify the options available for control.

Mole control

There are two methods of controlling moles: indirectly or directly. Indirect control involves killing earthworms which constitute the mole's diet. This now involves using carbendazim or thiophanate-methyl/lindane based products.

Direct control involves killing the moles and this can be achieved by poisoning or by trapping.

Poisoning can be carried out using aluminium phosphide tablets which release phosphine gas into mole runs. Products such as these can only be used by qualified users in the course of their business. See Part 1, Schedule 1 Poison, under Poisons Rules, 1982. Gassing will only work where there are closed tunnels which are gas-tight and which will allow the fumes to travel along for some distance.

Poison baits can also be used, with earthworms being dipped in strychnine and left in the mole run as bait. Once again, care must be taken as strychnine can only be used with the appropriate licence, usually issued only to professional mole catchers.

Coupled with poisoning, trapping is also an effective means of controlling moles. As a rough guide, if mole damage becomes evident on a green, aluminium phosphide should be used immediately by an appropriately trained operator. In contrast, if problems occur elsewhere then traps should be used, as one then knows for certain whether the mole is dead or not.

Rabbit control

Control of rabbits can be achieved by shooting, gassing and, in the short-term, by using repellents. The most efficient of these is shooting, although problems can occur as a result of complaints from club members. This operation is most effective if carried out in the early morning.

Gassing is also extremely efficient, but must be carried out by a licensed operator.

Repellents only give short-term control, and are ineffective following rainfall and after a period of growth.

Any control strategy for rabbits should incorporate the above coupled with thinning out of any bushes, etc. which act as natural cover.

Fox control

Foxes can cause problems with digging up greens and urinating onto the turf. Any control programme for these must be based on discouragement either by killing off rabbits (a food source) or by physical discouragement of the fox itself by the use of, for example, an electric fence.

Goose control

Geese can also be a problem by grazing down grass and also defecating onto the turf. Means of controlling these involves the use of bird-scaring devices or plastic swans. The swans are moored in water as geese apparently do not land on water already occupied by swans. The geese then theoretically fly off somewhere else, minimising damage to surrounding grassland.

A final alternative is the use of electric fences around greens in order to discourage encroachment onto the playing surface.

(Anon : B.184)

PLATE 7: The leatherjacket larva of the crane fly is the most damaging insect pest of turf in the British Isles.

PLATE 8: Other insect pests of British turf include the fever fly grub (top) distinguished by its shiny brown head, and the larvae of the chafer beetle (below) distinguished by six jointed legs.

SECTION 11
TURF WEEDS AND MOSS

❖❖❖

Weeds of Turf

Weed Control

Aquatic Weeds

Moss and Moss Control

Algae : Lichens

*The Care of
the Golf Course*

WEEDS ON THE GOLF COURSE

Weeds are traditionally defined as plants growing out of place. A rose could be classed as a weed in a cabbage patch, as could a potato plant in a wheat field. On the golf course, some wild plant species are welcomed in areas of rough and semi-rough, an indication of the growth in ecological awareness. On fairways and particularly greens and tees however, bent and fescue grasses dominate and all other plants are considered weeds. Under the heading of weeds we must therefore include broad-leaved weeds, undesirable grasses and mosses, all of which can occur commonly on the golf course. For the purpose of this article, we will concentrate largely on broad-leaved and grass weeds.

So why do we strive so hard to produce a turf sward limited to 2-3 turf species? Why are other plant species considered undesirable? For a start, the presence of weeds often produces an untidy appearance and the uneven surface resulting may interfere with play. The weeds will inevitably compete for nutrients and water with the desirable turf grasses and may smother out the grass as in the case of rosette forming plants, such as plantain and dandelion. Furthermore, annual meadow-grass which is considered a troublesome grass weed, is often more vulnerable to disease attack, in particular from fusarium and anthracnose.

Weeds can be introduced into a turfed area as seeds or plant fragments by a number of different means. Natural methods include transport by birds and animals or distribution by wind and flooding. In addition, various management practices can be responsible, such as transport by mowers or other machinery. The use of poor quality materials, for example contaminated grass seed or turf or unsterilised compost, is also a potential means for introducing weeds.

Broad-leaved weeds

Broad-leaved weeds can be categorised as annuals, biennials and perennials. Annuals, as their name suggests, are plants which flower and seed in one year. They are generally most troublesome in new seed beds, but are often mown out when regular mowing gets underway. Of biennials (plants which grow and flower over two years) and perennials (which usually flower and seed over more than 2 years), the latter are of more significance in established sports and amenity turf. Plantains, daisy, speedwell, buttercup, dandelion and white clover are amongst the very common perennial species.

Broad-leaved weed control in seed bed preparation

When sowing or turfing new areas the prepared seed bed should be as clean as possible, free from viable weed seeds and plant fragments. A flush of weeds, when seedling turf is establishing, will not only choke the young grass and compete for valuable nutrients, but may also be difficult to control chemically without damaging the young grass. Commonly, total herbicides in alternation with fallowing and cultivation are used to clean seed or turf beds. This method helps bring potential weeds in the rootzone to the surface in order that they can germinate and be chemically destroyed. Where rhizomatous weeds (weeds with underground stems) are present, a translocated total herbicide such as glyphosate would be most appropriate. Clearly, the efficiency of this method varies depending on the length of time the area is left fallow. Some weed seeds germinate over both spring and autumn and consequently the fallowing period should span these seasons to be as thorough as possible.

An alternative means of producing a clean seed bed involves soil sterilisation. The soil fumigant methyl bromide is quicker and more effective than fallowing, but far more expensive and can be responsible for killing beneficial organisms present in the soil. Similarly, the soil sterilant Dazomet is a cheaper, safer but less efficient alternative.

If weeds do appear in seedling turf, often a significant proportion of these plants can be mown out once regular cutting gets underway. There are herbicide products approved for use on seedling turf but young turf is particularly vulnerable and any chemical treatments early on may run the risk of setting back growth.

Cultural control of broad-leaved weeds

Established turf with strong dense growth rarely has serious problems with weeds. Weeds only have the opportunity to establish where the turf sward has been weakened or when conditions are more conducive to weed growth than turf. Broad-leaved weeds which persistently appear year after year may be indicative of some underlying problem. For example, white clover is often indicative of low nitrogen levels, whilst creeping buttercup is commonly found in damp, poorly drained areas. Close mowing, scalping or drought stress can leave a turf surface thin and open to weed invasion as can over acidic or alkaline conditions. The application of lime or alkaline top dressing can encourage a range of weeds, not to mention earthworms. Even the presence of worm casts provide an ideal site for weed seeds to germinate and establish. This being the case, the first step towards broad-leaved weed control is to identify any causal factors which may be rectifiable. Under such circumstances, chemical control may remove weeds in the short-term, but the chances are that the weeds will return.

Chemical control

For more immediate control a wide range of selective broad-leaved herbicides are available. These can be broadly split into 2 categories: those which act largely on contact with the leaf and those which are absorbed through the leaves, stems and shoots and are translocated throughout the plant. The contact herbicides have a relatively quick weed knockdown effect and are often used in mixes with translocated herbicides. Translocated herbicides on the other hand are able to travel through the plant destroying weeds with underground rhizomes. or deep tap roots which contact herbicides cannot reach. Translocated herbicides, e.g. 2,4-D, mecoprop, dicamba and dichlorprop are growth regulators which, once absorbed into the plant, upset the normal metabolic processes. Often rapid growth occurs causing leaf and stem distortion after three to four days, although plant death may not occur for several weeks.

Weed species vary in susceptibility to different herbicides and use a variety of means to avoid the toxic effects. For example, type, size and angle of leaf are often instrumental in this respect. Where weeds have some resistance to one chemical, mixes or alternative chemicals are often available. For some weeds particular active ingredients are most effective, for example, dicamba is useful against knotgrass (*Polygonum aviculare*).

The timing of treatments is important. The optimum time to treat most weeds is during periods of strong growth which often prevail in late spring/early summer. Needless to say, all herbicides used must be approved for the purpose and necessary procedures must be carried out during application in accordance with the pesticide legislation.

Grass weeds

The three most common weed grasses likely to invade fine turf are Yorkshire fog, perennial ryegrass and the notorious annual meadow-grass. The similarity between grass species makes it extremely difficult to chemically control one particular species without harming others present. There are currently no approved chemicals for controlling weed grasses in fine turf and turf management programmes must be geared towards discouraging unwanted grasses. When the coarser grasses perennial ryegrass and Yorkshire fog occur in small areas hand weeding, plugging or returfing may be considered.

Conclusion
Despite the difficulty regarding the control of grass weeds, the majority of broad-leaved weeds can be eradicated relatively easily using chemical herbicides. However, it must be stressed that herbicides are only one means of weed control and should only be used as part of a comprehensive programme. Prevention is far better than cure and every effort should be made to reduce the risk of weed invasion when seeding or turfing new areas. A good management programme is then essential to produce a strong, healthy sward. This should reduce the likelihood of large weed populations establishing and ultimately reduce the need for chemical control.

(SLM : B.185)

CONTROL OF WEEDS WITH APPLICATION OF SELECTIVE WEEDKILLERS

(1) General
Selective weedkillers or herbicides will control most weeds of turf. They may contain one or more active ingredients. At least one of the active ingredients is normally a foliage-applied translocated herbicide with growth-regulating activity, such as MCPA, 2,4-D or mecoprop. These chemicals are taken into plants chiefly through leaves, but also through roots, and upset normal plant growth processes and distort growth within susceptible weed species. Effects can be seen in twisting of leaves and distorted growth within a day or two of application, but weeds may not die for four to eight weeks. Resistant species may take in less chemical (e.g. because of angle and type of leaf, which partly accounts for selectivity between grasses and broad-leaved species) and also avoid the toxic effects in various ways. Some herbicides, e.g. ioxynil, act primarily by contact, producing a rapid contact scorch and then yellowing of foliage on susceptible plants as photosynthesis and other processes are affected.

Selective herbicides are sold as proprietary products containing variable amounts of active ingredient (a.i.). For some herbicides, the active ingredient is expressed as acid equivalent (a.e.). Although the two terms are not the same, they have a similar meaning for the layman, both being used to distinguish the active ingredient from the 'carrier' or solvents in a proprietary product. The proportion of active ingredient varies between products. Thus, if two firms sell weedkillers with the same active ingredient, firm A may formulate its product with 20% a.i. while firm B formulates its product with 30% a.i. Manufacturer's label recommendations must be followed at all times.

(2) Approved Products
All pesticides, including herbicides, currently used must be approved by MAFF; this can be checked by ensuring the product label displays a MAFF number. Details of the approval process are given in Section 10.

(3) Choice of Application Equipment
Herbicide application by sprayer generally gives the best results for professional users. The spray droplets give good cover, reaching at least partially the undersides of leaves and lower parts of the plants, but spray drift may give risks to non-target plants, the operator and the general public.

There is a wide range of spraying equipment available. For comparatively small areas or for spot treatment (putting greens) a knapsack sprayer or pedestrian operated trolley sprayer may be acceptable. For greens and tees there are sprayers mounted on compact tractors, while for larger areas, e.g. fairways, full-size tractor-mounted or tractor-drawn models are available. (Some herbicides, e.g. ioxynil, are not

228

approved for use in knapsack sprayers.)

The volume of liquid applied by a sprayer depends partly on the machine itself (e.g. pump output), partly on nozzle size, and partly on speed of movement over the ground (see "Calibration of equipment" below). The following are generally accepted definitions of the various volumes of application appropriate to conventional sprayers with nozzles:–

low volume	–	55 – 225 litre ha
medium volume	–	225 – 675 "
high volume	–	675 – 1125 "

Details of application volumes for herbicides may be found on product labels and must be strictly followed.

Controlled droplet application (CDA) sprayers based on a spinning disc principle work at very low (11–55 litre ha^{-1}) or ultra-low volumes (1–11 litre ha^{-1}). Direct injection equipment is another innovation which may become increasingly significant in future.

For areas containing low populations of weeds only, spot treatment may be appropriate. This is often difficult to achieve with any degree of accuracy in practice.

(4) Checking Spraying Equipment

Prior to every spraying operation make sure that the application equipment is in good working order and that pressure hoses, joints and unions are watertight. Ensure that the jets and filter screens of spraying machines are free from blockages and are suitable for the job in hand. The nozzles fitted should be of the type and size specified by the equipment manufacturer or, for particular jobs, those recommended by the chemical manufacturer as described on the product label.

Make sure nozzles are clean and giving their proper spray pattern. As part of the calibration process check their uniformity of output, by operating a stationary water-filled sprayer with a beaker under each nozzle and rejecting nozzles from which output differs from average by more than ±5%.

The spray boom needs to be positioned so the nozzles are at the correct height from the ground, so that the 'cones' or 'fans' of spray just overlap when they meet the turf surface.

The nozzles of hand-held booms on knapsack sprayers or the working height of controlled droplet applicators may be difficult to keep a consistent height above target level during operation, but unless this is done, calibration will be meaningless and the application rate quite different from what is intended.

Cleanliness of spray machines is of paramount importance, especially where one machine is used for many different products. If equipment is shared with other users, it is advisable to wash it out thoroughly both after spraying is complete and also before the next use. Ideally, a separate sprayer should be kept for total herbicides or other similar chemicals, to avoid problems of contamination which could result in damage to turf.

(5) Calibration

Correct calibration of spraying equipment is essential.

(6) Mixing

Mix, as accurately as possible, only the quantity of spray required for the area to be treated. This will avoid the need to dispose of excess material, which is wasteful of chemical and difficult to do safely.

Always wear suitable protective clothing when mixing chemicals. (Refer to product label for details.) Follow any specific instructions given on the label but, as a general rule, add half the required quantity of water, then the chemical, then the remainder of the water (which can be used to rinse out the container in which the chemical was measured). Powder formulations can usually be added to the water and stirred to give a suspension or solution, but it may be necessary to pre-mix the powder by adding a small amount of water to it and mixing thoroughly, to the consistency of a thin cream. This 'cream' can then be added to half the quantity of water in the spray tank and topped up in the normal way.

(7) Patterns of Spraying

Accurate marking of strips is essential to minimise misses or overlaps. If chemicals do not contain a dye, or sprayer wheelings cannot be followed, lines and/or marker pegs should be used or a marker dye added to the spray, particularly on important areas such as golf greens.

For such areas, it is also advisable to spray twice over with a half-strength tank mix, the second time at right angles to the first. This makes misses or overlaps less serious.

All spray work using a boom should be done in parallel lines, not curves (to avoid different speeds at the two ends of the boom). Even with single-nozzle equipment, parallel working is more methodical.

(8) Special Points on Applying Growth-Regulator Herbicides Against Weeds
(8a) Timing

Apply any time from spring to early autumn, preferably in fine, warm weather when the soil is moist and growth is vigorous. Late spring is generally considered best. Avoid applying herbicide treatments during hot, dry weather, or in late autumn (when weed control may be good but the turf may not fill in adequately before winter). Heavy rain shortly after application may reduce effectiveness. Wind gives risk of drift, but a slight constant breeze may allow better work than light variable winds.

(8b) Fertiliser

Growth-regulator herbicides act best when both weeds and grass are growing vigorously. Therefore, if the turf normally receives nitrogenous fertiliser, give some a week or two before spraying. Fertiliser/herbicide mixtures are convenient and avoid risks of spray drift, but they do not boost growth in readiness for herbicide treatment like a separate fertiliser dressing, and a granular herbicide may be washed off by rain more easily than a spray, especially a rain-fast one.

(8c) Mowing before and after spraying

[i] *Turf mown infrequently (every seven to ten days, or more)*

A large leaf area of weeds allows maximum herbicide absorption: therefore delay spraying until a few days before a cut. But then make sure not to cut for two to three days, to give time for herbicide absorption before weed leaves are removed by mowing.

[ii] *Frequently mown turf*

Weed growth between cuts will not matter. Some people would advise not to spray freshly cut grass, but many greenkeepers mow fine turf and spray the same day with no apparent damage. Also, there is no need to refrain from mowing to allow herbicide uptake if all weed foliage is below mowing height.

(8d) Disposal of clippings

After use of growth-regulator herbicides, the clippings from the first four mowings must not be used directly as a mulch round broad-leaved plants or shrubs but may be incorporated into compost heaps, provided that they remain there for at least six months before the compost is used for broad-leaved plants or shrubs. After the first four mowings no special precautions are needed.

(8e) Grass Weeds

The three most common grass weeds found in fine turf are annual meadow-grass (*Poa annua*), Yorkshire fog (*Holcus lanatus*) and perennial ryegrass (*Lolium perenne*). There are no suitable chemicals available for their control in fine turf and the best way to avoid them is by employing suitable management practices. Removal of grass weeds is possible on a small scale by, for example, hand weeding, plugging or returfing.

Certain resistant weeds may require more than one application of herbicide for effective control. Consult the product label for instructions on repeat treatments.

(9) Precautions

Growth-regulators are very powerful and can affect non-target plants even in minute doses. Risks are very real where crops and plants other than grass and cereals are grown in the vicinity of spraying. Do not treat areas of turf near valued plants in flower beds, etc. except on a calm day. If contamination of such plants is suspected, wash them down copiously with clean water. Clean out spraying equipment thoroughly after use.

All herbicides are potentially harmful to the user; follow safety instructions on the product label carefully. Always be careful when measuring out and mixing concentrated herbicides, avoid inhaling the spray, and store and dispose of containers carefully. Always wear minimum protective clothing, i.e. gloves, protective clothing and face mask. Above all, read everything on the label before opening the container. It should be understood that herbicide users are under an obligation to comply with legal requirements governing the usage of such materials and that the instructions included with each product are mandatory, including instructions regarding application rates. Users should be familiar with the Food and Environment Protection Act (1985) Part 3 : Control of Pesticides Regulations (1986).

(CGC 1 : 86)

AQUATIC WEED CONTROL

Excessive weed growth in drainage channels, streams and rivers can obstruct the flow of water, causing flooding, impeding drainage and, through increased silting, channel deterioration. The appearance of water features on golf courses may be impaired by weed growth itself, or by the collection of rubbish and debris caught in the weeds. Furthermore, weed growth may interfere with the use of water for irrigation purposes.

The weeds found in or near water can be put in different categories, from truly submerged weeds to bankside plants. Algal growth may also constitute a problem, particularly in sluggish or static water.

Methods of Control

Cutting

The traditional method of eradicating aquatic weeds in small areas has been to cut using scythes, hooks or chain scythes, followed by raking and clearing. In larger areas or depths of water, specially designed weed cutting boats or weed cutting 'buckets' on long-reach excavators can be employed. These methods are both slow and laborious and can also stimulate rapid regrowth, thereby exacerbating the problem.

With both mechanical and hand cutting it is essential to remove all cut material from the water to prevent it blocking pump intakes, etc. and deoxygenating the water as it decomposes.

Chemical Control

The following list details those herbicides which are approved for controlling aquatic weeds or weeds growing along the banks of watercourses. Water that has been treated with these products can only be used for irrigation purposes after defined periods of time have elapsed to prevent any phytotoxicity effects. This period is known as the "safety interval before irrigation".

CHEMICAL	WEEDS CONTROLLED	SAFETY INTERVAL BEFORE IRRIGATION
asulam	docks, bracken	nil
2,4-D	water weeds, dicotyledon weeds on banks	3 weeks
dichlobenil	aquatic weeds	2 weeks
diquat	aquatic weeds	10 days
fosamine	woody weeds	nil
glyphosate	reeds, rushes, sedges, waterlilies, grass weeds on banks	nil
maleic hydrazide	suppression of grass growth on banks	3 weeks
terbutryn	aquatic weeds	7 days

When using herbicides the manufacturer's instructions found on the product label should be followed carefully – many of them are now legally binding. All those concerned with pesticides should make themselves aware of legislation and obligations by consulting the publications listed below.

Additional Information

There are several informative leaflets available from the MAFF Publications Unit, Lion House, Alnwich, Northumberland, NE66 2PF.

These include a general leaflet "Pesticides: Guide to the New Controls" reference UL79 and a booklet "Guidelines for the Use of Herbicides in or Near Watercourses and Lakes" (B2078). This is essential for all those people intending to apply aquatic herbicides as it details the choice, correct application procedures and obligation to consult the appropriate River Authority Catchment Board, River Purification Authority or Water Undertaking before the spraying of such areas is carried out.

Other relevant publications are listed in the Bibliography.

(CGC 1 : 87)

INTEGRATED PEST MANAGEMENT: MOSS, ALGAE, LICHENS

INTRODUCTION

Integrated Pest Management (IPM) is a system of controlling pests (weeds, diseases, insects) at or below acceptable levels. The term "pest" is used to describe the unwanted presence of any living organism, such as weeds, diseases, insects, etc. The system of IPM depends on correct identification of pest problems (present or anticipated), a clear indication of acceptable action thresholds, full understanding of all available control options (biological, cultural, chemical) and implementation of selected control(s). The choice of control options should be based on effectiveness, environmental impact, site characteristics, worker or public health and safety and economics. The aim of IPM is therefore to manage pests in a manner which is sympathetic to the environment.

MOSS
Introduction
Although there are about 600 species of moss in the UK, their occurrence in amenity turf is restricted to three main types.

Main groups of mosses
Type 1. Fern-like, usually trailing: *Hypnum* and *Eurhynchium* spp. Present in many types of turf but often overlooked. Characteristic of moist, rather spongy swards where there is a soft surface mat. Such mosses are often a problem in turf cut from the rough where the fibre is thick.

Type 2. Tufted, mat-forming: *Ceratodon purpureus, Bryum* spp. Very troublesome types of moss, especially on acid soils. *Ceratodon purpureus* is common and is the so-called 'winter' moss since it appears to die out in spring when active growth starts, only to reappear in the autumn. Tends to become progressively worse unless checked.

Type 3. Upright: *Polytrichum* spp. Most common on dry mounds surrounding greens, bunker faces, etc. Not normally very troublesome, except occasionally under acid conditions.

Causes of moss invasion
Moss soon establishes on thin swards where there is a lack of competition from vigorous turf. Most mosskillers are palliative – mosses soon return unless the factors responsible for a thin sward are removed. A strong, healthy turf is the best answer to moss.

The following factors can favour the growth of moss:
1. A moist turf – poor drainage encourages the fern-like and tufted mosses.
2. A very dry soil, e.g. over drains, on mounds and ridges – inadequate watering or over-drainage – encourages the upright type.
3. Cutting too closely or poor surface levels causing scalping.
4. A soft, spongy sward with a thick fibre (thatch) layer.
5. Low fertility, e.g. deficiencies of plant foods, lime, etc., or insufficient soil depth.
6. Over-consolidation of the soil – compaction.
7. Shade.

Control of moss
As with all pest problems, the control of moss on areas of amenity turf can be achieved by understanding the conditions which favour the problem. If mosses are encouraged by poor surface drainage, management practices to alleviate this stress will aid reduction of the moss presence. Alternatively, *Polytrichum* mosses are an indicator of excessively dry conditions, e.g. mounds and banks, thus care to ensure adequate water availability should lessen the presence of these particular species. Moss is also favoured by excessively close mowing or scalping, low fertility, excessive acidity, shade, compacted soil and the presence of thatch. The correction of such factors can significantly reduce persistent moss problems.

Products currently available with approval for chemical control of moss both on amenity turf and on non-turf areas can be found listed in *BAA Handbook of Amenity Pesticides* (BAA Ltd) or *The UK Pesticide Guide* (CABI/BCPC).

ALGAE
Introduction
Bare patches in amenity turf are readily covered by an algal scum. Once grass is established, the algal growth usually disappears. The green algae known colloquially as "squidge" sometimes coats the turf surface with green slime. Although no direct damage is caused to the turf, if this occurs on sloping ground, dangerous playing conditions can be created.

Control of algae
Cultural control of algae in turf should always be attempted by improving grass growth and taking steps to dry the surface – spiking and sanding are often useful. If the problem persists, treatments as for control of moss should be implemented with the application of currently approved chemicals.

LICHENS
Introduction
A lichen is a mutually beneficial association between a fungus and an alga. Their presence in turf is encouraged by similar conditions which have been described for mosses where turf growth is weak. They are generally regarded as a relatively minor turfgrass pest.

Control of lichens
Cultural control can be achieved by encouraging more vigorous grass growth. Adjustment of fertiliser application may be all that is required to alleviate this problem but if chemical control proves to be necessary, methods described for moss control will be successful.

(IS No.3 Ref. 02/04)

CONTROL OF SQUIDGE
During the cold wet winter months when grass growth is slow, turf may be affected by a problem known as squidge. Squidge is caused by an extensive colonisation of the turf by algae (tiny one-celled plants with no true stem or leaves). Algae are common in turf but they generally do not occur in sufficient numbers to cause problems. The algae which cause squidge produce copious amounts of slime to protect themselves from desiccation during dry weather. Rainfall is absorbed by these algae to form a gelatinous mass which rises to the turf surface rendering it very slippery and consequently presents a hazard to greenkeepers and the golfer. Squidge (the term was first used by Scottish greenkeepers) gets is name from the fact that if affected areas are walked on the algal slime rises to the surface, sticks to foot-wear and becomes exceedingly squelchy – an apt description of the problem.

Recognition
Squidge is usually first seen as dark green or black gelatinous masses on the turf surface. Often these masses are discrete from each other measuring approximately 10 mm^2. In severe cases these gelatinous masses will coalesce and form large areas of affected turf. Examination using a high power microscope often reveals several different algae present (over six different types have been identified in research at STRI) together with moss protonema, fungi and various soil fauna in the slime. The turf is also very slimy to the touch and in severe cases handfuls of algae can be removed from a small area of turf.

Recommendations for Control
Long term control of squidge can only be achieved by rectifying the conditions

which favour its development. Squidge is often found on sloping turf where water is running across the surface rather than through the soil profile. Slitting or spiking and installing a drainage system where necessary will aid water movement downwards and consequently create a drier turf surface, to the detriment of the algae which cause squidge. Operating machinery on slopes which are affected is very dangerous and it is therefore best to do all slitting and spiking by hand until the problem has been alleviated. Top dressing with a coarse sand will also provide a free draining surface and thus inhibit squidge development. Shaded and sheltered areas are also prone to squidge development due to slow evaporation of surface water by the wind or sun. Shaded areas could be opened up by possibly removing bushes or trees etc. which cast excessive shade. Highly acidic turf is also prone to squidge due to the absence of predatory soil animals who normally feed on squidge, but cannot tolerate acidic conditions. Applications of lime can therefore be made to control squidge but this is recommended in only exceptional circumstances as lime can favour certain diseases such as fusarium patch or take-all patch.

When a squidge problem occurs the first control measure to be deployed is to remove excessive algae and slime from the turf using a brush or reverse side of a rake. Once the majority of the squidge has been removed, certain pesticides may be effective in suppressing recolonisation to allow time for the predisposing cultural conditions to be rectified. Research at STRI has evaluated 6 possible chemical treatments for squidge and of these, three proved effective – cresylic acid, dichlorophen and sulphate of iron. However, satisfactory results were only achieved with repeated applications – three applications at ten day intervals. Finally, it must be remembered that these chemicals are only useful in creating enough time to rectify the underlying problems and cannot be relied on solely to give effective control.

(CGC 1 : 90)

PLATE 9: Protective clothing (as specified on the product label) must be worn when using pesticides. (Courtesy SISIS Equipment (Macclesfield) Ltd.)

235

SECTION 12
GOLF COURSE CONSTRUCTION AND DRAINAGE

❖❖❖

New Golf Courses

C.D.M. Regulations

Golf Course Pathways

USGA Greens

Drains & Drainage

Seeding & Turfing

Sands for Construction

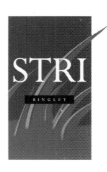

*The Care of
the Golf Course*

SOME PROBLEMS ASSOCIATED WITH NEW GOLF COURSES

The ultimate aim when constructing a golf course is to provide:- satisfactory surfaces on greens, tees and fairways; a course which can be easily managed; pleasing aesthetic qualities as well as strong strategic features. Problems associated with a deficiency in any of these factors are to be found in the many disciplines associated with the building of the course.

Architecture

The tee surfaces need not exceed 300 mm above original surface unless the architecture of the hole demands. "Helicopter landing pads" are not only obtrusive but add unnecessarily to the maintenance burden. Equally, batters stronger than say 1:3 impose an unnecessary burden on the mowing regime, making it difficult to mow with ride-on triple machines and necessitating increased use of time-consuming hover mowers.

Often little thought has been given to the area of teeing ground in these days of high intensity of play. On a members' course you are looking for areas of the following minimum order:-

$$
\begin{array}{lll}
\text{Par 3} & - & 500\,\text{m}^2 \\
\text{Par 4/5} & - & 400\,\text{m}^2 \\
\text{Ladies} & - & 100\,\text{m}^2
\end{array}
$$

Areas of lesser dimension give the greenkeeping staff real difficulty in their endeavour to maintain level stances.

Additionally on a pay as you play course where wear is likely to be of an even greater intensity, two separate teeing grounds at each hole should be a definite aim. Not only does this assist maintenance of satisfactory overall grass covers and level stances on the surfaces, but adds to variation when playing the holes and distributes wear over a larger area of the fairways.

Narrow landing areas lead to greater intensity of wear over a confined area, thus scuffing and divot marking restricts the greenkeeper's ability to offer good lies in the more important parts of the fairway.

At the green end of the hole narrow approaches constrict traffic, therefore increased compaction and subsequent thinning out of the swards in these very important areas is almost a certainty.

Poor position of sand bunkers or grass mounds and hollows immediately adjoining the green can confine traffic to restricted areas, thus destroying what could be very good lies on turf surfaces immediately adjoining the green.

Lack of thought when considering tee positions for the following hole leading to only one walk-off route or a restricted route from the previous green adds to compaction, not only along the route to the next tees but within that part of the putting surface upon which the players' funnel in order to leave the green. It is very difficult, if not impossible, for the greenkeeping staff in such a situation as this to offer uniformity within the putting surface of the green.

Engineering – greens

Subsoil formations should be free from water collecting hollows and the extreme margins of the putting surfaces should be swept up as required to marry in with the toe of any adjoining surround mounds - this peripheral area extending in width to say 2-4 m is very important. An acute change in level within it creates problems for the greenkeeping staff when mowing around the perimeter of the putting surface or collar and toe of an adjoining surround mound. Only a ragged finish to mowing is achievable. This is not only detrimental to appearance but prevents the offering of good lies.

On approaches, surrounds and walk-offs when earthworks are completed adequate subsoil cultivation, particularly in heavy clay soils, should be allowed for to reduce the possibility of surface wetness arising in the future. This item of work should be completed both before and after any pipework has been introduced, as it assists in moving water through the subsoil to the pipework.

It is useful to introduce irrigation pipework at this early stage of the greens' construction with upstands in the intended position for pop-up heads. Any disruption to surface levels between the boxes and formations is corrected during the course of completing the next stages of the works. Introduction of irrigation pipework, following final preparation of trimmed soil surfaces or establishment of a grass cover, can have a detrimental effect on the surfaces from the point of view of mowing and play. A golfer quite reasonably expects a good lie if his ball is a mere 2-3 m off the edge of the putting surface.

Adequate falls are necessary on the trenches for all drainage works which should lead off to positive outlets. Within the putting surfaces perforated pipes to the appropriate BS number should be supplied and laid with purpose made connections between laterals and mains. Following laying of pipes, trenches should be backfilled with an approved 3-6 mm hard aggregate. A well-designed and adequately introduced pipework system is an essential prerequisite to draining water away from the future putting surfaces, whether or not drainage layers are to be introduced.

Should there be lack of stability in the subsoil formation, surface geotextile membrane should be supplied and laid, cutting it to allow aggregate to be placed in drain trenches and over the pipes to connect directly with the aggregate of the drainage layer to be introduced as the next stage of the works. Should introduction of the geotexile membrane be omitted where there is lack of stability in the formation there will be a loss of aggregate into the soft subsoil, thus reducing the water storing capacity of the aggregate. Additionally, there might be differential settlement of the aggregate leading to difficulties in maintaining satisfactorily levels within the putting surfaces.

The use of a selected fill drainage layer is the norm nowadays. A one-stage layer of suitable 2-6 mm aggregate can be used, but preferably a two-stage layer might be considered of 6-10 mm aggregate topped by a blinding layer of 1-4 mm coarse sand or fine gravel. The blinding layer should consist of a minimum 50 mm firmed depth. The purpose of this blinding layer is to prevent the migration of fine silt and clay particles which would ultimately block up the surface of the drainage layer and very soon slow down and eventually stop its drainage capability. The intermediate layer or blinding layer has to be carefully selected with regard to grade, so that it will be supported by the drainage layer and yet will act as a barrier between the growing medium and the drainage layer. Drainage problems which the STRI are faced with today are very often found to be as a direct result of wrongful selection of the blinding layer and gravel, or indeed the complete absence of a blinding layer.

High proportions of sand are used in modern day rooting mediums. The sand used should be lime-free, predominantly single-sized within the medium to medium-coarse range (0.25 to 1.0 mm diameter). Failure to acknowledge the need for correct choice of sand can lead to very serious drainage problems indeed, *viz* use of a sand with wide particle distribution leads to fines migrating through interstices between the larger particles, thus impeding speedy movement of water through the medium. Whilst an all-sand rooting medium has been tried in the past, the more normal procedure nowadays is to introduce a small percentage of suitable topsoil or peat into the sand, principally to offer a rooting medium within which the environment to develop a grass sward is less keen. Such an approved mixture has buffering action which eases the greenkeeping staff's task to offer uniform putting surfaces through 12 months of the year. USGA-type rootzone mixes are now the most popular.

The quality of mixing the two ingredients is of high importance. Inadequate mixing creates lack of homogeneousness and this in turn gives differential movement of water off the surface to the underlying drainage layer. Wetness and lack of uniformity in the putting surfaces can ensue.

Engineering – tees

Subsoil formations must be well tracked in with a 360° machine or tracked shovel to reduce risk of settlement in the future. If this is not seen to be done then in the future added expenditure will be necessary for labour and supply of top dressing to improve surface levels, such that level stances are offered - at worst the tee may have to be lifted and relaid. A minimum fall of 1:100 is required on the formation to facilitate surface water run-off in the future.

Unless it is extremely poor, indigenous topsoil can be placed to provide the minimum 150 mm firmed depth rooting medium required. To avoid unnecessary damage to the natural drainage qualities of the indigenous topsoil, the topsoil must be handled at all times under dry conditions, *viz* stripping, transport, stacking, replacement only in the dry.

Engineering – through the greens

On roughs, semi roughs and fairways where major grading work is required to obtain the necessary sight lines, natural drainage properties of the soils (both top and subsoil) are inevitably reduced. To avoid gross deficiency in drainage quality on completion of works:–

[a] Work only when ground conditions are fit and cease activities in periods of adverse weather conditions.

[b] Allow for subsoil cultivation. If pipework is required to facilitate movement of water off the surfaces in the future, carry out subsoil cultivation before and after introduction of the pipework – this facilitates movement of water through the subsoil to the pipes.

Cultivations during the course of seed bed preparation should be carried out only when ground conditions are suitable, to prevent further reduction in drainage capability of the topsoil and to provide the fine seed beds required for satisfactory establishment of a bent/fescue seeds mixture.

On bunkers sand splash on to collars and periphery of putting surfaces can give problems should bunkers be built to close to the greens. Drainage of bunkering is facilitated given adequate falls on the bunker floors and introduction of an emptying pipe drain leading off to a positive outfall. Movement of stones working up out of a stony subsoil through the sand can be prevented by introduction of geotextile membranes.

Supervision

Adequate on-site supervision is a very important discipline to be imposed upon the works. Monitoring of materials as they are delivered to site, each individual load being examined as it arrives, together with examination of surfaces immediately they are offered by the contractor can be readily handled under such a regime. Additionally, minor adjustment to formations can be instructed when the machines are still in position.

Maintenance

On older constructions long-term damage has occurred from over-watering with irrigation systems. Sandy constructions which are now the norm require even greater care in the approach to application of water. The limited water-holding capacity of an adequate sand means that drought effects can occur very quickly and dramatically unless a careful watch is exercised. Too much water can lead to rapid leaching and consequent loss of colour and vigour and the ingress of the weed *Poa annua* (annual meadow-grass).

The benefits of USGA-type constructions are gradually being appreciated by the golfing fraternity, particularly those wishing to play on inland courses during wet winters, but much is still to be learned about the general management and care of these new profiles. Recent research carried out at the STRI suggests that the routine fertiliser regime will require changing radically with greater emphasis on the use of potash fertiliser particularly on very sandy constructions. Also there will be an increasing demand for "slow release" nitrogen fertilisers, e.g. IBDU or coated fertiliser, to sustain grass vigour during the growing period as the old favourite sulphate of ammonia, which is contained in many available compounds, is too rapidly used up and the lack of sufficient humus in the soil means an inadequate nitrogen reserve for any long-term effects. This is an explanation for the general poor colour of many new greens.

Disease can be a serious problem on newly constructed sandy golf greens. Take-all patch caused by *Gaeumannomyces graminis* can be very damaging to bentgrass especially during the first few years after establishment. This is particularly unfortunate because this disease is difficult to control with fungicide.

(DDW : B.187)

CHECK IT OVER : QUALITY CONTROL FOR SUCCESSFUL CONSTRUCTION

Thorough planning is the first essential in construction. Unfortunately there are many failed projects due to the lack of observance of this basic principle.

Construction must satisfy the demands of the user as well as being sustainable over time. For example a golf green constructed to a modern specification may be inappropriate amongst 17 clay-based traditional greens. Consequently the requirements for management will be at variance with established practices in order to compensate for the very free-draining nature of the rootzone and the golfers will have to adapt their game to the different playing qualities of the new green.

Once the criteria for construction have been established, sound design underpins all phases of the work. Documentation must provide clear direction and leave no room for misinterpretation. Accurate drawings should convey key information which is invaluable during construction by showing existing and finished levels, position of drainage, etc. Inclusion of detailed conditions of contract defines the obligations on the contractor and provides further safeguards for both the client and contractor. This is particularly important when working in built-up areas or where there is potential conflict with the public. Furthermore the site must be protected and treated with respect. Therefore haulage routes and site access must be clearly defined before work commences.

Problems can arise where underground services (gas, electricity, water) cross the site and these must also be resolved at this stage.

With the necessary documentation completed, selected contractors can be approached to tender for the works. This short-list will include qualified contractors well-versed in the principles and practices of golf course construction. The competitiveness of the price submitted is the overriding factor in selection, but track record and first hand experience of quality of previous workmanship do have an influence, notably if quotations are very close.

Timing of works is critical, particularly in high rainfall areas and intractable soil conditions. If a delay is enforced or an unrealistic timetable set the risk of down time due to deteriorating weather and ground conditions will be increased as the project extends into the autumn or possibly winter months.

If the project is to be completed "in-house" this needs to be co-ordinated with the demands of routine management so that standards are not sacrificed due to an over stretched work force.

A schedule of works can be of significant help as phases of the project can be set against a time scale. With this information materials can be delivered to site when needed and additional manpower or machinery made available at key stages to maximise efficiency and prevent hold-ups. Perhaps bulk materials such as rootzone and drainage aggregate can be transported to the working area over the summer months, thereby minimising damage along haulage routes.

False economy in material selection or improper specification are common causes of failure in construction. The maxim of "you get what you pay for" often holds true and substandard materials can ruin an otherwise sound construction project.

Materials need to be properly specified in the first instant. Terminology such as a 70:30 mix is still common place but this could be 70% clay and 30% sand!

We need to be more rigorous in our definitions, with mechanical analysis providing an accurate determination of the suitability of the material, together with other performance parameters as deemed necessary.

Stone carpets composed of limestone or soft sandstone may break down over time. The intermediate blinding layer may be omitted (leading to downward migration of finer particles which block the drainage spaces in larger aggregate) or worse still a geotextile membrane may be inserted as a substitute for the blinding layer!

Small variations in particle size distribution can have a major influence therefore visual analysis alone is totally insufficient. Bulk deliveries to site may also exhibit marginal but important differences. Retention of the original approved sample provides the standard for the subsequent testing and comparison of representative samples from bulk deliveries. There may be a slight lag-time involved in laboratory analysis but this is outweighed by the overriding requirement for consistency of supply.

These considerations should also apply to turf selection, with immediate rejection of delivered turf if it does not match the original sample in terms of grass composition and quality, depth of fibre or soil substrate.

On-site supervision is another essential ingredient for construction projects, notably when a contractor is engaged.

There is no substitute for a professional "engineer" monitoring progress at **regular** intervals and ensuring work proceeds in strict accordance with the specification. Minor adjustments or contingency plans may have to be invoked as work proceeds, therefore there is no substitute for close on-site supervision.

Machinery and equipment employed during construction must be both efficient and reliable. If work is to be sub-contracted then the calibre of operator and machinery must be verified beforehand.

In conclusion, it would be unwise to assume that a reputable name in construction is sufficient guarantee. Even if the construction work is to be completed in-house there are several guiding principles to be observed which are summarised in the following checklist.

- Compilation of detailed documentation.
- Thorough on site supervision throughout construction.
- Selection of good quality materials.
- Consistency of material supply.
- Appropriate timing of works.
- Use of reliable and efficient machinery/equipment.

(JWT : B.190)

HEALTH & SAFETY : CDM IMPOSE NEW OBLIGATIONS

In response to the EC directive relating to temporary and mobile construction sites, the Construction, Design and Management (CDM) Regulations were brought into force on 31st March 1996. These Regulations form an addition to the existing Health and Safety Legislation.

These new rules place obligations and duties on all those involved in design and construction work and breach of the legislation is a criminal offence.

The wording of the Regulations is such that virtually all construction and drainage work is covered by the legislation, except for projects involving four or fewer workers and lasting less than thirty working days or that where the Local Authority is the enforcing authority.

The obligations on designers apply to any design work. The creation of the Planning Supervisor introduces a new element into project work. Clients also have their own specific responsibilities.

Local Authorities, government departments, private industry, consultants, contractors, the self-employed and private individuals are all affected if they are involved in the commissioning, construction and design of sports turf projects.

In brief, the requirements are as follows:

The Client

i.   Must select and appoint a competent Planning Supervisor, Principal Contractor and, likewise, ensure that Designers and other Contractors are also competent and will allocate adequate resources to the project.

ii.   Provide the Planning Supervisor with relevant Health and Safety information.

iii.   Ensure that the project does not begin until the Principal Contractor has prepared an adequate Health and Safety Plan.

iv.   Ensure that the Health and Safety File is available for inspection after completion of the project.

The Planning Supervisor

The Planning Supervisor's task is to co-ordinate Health and Safety, ensuring that

i.   Designers comply with their duties and co-operate with each other on Health and Safety matters.

ii.   A Pre-Tender Health and Safety Plan is produced.

iii.   If required, advice is given on the competence of Designers and/or Contractors.

iv.   If notifiable, the Health and Safety Executive is notified of the project.

v.   The completed Health and Safety File is delivered to the Client on completion of the project.

The Designers

i.   Must make the Client aware of their duties.

ii. In carrying out design work, must take into account hazards and risks involved in construction and subsequent maintenance. Where possible, must avoid risks or reduce the risk at source if avoidance is not possible. When risks cannot be avoided or reduced, must consider measures which will protect all workers.

iii. Ensure that the design includes adequate information on Health and Safety and pass this on to the Planning Supervisor.

iv. Must co-operate with the Planning Supervisor and other Designers.

The Principal Contractor

The Principal Contractor has substantial duties which include:

i. Developing the Health and Safety Plan.

ii. Ensuring that other Contractors are competent, adequately resourced and co-operative.

iii. Obtaining information regarding risk assessment and detail of how High Risk work is to be carried out. Disseminating the information about risks to other Contractors.

iv. Ensuring that workers are trained in Health and Safety matters.

v. Enforcement of site rules.

vi. Monitoring Health and Safety matters.

vii. Ensuring workers are informed and consulted.

viii. Site security.

ix. Passing information on to the Planning Supervisor for inclusion in the Health and Safety File.

Other Contractors

Other Contractors and the self-employed have duties regarding the management of Health and Safety matters during construction work.

More comprehensive details of the Regulations can be found in The Approved Code of Practice: *Managing for Health and Safety* and *A Guide to Managing Health and Safety in Construction*, both published by the Health and Safety Executive.

Documentation

No-one would challenge the need to raise awareness regarding the Health and Safety of those carrying out construction work or who are affected by works or who subsequently have to maintain such constructions. It is quite clear, however, from the documentation currently being produced that there is no clear general opinion as to what constitutes a hazard when carrying out sports turf construction work.

The Health and Safety Executive have published a number of documents relating to the CDM Regulations. Some of the important points which apply to sports turf construction projects include:

> "Regulations should be adapted to the scale and complexity of the projects. Projects involving minimal High Risk work will call for simple Health and Safety planning and few, if any, specialist skills" .... "those involving High Risk will call for correspondingly more detailed assessment and specialist skills".
>
> "The detail and size of the Health and Safety Plan depends on the nature and extent of the project" .... "The Health and safety Plan needs to be relevant to the circumstances of the project". (Approved Code of Practice).

Many sports turf construction projects will involve little in the way of High Risk works.

The inclusion of large quantities of standard material in the Health and Safety Plan which are not relevant to the project will not serve the purpose of "making plain Health and Safety issues specific to the project" and would indicate that the Regulations are not being complied with.

The intent of the legislation is to improve the Health and Safety record of the construction industry. Much of the documentation currently produced in response to CDM will not achieve this.

The key points in the production of any documentation, and certainly that relating to Health and Safety, are that it should be:-

    (a)   Clear.
    (b)   Concise.
    (c)   Relevant.

If the documents are not clear they will not be understood, if not concise they will not be read and if not relevant will be held in contempt.

These points are nowhere more important that in the preparation of the Pre-Tender Health and Safety Plan. Contractors, particularly at this early stage, should not be expected to trawl through quantities of irrelevant material extracting the pieces of information which they need to know.

If there is a place for waffle, it is not in Health and Safety documentation – this is far too important.

(STP : B.191)

DRAINAGE PROBLEMS ON THE GOLF COURSE

Introduction

Water, wet feet and unnecessary wear result from poor drainage on the golf course and it also creates a hindrance to play and complicates maintenance works. Satisfactory drainage is, therefore, essential on a golf course if the most pleasing and best possible conditions for play are to be provided for the maximum period throughout the year. In golf course design and construction, measures are usually taken to ensure adequate and efficient drainage and it is often the clubs with old-established parkland courses on inland sites which suffer most from drainage faults. In many of these cases the greens were not drained intensively enough to provide the conditions needed for the high levels of golf played today. Often, drainage which does exist is of an old agricultural type which becomes silted up or lacks the intensity and requirements for the drainage of a modern golf course. One often finds time and money being spent on trying to modernise such systems and in the majority of cases it is very questionable as to whether the improvements obtained justify the effort and expense. Where a real drainage problem occurs it is generally wise to ignore what exists and study the situation anew, bearing in mind the exacting requirements of today's golf courses and modern techniques.

Fairway Drainage

Introduction of pipe drainage into the whole of the fairway area on a golf course is rarely necessary and more often than not problems are confined to local regions. These may be parts which are relatively flat and where surface water run-off provides little aid to drainage, they may be low-lying regions of generally undulating land or parts where changes in levels on an area with generally sloping ground checks subsoil water flow and/or surface water run-off. The drainage requirements of such parts should be given individual study as the pattern of pipe drains needed and their intensity will be dependent on the contours of each region and its soil type.

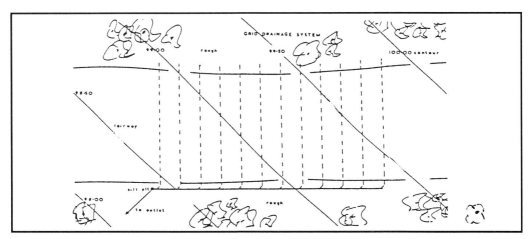

FIGURE 17: On fairways a grid system of drains can be used where the fall is diagonally across the line of play.

Generally on fairway areas a grid system of drains is most commonly used, for example, on an area where the maximum fall is diagonally across the line of play the lateral drains would run more or less straight across the fairway to feed a main drain running parallel to its lower side (see Fig. 17). On the other hand, where the contours form, for example, a shallow, fairly wide valley running across the fairway a herringbone system might be considered (see Fig. 18). In this case the main drain would run across the fairway through the lowest levels of the valley and lateral drains would feed this at an angle of 45-60° from both sides. No hard and fast rules can be made on the intensity of the lateral drains but they could be spaced as wide as 10 metres on lighter, naturally free-draining land but as close as 4-5 metres on heavier clay soil with slow natural drainage.

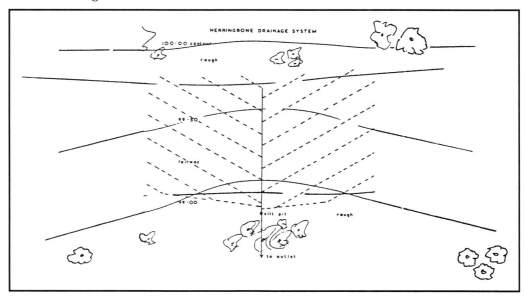

FIGURE 18: On fairways where the contours form a fairly wide valley running across the fairway, a herringbone system of drainage can be used.

As an alternative to pipe drainage of wet areas, consideration could be given to mole draining as this can be beneficial, though the operation would have to be repeated on occasions. The work could not be effectively done in very stony subsoils and it is most efficient where the clay content is 35% or more. Mole drains prove most beneficial when their spacing is no more than $4^{1}/_{2}$ times their depth which is usually between 460 and 610 mm. Pipe main drains laid a little below the depth of the mole drains should be provided, their trenches being backfilled with small gravel or hard broken stone except at points where they join open outlets, e.g. ditches.

On a fairway area where slow surface water drainage causes problems due to the heavy nature of the topsoil, or the fact that it is a catchment area and in spite of satisfactory under-drainage, a suitable pattern of slit drains supplementing the pipe drainage would give much improved conditions. Slit drains 50 mm wide cut at intervals of 610 mm to 1.2 metres according to site conditions and to a depth which would allow their backfilling to directly link up with the backfilling over the pipe drains would allow surface water to quickly bypass the slow-draining soils. The narrow trenches would be excavated with a small trenching machine and they are usually cut across the fall of the land. Backfilling is done with suitable small gravel or hard broken stone topped off with suitable lime-free sand (or completely with lime-free sand alone) right up to ground level. This relatively new drainage technique can be done by contract or by the green staff using suitable plant hire equipment.

Drain Laying

Pipe drainage systems should be formed with clayware field drain pipes (BS 1196:1971) or now much more commonly with perforated plastic drain pipes (BS 4962:1989) of appropriate sizes and all connections should be formed with purpose made junction pipes. Sealed pipes should be used in the vicinity of trees. The drains should be laid at a minimum depth of 610 mm to invert below ground level and at even falls of no less than 1 in 200, though 1 in 300 could be accepted as an absolute minimum where circumstances demand. Lateral drains should run at an angle across the maximum fall on the land and wherever possible systems should be designed to utilise existing falls on the land so that the drains can be laid at a constant depth. Where this can be done, introduction of the drainage system is simplified, excavation is kept to the minimum as is the cost of backfilling materials, but the essential requirements, with regard to depths and falls, must be satisfied. Where this cannot be done, the requirements must be obtained by laying the drains to increasing depth to obtain the falls advised.

Drain trenches should be some 50 mm wider than the diameter of the pipes (unnecessary width involves increased excavation and backfilling) and after the laying of the pipes, backfilling should immediately follow. Trenches of all drains which are expected to collect and carry water should be filled with suitable small gravel (8–10 mm diameter) or hard broken stone.

All drainage systems should have positive outlets otherwise they will not function correctly. Outlets can be ditches, streams and rivers or existing surface water drains might be used if they have adequate capacity. The water levels at the outlets, particularly in the winter, in relation to the depths of the drains is of consequence as an unimpeded water flow is important. Soakaways are of limited value unless they can be situated in an area where the subsoil has very good naturally free draining qualities.

CROSS SECTION THROUGH
TYPICAL PIPE DRAIN

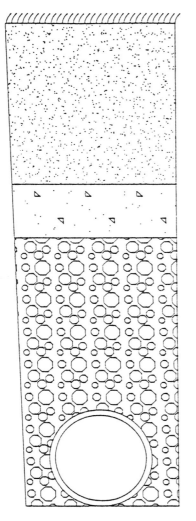

FINAL TRENCH BACKFILL
100–150mm TOPSOIL, SAND/SOIL
MIX OR SAND DEPENDING ON
SITUATION

50mm COARSE SAND/GRIT
BLINDING LAYER

6–10mm GRADE
PERMEABLE BACKFILL

PERFORATED PLASTIC
DRAIN PIPE

FIGURE 19: Cross-section of pipe drain suitable for drainage of fairways, etc.

(CGC 1 : 67)

FAIRWAY DRAINAGE

The attention paid to fairway drainage on new courses is often minimal, yet greens and tees are constructed so as to be playable even after prolonged heavy rain.

It is certainly true that the greens and tees do receive the most concentrated wear and the surfaces must be to the highest standard. It is, however, of little use if the areas in between can only be negotiated wearing wellington boots or in an amphibious vehicle.

In dry years, for example 1989–1991, with soils retaining moisture deficits until January after summer droughts and limited winter rainfall, fairway drainage was not an issue for the majority of courses. The arrival of wetter conditions during the late summer and autumn of 1993 focused attention on this aspect of the performance of the golf course.

It is true that the performance requirements for fairway drainage are far less precise than for virtually any other turf surface played on in the winter months. The areas involved are, however, large and within the course or even within fairway areas there can be substantial variations, both in topography and soil type. Certain areas are more important than others, for example landing zones. The design on a cost-effective drainage system is therefore quite a complicated business.

On an existing course, problem areas are well known through past experience and examination of the soils and swards reveals the tell-tale signs of poor drainage.

For a new course the problem is greater. How will the fairway drain when it comes into use? If major grading has not taken place the soil and pasture can give clues, as can previous users of the land. If the area has been under cultivation, however, what will the drainage characteristics of the land be when grassed and subject to wear? If major earthworks have been undertaken, soil structure will have been damaged to a greater or lesser extent. In such situations the land may take some time to settle down. In the short-term drainage may be quite poor. Given a few years for the soil structure to return, drainage might be adequate for the purpose without major additional drainage work. Does the designer take the risk that conditions will not be too wet in the first few years and save the client expenditure, or does he introduce an expensive system which is only required in the short-term? Choose the first option and the course may have to close within the first month of opening following a particularly wet spell of weather.

From the designer's point of view the poorest drained sites are the simplest to produce a drain layout for. If the soils on site are destructured clays and the annual rainfall over 1.25 m drainage is going to be a problem, intensive pipe drainage from boundary to boundary is the order of the day.

Comparatively sandy soils in wetter parts of the country or clay soils in the drier parts require greater judgement, thought and if truth be told, a certain amount of luck.

Existing drainage systems

On land which has been drained on one or more occasions in the past, the old drainage pipework can be as much of a hindrance as a help. This is particularly so where no layout drawings exist. Where the old system of drains is shallower than the new system, the old pipe should be connected directly into the new. If the drain is missed or carries a greater flow than the new system can cope with, water can discharge to the surface causing deterioration.

If the old drains are deeper than the new, water can easily discharge from the new system into the old. If the old system cannot cope with the increased flow, through blockage or just lack of capacity, drainage problems can arise at one or more points along the system.

In many cases it would be desirable to completely destroy the old drains by ripping or subsoiling. On most existing fairways this is not a practical option. Every effort should be made to locate the old drains to ensure that where they are connected to the new system, there is adequate carrying capacity. Where possible, old drains should be checked, cleaned out and incorporated into the new design flow. Old mains should only be used to pick up water from new laterals if their condition is not at all suspect.

Particular care should be taken on steeply-contoured ground or land surrounded by strong slopes. In this situation even small diameter pipes can build up a considerable head of pressure.

Iron oxides – red ochre

On certain acid soils iron compounds in the soil can be leached into the drainage system. On exposure to air in the permeable backfill or within the pipe the iron compounds come out of solution and form a red sludgy deposit which in severe cases can rapidly block drains.

In most situations drains can continue to function if occasionally rodded or jetted. Extreme conditions in this country are fairly few and far between, these limited to acid peaty soils or reclaimed land.

Filter wrapped pipe should not be used in this situation, as ochre can be flushed out of an ordinary pipe fairly readily, unless the sludge has dried out. Once a filter blocks, which only requires a small amount of ochre, there are no means of unblocking it. Filter units of pine bark within the drainage system have been shown to have some promise.

An initial assessment as to whether drainage is justified should be taken in severe cases. Open ditches encourage the iron to come out of solution where the sludge can be removed; the provision of numerous access points to drains with simple layouts and if possible, numerous outlets will help in allowing the drains to continue to function.

Settlement

If porous backfill over drain runs is not adequately firmed, some settlement can occur leaving a slight depression. It is not usual for settlement so caused to be very marked, because of the nature of the selected fill, i.e. comparatively uniform, clean aggregate. Where topsoil or sand is replaced along the tops of drains there can, if materials are not carefully selected, be some migration of particles into the underlying stone backfill.

The main cause of a marked subsidence along drain lines is not associated with either of these factors. When drains are introduced into soil with even a moderate clay content, problems have been encountered, particularly with the extreme drought experience in the 1995 summer. The problem is quite simply that in dry conditions clay soils shrink. The drains are lines of weakness and the soil pulls back from the edge of it, causing the trench to widen and the backfill to drop. In extreme conditions the shrinkage can continue and cracks open up below the pipe, allowing the pipe to move out of alignment. Observation would indicate that recently-introduced drains are often the most vulnerable as the weakness along the drain line is most marked. Drains cut into an existing turf are more likely to settle than drains introduced during cultivation work. This is directly related to the relative continuity of the surface. When the turf is well-established and there are no marked lines of weakness, shrinkage leads to minor cracking more or less evenly distributed over the surface. Where there are lines of weakness, i.e. drain lines, the shrinkage is concentrated along slit lines.

In extreme conditions experienced recently, the drying and shrinkage of clay soils has been so severe that even drains introduced many years ago have been subject to settlement. In some cases where the surface has held, the shrinkage of the subsoil has still resulted in the collapse of the underlying aggregate, but leaving the surface apparently unaffected. The voids left have, however, not been filled even after the soil wets up again and the surface has subsequently collapsed after the passage of vehicles.

Counter-measures

It is best if drainage work on heavy clay soils is carried out when the soils are fairly dry and it is important to get a vigorous sward established over the drains as soon as possible. It is, however, difficult to counter problems which are due to exceptional weather conditions.

Organic soils

Soils which are wholly organic are invariably formed in wet conditions brought about by high rainfall or flooding and poor drainage.

Saturated peats are unstable and difficult to work on. Preliminary work involving the excavation of open ditches may produce a surface which can be worked on, but only with track-laying machinery. Following drainage, soils will shrink causing levels and gradients to be affected. The soil is still by nature water-retentive and only following intensive drainage work can many surfaces be made reasonably dry for winter play. The presence of iron ochre can be an additional complication. Peaty soils overlying a mineral subsoil can be easier to deal with. As with all soils, if peat is worked on in wet conditions, it will only get worse.

Flood plains and low-lying sites

Sports facilities of all kinds are often sited on flood plains, simply because they are unusable for anything else. The degree of the problem depends on the frequency with which the land is likely to be flooded, although even when not actually under water, drainage outfalls may be restricted in their efficiency as water levels rise.

There are often problems in achieving a satisfactory outfall and gradients along drain lines can be marginal. The combination of limited gradients and periodic flooding is likely to lead to problems of drains silting up.

Unless a pumped drainage system is introduced, irrespective of the intensity of the drainage system installed, the playing surface is likely to suffer when general water levels are at or close to the surface.

The above represent just some of the factors which may need to be considered when dealing with fairway drainage.

(STP : B.184)

CONSTRUCTION OF CATCHWATER/ CUT-OFF DRAIN

The purpose of a catchwater drain is to intercept any flow of water that might enter an area over the surface or along water-bearing strata. Such a drain is often useful for intercepting water around the perimeter of a golf green or tee. Catchwater drains are usually located at the toe of banks or slopes, i.e.

For full effect, catchwater drain trenches should be filled with permeable material usually up to within 25 mm of ground level. The requirements of the sport, however, may dictate that a turf cover is maintained above the drain so that play is not interfered with, e.g. around golf greens.

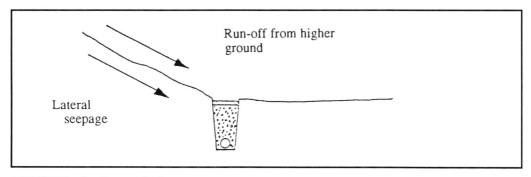

FIGURE 20: Catchwater drain.

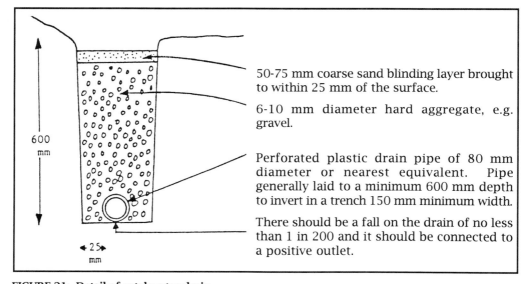

600
mm

◄ 25 ►
mm

50-75 mm coarse sand blinding layer brought to within 25 mm of the surface.

6-10 mm diameter hard aggregate, e.g. gravel.

Perforated plastic drain pipe of 80 mm diameter or nearest equivalent. Pipe generally laid to a minimum 600 mm depth to invert in a trench 150 mm minimum width.

There should be a fall on the drain of no less than 1 in 200 and it should be connected to a positive outlet.

FIGURE 21: Detail of catchwater drain.

N.B. If a turf cover is required over the drain line, then the turves should be laid slightly dished to hold water.

(IS No.11 Ref. 02/04)

PATHS: THEIR APPLICATION AND INSTALLATION

Traffic routes within golf courses such as approaches to greens, the walk across the surround to the next tee, and from tee to fairway are often narrow, controlled by artificial features such as bunkers and mounds, and it is in these areas that the turf cover is readily destroyed by constant traffic. Often, the natural contours of the site have been utilised in a very clever way by the architect who designed the course to provide interest and a real test of players' abilities. It is perhaps unfortunate that in the days when the majority of our older courses were designed and built, no architect, however brilliant, could have foreseen the tremendous upsurge in the popularity of the game that has taken place over the past 20 years and the enormous pressure this has placed on these areas of our courses, where, of necessity, traffic is channelled.

Heaven forbid, however, that British architects should venture down the road being followed by so many American architects who have taken on the role of God and literally move mountains of earth to create forced, artificial features to greens, "spectator mounds", and provide for the ubiquitous tarmac roadways for golf buggies. All this, with no regard whatsoever for the damage to soil structure and drainage, the maintenance of which is paramount in our climate and with our soils if a satisfactory quality of turf and year-round playability are to be provided.

The traditional British golf course Architect's approach was and is to make the very best of the site contours and to fit the design and layout into whatever nature has provided. It has served well, in many cases brilliantly, for a century or more, and you will find many a Scottish green design slavishly copied in the totally alien environment of America or Japan where it looks completely out of place.

As an example, Royal Troon golf course has been designed to accommodate minimum wear patterns. Here, the 2nd to the 5th holes out exemplify what should become an integral part of modern golf course design, and indeed should be applied wherever the strategy will fit in on older courses. This course design deals with not only golfing aspects either, although the stratagem does offer a great variety of choice in the way these holes are played. At each of them there are two separate sets of tees – the regular summer tees set to the right nearer the sea, whilst on the opposite side of the green and thus well away from the summer wear patterns there is an alternative set of tees. Most of these are used mainly in the winter period but they can, in emergency, be pressed into summer use. Indeed, this concept is so useful, especially on a busy course such as Royal Troon, that successive Green Committees with the ready forbearance and, indeed, support of members have extended the provision of alternative tees and access routes at as many holes as practicable. The idea is simple, provides much needed extra teeing space, alters traffic patterns both near greens and on carries which are pretty fragile on links courses, quite often varies the landing zone on fairways, and, where there is space in siting these alternative tees, may not even shorten the course. Where there is the space available, this approach is recommended.

One will have gathered by now that paths on the golf course should be resorted to when all else has failed and, to some extent, one should regard their introduction as a failure.

Maintaining Grass

Before even considering the provision of paths which, no matter how well-built or disguised always look out of place on the golf course proper and far too often intrude into areas which come into play, we must reassess maintenance practices.

If turf is to be tough and hard-wearing it must be mature, well-established in free-draining soil and contain the right grass species. On the majority of our golf courses the finer browntop bents and, in the right situations, fescue grasses fill the bill. To survive however, even these hardy grasses need good soil aeration to encourage a vigorous root system and an occasional rest from the battering of traffic to allow recuperation and for any necessary repairs to establish. We are, after all, dealing with living plant material.

Let us be quite clear that it is constant foot and trolley traffic over the same narrow routes used by golfers that compacts and seals the top, reduces air content in the soil, affects drainage and physically wears away the leaves and mat of plant tissue. The advent of golf trolleys has made the situation far worse since their use inevitably dictates certain routes, usually the shortest and easiest between two points. It is the constant hammering that the same tracks receive summer and winter which results in deterioration – wide or narrow wheels make little difference, although the heavier battery-powered units with a skidding drive-wheel on wet ground add to the problems.

The first and essential operation must be to ensure that adequate aeration is carried out and as early as possible in September since we want better root action, and encouraging moisture to penetrate hard paths is just as important as letting in air and relieving soil compaction. Suit the tool to the circumstances, be it hollow tine coring, deep or shallow slits, or in compacted conditions, which so very often apply, the favourite is the Verti-Drain or a tool for air injection.

Having achieved a basis of more open soil, keep up regular but more shallow slit tine aeration as ground and weather conditions permit through the autumn and winter. Move traffic off the worn places and carry out such repairs as are necessary by turfing wherever this is practical. For preference, use a tough, mature turf off the course rather than softer, immature, bought-in material – seeding is rarely satisfactory.

Where aeration has been tackled properly in autumn, a little mild feeding may help in the spring or late summer. Above all, limit maintenance traffic in these places. Effective winter aeration is quickly nullified by thumping around surrounds with heavy tractors or gang mowers twice a week. Equally, there is no excuse for thoughtless greenkeeping staff regularly tracking these routes with a Cushman or Hydromain when carrying out routine tasks such as hole changing, tee repair, etc.

Traffic Direction

One absolutely clear thing is that golfers carrying clubs and especially when hauling trolleys will have to be given far stronger direction as to the routes that they can use, particularly between October and April. In the non-growing period constant traffic over the same ground can lead to bare soil or, at best, a broken, disturbed surface, and that can occur whether the winter is hard or open since the briefest interlude of improved weather nowadays means a positive deluge of golfers on the course.

The best approach is undoubtedly that adopted by some tough-minded Committees who impose a complete ban on trolleys for a set period of the worst weather and ground conditions each winter.

Actual routing of traffic can take many forms, from simple metal hoops to deter the right-of-way developing around the collar of greens or the damage developing within inches of the run into greenside bunkers. White lines along with appropriate notices are also used to good effect, occasionally both summer and winter. Where golfers are used to them and prepared to accept them, white lines are particularly versatile – as one set of lines fades the next can be marked out a little further away to avoid tracks developing right at the edge of the lines. At some clubs there is nothing else for it but to resort to posts and ropes to provide physical barriers.

When All Else Fails

In situations where the above measures are clearly failing to provide satisfactory conditions, one is forced to resort to pathways. These will commonly be required alongside tees, preferably sited to provide as wide an access at either end as possible – try to limit the tendency of paths to become extended by muddy tracks at entry and exit points.

Paths should be at least 1.2 metres wide to take two pedestrians side by side or a pedestrian pulling a golf cart. Where there is choice, the route should be as direct as possible to avoid golfers taking shortcuts; where deliberately longer to get round an obstacle and prevent damage close into greens, then clear signposting is essential.

Construction

Sound basic construction will provide not only a well-drained, firmer and longer lasting path, but will allow one to get the best out of the more expensive surfacing materials.

Cut out the basic shape, removing turf and topsoil, to the required depth which is usually 150 mm. To provide a neat, firm mowing edge and to help contain the construction materials, it is better to use edging boards nailed to supporting pegs, the wood treated with appropriate preservative. Finish the top of the edging flush with the adjacent soil level. The two edges of the path should be an equal distance apart and having set in and established the first edge, use a simple wooden measuring gauge to ensure the second one is parallel. The path should have a slight crossfall.

Fill in with hardcore or crusher-run material to a minimum firmed depth of 100 mm, rolling to consolidate. Drainage into surrounding topsoil may well be adequate where soil conditions are pretty open, but on heavy clay soils make provision where necessary to tap into existing drains or provide new ones, especially through lower-lying sections of the path.

For pathways down slopes some care is needed to minimise erosion problems. A trap drain along the higher side of the path may be necessary, and wooden cross battens angled across the slope of the path with, say, 12 mm upstands to check the downward flow of water. The alternative would be to use proprietary products such as Fin drains.

Surfacing

Over the years many different types of surfacing material have been tried with varying success. On links or on courses where it is freely available, crushed shell can be very effective, but does need to be well bedded down to provide a tight, well-bound surface; if near putting greens, the material used should not be too noisy when walked upon.

Coarse stone, particularly if it has no finer particles mixed with it, is totally unsatisfactory, being unstable, uncomfortable to walk upon and often too easily spread by feet or trolleys on to mown areas, damaging cutters. Any stone content which is used must have sufficient fines in order to help bind it and form a stable surface. Quite often the 5 mm down quarry waste materials that have been used for surfacing hard porous pitches are very satisfactory, obtained in grey, tan or ochre colours – red shales or white limestones either look out of place or glare off the surface in summer can affect the eyes.

In recent years tree bark has been much used, often to quite good effect. However, choice of product needs care, the finer and softer grades of bark rapidly break down in this situation into a wet organic mush, often after only a couple of years or so. Coarser and harder grades of bark last rather better but are still expensive and, of late, there has been a move to use wood chips or wood fibre. These products may cost slightly more but last far longer, are clean and comfortable to walk on and do not damage golf balls or other equipment.

These latter points sum up the requirements for the surfacing material itself and if the design is right, pathways should merge naturally and as unobtrusively as possible into the golf course site.

(CGC 1 : 71)

STRI THOUGHTS ON GOLF GREEN CONSTRUCTION

Past activities

Many methods and materials have been used for golf green construction in times gone by, but particularly before the early 1960's when the first USGA specification greens (or whar purported to be USGA specification greens) were constructed.

Invariably, green construction was a reflection of site materials, climatic conditions and available resources (particularly finances). There is also no doubt that available knowledge (or ignorance) was also of significance to the way in which greens were built.

Those fortunate enough to have relatively free-draining soils, as seen on many links and some heathland courses, have usually built greens to satisfactory standards as long as they treated the site and its materials with respect. Those less fortunate who had to develop sites with poorer draining soils frequently showed a diversity of constructional methods and standards, ranging from an end product that may have been excellent, to greens that could be simply described as disastrous in every respect. One must also not forget that greens built say 40 - 70 years ago may very well have been produced to architectural and constructional standards appropriate for the time (less play and certainly less winter golf), but in the 1990's with the pressure of all the year round play and the vastly different maintenance equipment available, those previously accepted greens are no longer judged satisfactory.

In the past it has usually been the golf course architect who has taken on the responsibility of constructing and designing greens. Very few architects employed agronomists to help them with this particular discipline.

The Present

Since its earliest days the STRI has, when requested, helped architects, developers and contractors with the construction of golf greens. The advisory agronomists have also given assistance to innumerable golf club committees and greenkeepers wanting to reconstruct old greens or maybe extend the course and construct new greens, etc. It has been clear for some time, however, that the demands and expectations of all concerned with golf course development are changing and in today's world not to regularly examine your philosophy, policy and strategy would be unwise to say the least. In this context therefore, after appraising all the technical, practical and contractual aspects of golf green construction, the STRI at present almost always recommends the installation of the USGA specification of golf green construction. It is worth noting that the USGA specification rootzone was the most successful when compared to other rootzones, in recent research at Bingley funded by the R&A. The occasional exceptions to advising the USGA specification are on those sites where prevailing conditions and materials are very free-draining, such as on many links sites and some heathland sites.

No doubt some involved in giving advice on constructing golf greens will say that such a policy from the STRI is not necessary, as there are many (some would say most) greens built in recent years which perform satisfactorily and that have not been constructed to the USGA specification. One cannot dispute this, but at the same time one should also not forget the many greens that have been constructed or reconstructed in recent years that have turned out less than satisfactory. I also suspect that there will be some who will say that the USGA golf green specification is totally inappropriate for UK conditions and that if USGA specification greens were constructed everywhere, all greens would be the same from course to course. I would not accept such contentions as there are significant quality and performance parameters within the USGA specification which allow materials to be chosen according to site conditions and circumstances. For example, within the hydraulic conductivity range quoted in the USGA specification the rootzone performance should, for UK conditions, be within the normal range (150-300 mm per hour), not the accelerated range (300-600 mm per hour), and indeed it would probably be appropriate in most instances to choose a rootzone material at the lower end of the normal hydraulic conductivity range. It is also possible that some greenkeepers will not be terribly enthused towards the USGA specification, some of the comments we hear from time to time orientate around the rootzones being too difficult to manage, particularly in terms of nutritional and irrigation requirements. Certainly there is no disputing that maintaining USGA specification rootzones is quite different to slower-draining more soil-based rootzones, but again it is often a question of understanding and adjusting the philosophies and practices to meet the freer-draining USGA specification rootzones. At some sites I feel that lack of enthusiasm towards so-called USGA specification greens is for a multitude of reasons, not the least of which is that so many USGA specification greens are really not such. It must also be recorded that there are quite a few greenkeepers who are delighted with their greens built to a USGA specification. The promotion of a rootzone complying to the USGA specification may also result in the suppliers of rootzones having a clearer definition of what is required and thus they can find materials, blend them and supply rootzones with greater confidence in their suitability and performance for the end user.

Responsibilitites

Besides specifying the USGA method of golf green construction, the STRI also insists on proper and appropriate contractual arrangements with all parties that it advises. Whilst the STRI can draw upon the services of our own Jonathan Tucker (who is an Associate member of the British Institute of Golf Course Architects) for golf course architecture and golf green design, we will be very happy to also act as agronomists to any golf course architect, subject to agreed contractual arrangements.

It seems, in view of changing demands and the circumstances in which golf course architects occasionally find themselves, that greater use will be made of agronomists for specifying constructional materials and work. A further role could be that of perhaps monitoring work on behalf of the architect, but we feel great care should be taken not to confuse monitoring with supervision. Supervision is a responsibility that requires regular and frequent site presence to the extent that probably an agronomist's time could be totally taken up by two or three projects. It is unlikely that architects would see the need for an agronomist to act in this fashion.

Architects, agronomists, contractors and suppliers may very well wish to have different roles and responsibilities according to the nature of the project. Such flexibility would present no difficulty to the STRI as consultant agronomists as long as the responsibility, and therefore liability, of the agronomist's role is clearly identified and contracted. At the moment, if the STRI were to give requested guidance on its perceived role in a golf course or golf green construction, we would very much like to work for and with the architect (using the USGA golf green specification except in special circumstances). Once the appropriate specifications have been produced the testing of subsequent materials to the USGA standard would present no problem, the STRI having excellent laboratory facilities and is indeed only one of two laboratories in the United Kingdom recognised by the USGA for testing to its specification. After testing and approving samples of materials (which will be submitted by the contractor or via his supplier), the STRI would always recommend the regular testing of materials brought to site. As a very minimum, materials used in each golf green constructed should be tested. The collection of samples should be the responsibility of the agronomist and contractor or possibly the architect and contractor working to agreed sampling procedure. It would seem wise to always have the contractor's representative present during sampling work. Following the production of the specification and testing of materials further involvement of the agronomist in a monitoring or supervisory role could be at the discretion of the architect. Past experience has shown that some architects (maybe the minority but perhaps increasing) will use a consultant agronomist but there will always be those who consider themselves to be their own agronomist!

Future possibilities

The STRI is always looking to improvements and methods of construction appropriate to conditions in Britain but until there are alternatives that can be substantiated from the scientific viewpoint, we will have to continue supporting the only scientifically credible method of golf green construction, i.e. the USGA specification, (Steve Baker the STRI's Senior Research Officer was a member of the USGA Advisory Committee which drew up the Green Construction Specifications). It would be nice to think that those involved in determining the future of golf in this country are aware of the need to seek an alternative to the USGA specification and that sooner rather than later this need is acted upon. Indeed an R&A 'Course Construction Guidelines Committee' to be chaired by architect Donald Steel has recently been convened to consider these issues and STRI will be represented on this committee through Steve Baker. No doubt research work is needed but perhaps a good starting point would be for a scientific appraisal of those successful greens in Britain not built to the USGA specification. If one can prove underlying parameters to successful non-USGA specification greens in Britain then this could be the first step towards a national, possibly more appropriate specification. To those who fear that standards will produce uniform greens from coast to coast, we would say that the immense diversity of architectural design, climatic conditions and greenkeeping standards should lead to quite significant variation in playing surface and performance whilst still providing all-year round golf.

Whilst the STRI have set their criteria of contractual involvement and responsibility for golf course development it would be happy to amend its position and fit in with any alternative and satisfactory arrangements that the industry consider appropriate.

Finally in an article about golf green construction, be it USGA specification or otherwise, we must simply not forget one absolutely crucial aspect, that is the subsequent standard of maintenance following construction which is the most important factor determining the standards achieved. It is a fact that those involved in designing, building and thereafter maintaining new greens ignore at their peril.

(JP : B.192)

THE USGA GREEN SPECIFICATION

The USGA first published "Specifications for a Method of Putting Green Construction" in 1960 after years of scientific research sponsored by the Association as well as several universities. Prior to this time, the convention when constructing golf greens in the United States was to use a soil mix generally comprising equal parts of sand, soil and organic matter. The new Specifications called for the use of locally available materials in the form of sand, soil and organic matter. The precise ratio of the components used in the final rootzone mix is dependent upon laboratory analysis, backed up by well-documented research and extensive field experience over many years.

Since the Specification's inception, many thousands of greens have been built all over the States and around the world. However, a number of **modified** specifications have been developed over the years and these constructions have often been mistakenly referred to as "Green Section Greens" which, in many cases, have failed. As a result, the USGA are very insistent that if it is intended to build genuine Green Section greens, then the procedures and techniques described in the Specifications must be followed exactly as outlined.

Whilst minor changes and improvements have been made to the Specifications over the years, the basic concept of this form of green construction remains the same. This comprises a gravel drainage carpet tapped by pipe drains, a coarse sand blinding layer and a specially prepared free-draining rootzone mix.

The procedures involved in a USGA green construction as revised by them in 1993 are as follows:

(1) THE SUB-GRADE. The slope of the subsoil formation surface should generally conform to the finished grade and it should be about 400 mm below the finished surface of the green, or 450-500 mm below when an intermediate (or blinding) layer is to be used. It should be thoroughly compacted to prevent settlement. If the subsoil is unstable, a geotextile membrane may be required.

(2) PIPE DRAINAGE. Drainage trenches should be cut into the sub-grade which are 150 mm wide and a minimum of 200 mm deep, with a uniform fall. If a geotextile membrane is employed, it should not cover the drain trenches. A pattern of drains should be designed so that the main drain (minimum diameter 100 mm) is placed along the line of maximum fall. Lateral drains of 100 mm diameter should run down and across the sub-grade to connect with the main and their spacing should not be ore than 5 m apart. Plastic pipe is preferred. A perimeter drain should be installed along the low end of the sub-grade.

(3) GRAVEL LAYER. The entire sub-grade surface should be covered with a layer of clean, washed, crushed stone to a minimum thickness of 100 mm conforming to he proposed final surface grade to a tolerance of ± 25 mm. If an intermediate (blinding) layer is not to be used, then the gravel should have no particles greater than 12 mm, not more than 10% should be less than 2 mm diameter and not more than 5% less than 1 mm. If an intermediate layer is to be used, then not more than 10% of the gravel should be greater than 12 mm, at least 65% between 6 mm and 9 mm, and not more than 10% less than 2 mm.

(4) INTERMEDIATE (BLINDING) LAYER. The need for a blinding layer depends on the particle size distribution of the gravel drainage layer and that of the rootzone mix. If gravel of the specification given above can be found, then a blinding layer may be omitted – otherwise it is essential to prevent the migration of rootzone material down into the gravel layer. A geotextile membrane is not recommended as a substitute for the blinding layer.

<table>
<tr><td colspan="2" align="center">Table A</td></tr>
<tr><td colspan="2" align="center">PARTICLE SIXZE DESCRIPTION OF GRAVEL AND
INTERMEDIATE LAYER MATERIALS</td></tr>
<tr><td>**Material**</td><td>**Description**</td></tr>
<tr><td>**Gravel:** Intermediate layer is used</td><td>Not more than 10% of the particles greater than $1/2$ in. (12 mm)</td></tr>
<tr><td></td><td>At least 65% of the particles between $1/4$ in. (6 mm) and $3/8$ in. (9 mm)</td></tr>
<tr><td></td><td>Not more than 10% of the prticles less than 2 mm</td></tr>
<tr><td>**Intermediate Layer Material**</td><td>At least 90% of the prticles between 1 mm and 4 mm</td></tr>
</table>

(5) ROOTZONE MIXTURE. The correct choice of locally available materials plays an essential part in the success of the Green Section's method of green construction.

In the vast majority of cases the indigenous soil to the site cannot be used on its own for the rootzone mixture. Consequently, the final mix has to be formulated from suitable sand, with organic amendments probably in the form of a suitable soil or peat. Laboratory testing of potential sources of these materials is regarded as being imperative in order to achieve the proper combination of physical and hydraulic properties required in the rootzone.

Before making a final selection of rootzone materials they must undergo a series of laboratory physical analyses, where values including infiltration/percolation capacity and water retention capacity are assessed.

Table B

PARTICLE SIZE DISTRIBUTION OF USGA ROOTZONE MIX

Name	Particle Diameter	Recommendation (by weight)
Fine gravel	2.0-3.4 mm	Not more than 10% of the total particles in this range, including a maximum of 3% fine gravel (preferably none)
Very coarse sand	1.0-2.0 mm	
Coarse sand	0.5-1.0 mm	Minimum of 60% of the particles must fall in this range
Medium sand	0.25-0.50 mm	
Fine sand	0.15-0.25 mm	Not more than 20% of the particles may fall within this range
Very fine sand	0.05-0.15 mm	Not more than 5% — Total particles in this range shall not exceed 10%
Silt	0.002-0.05 mm	Not more than 5%
Clay	Less than 0.002 mm	Not more than 3%

Table C

PHYSICAL PROPERTIES OF THE ROOTZONE MIX

Physical Property	Recommended Range
Total porosity	35% - 55%
Air-filled porosity (at 40 cm tension)	15% - 30%
Capillary porosity (at 40 cm tension)	15% - 25%
Saturated conductivity	
Normal range:	6-12 inches/hr (15-30 cm/hr)
Accelerated range:	12-24 inches/hr (30-60 cm/hr)
Organic matter content (by weight)	1% - 5% (ideally 2% - 4%)

The final rootzone mix should ideally contain no particles larger than 2 mm in diameter and less than 5 per cent silt and 3 per cent clay. The general guideline for the type of sand to be used in the mixture is that the majority of its particles should be in the range 0.25 to 0.75 mm.

Once the appropriate proportions of the rootzone components have been determined, then mixing can begin. Emphasis is placed on mixing all rootzone components off-site in order to achieve a completely homogeneous mixture.

(6) MIXING AND PLACEMENT OF THE ROOTZONE. The off-site mixing of the rootzone is normally carried out using a tractor and front end loader, working on a hard surface area to avoid contamination with other materials. Other options for mixing include the use of large concrete mixers or passing the components through commercial blending equipment.

Sufficient rootzone material should be prepared to provide a final firmed 250 mm depth over the putting green area. Placement of the rootzone should be undertaken using suitable equipment such as balloon-tyred dumper trucks and then spread with an appropriate blade on a balloon-tyred compact tractor or perhaps the bucket on a 360°-swing excavator, the latter often being an invaluable machine in the formation work and the placement of the gravel or blinding layers. The usual procedure would be to work in from the edges towards the centre of the green so that the prepared drainage layers are not disturbed. The balloon-tyred dumper wheels can be used to achieve initial firming, finished off with heeling and raking if there appears to be any remaining inconsistency in the degree of firmness.

The provision of a 250 mm depth of rootzone material lying above two porous drainage layers creates the perched water table concept. The interface between the coarse sand layer and the rootzone acts as a check on the downward movement of non-capillary water. This interface prevents the further downward movement of water until a point of near saturation is reached, at which point gravity overcomes the interface effect. When sufficient gravitational force accumulates, the surface tension effect which retains water within the rootzone pores is overcome and water drains out through the sand and gravel. Thus, the interface permits a droughty-type soil to remain at or near field capacity for longer periods of time.

(7) ESTABLISHMENT OF TURF. After final seed bed preparation, an application of fertilizer is recommended prior to establishing a grass cover by seeding or turfing. If seeding is carried out, the seed should be applied uniformly usually at half rate in two directions. Light and frequent watering may be required to ensure full germination and establishment of the seedling grasses. Once the new sward is well established, the mowing level should be gradually reduced to the desired height over a period of months. The Specification stresses the importance of not bringing the new greens into play too early.

Turfing might be considered if an early opening date is required. It is important that the turf used is grown on the same rootzone mix as the original construction. If this is not the case, then to avoid any layering/drainage problems a prolonged period of intense aeration, core removal and top dressing with the proper rootzone mix will be required to break up the imported soil base. Better still, the use of washed turf could be considered.

(TABLES COURTESY OF THE USGA)   **(RDCE after JRW : B.177)**

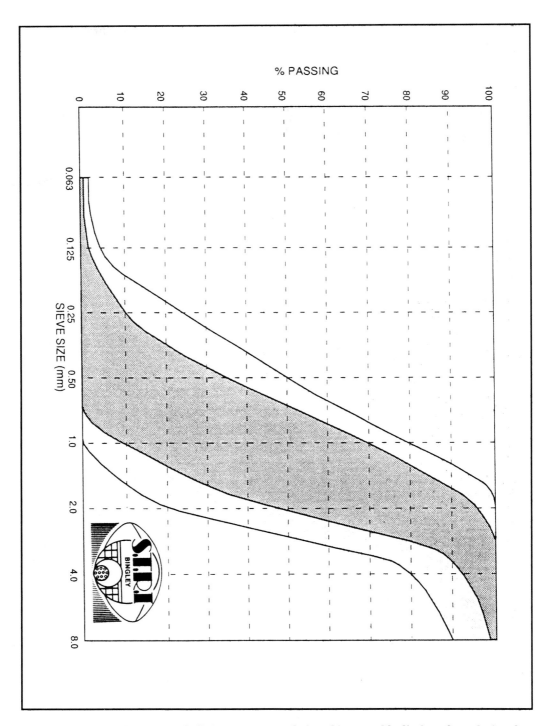

FIGURE 22: Grading curve defining recommended and acceptable limits of sand size for blinding a 5-10 mm drainage aggregate.

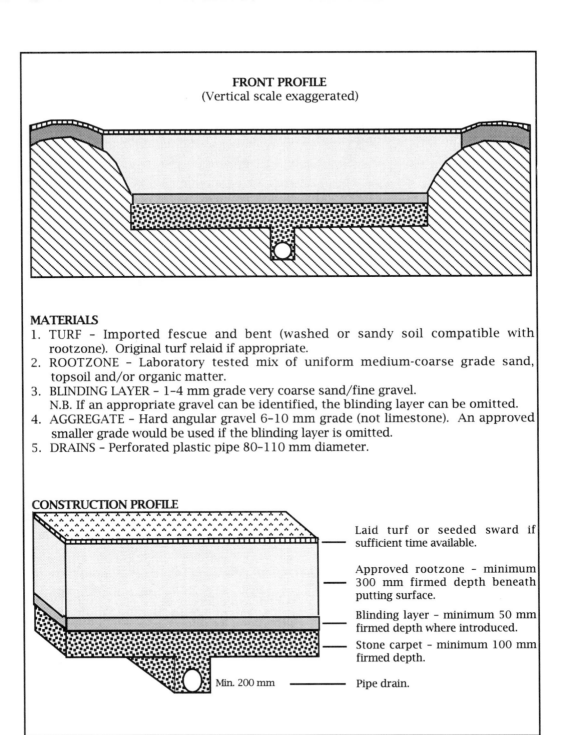

FRONT PROFILE
(Vertical scale exaggerated)

MATERIALS
1. TURF – Imported fescue and bent (washed or sandy soil compatible with rootzone). Original turf relaid if appropriate.
2. ROOTZONE – Laboratory tested mix of uniform medium-coarse grade sand, topsoil and/or organic matter.
3. BLINDING LAYER – 1–4 mm grade very coarse sand/fine gravel.
   N.B. If an appropriate gravel can be identified, the blinding layer can be omitted.
4. AGGREGATE – Hard angular gravel 6–10 mm grade (not limestone). An approved smaller grade would be used if the blinding layer is omitted.
5. DRAINS – Perforated plastic pipe 80–110 mm diameter.

CONSTRUCTION PROFILE

Laid turf or seeded sward if sufficient time available.

Approved rootzone – minimum 300 mm firmed depth beneath putting surface.

Blinding layer – minimum 50 mm firmed depth where introduced.

Stone carpet – minimum 100 mm firmed depth.

Min. 200 mm — Pipe drain.

FIGURE 23: Golf green construction : Drainage carpet method.

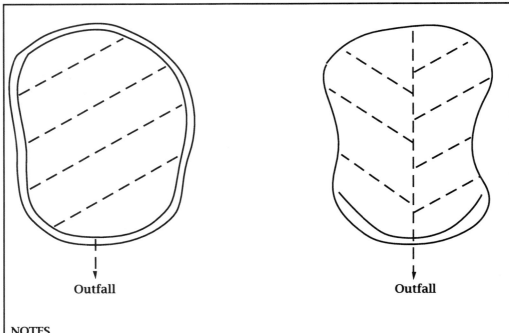

NOTES
1. Average size 500 m².
2. Provide overall fall of 1:80 to 1:100.
3. Minimum 70% of putting surface should be usable pin space.
4. Perpendicular drain spacing aproximately 5-7 m.
5. Perimeter drain must tap front edge of green.
6. Connections between drains using purpose made junctions.

FIGURE 24: Drain layouts for golf greens.

In executing the works, take recognition of and comply with all statutory Health and Safety Regulations.

This information is of a general nature and is intended only to outline the basic information. Such information is not intended to constitute a specification or comprehensive guidance in relation to any project/subject which should only be undertaken after consultation with those holding appropriate qualifications. The STRI employs persons so qualified who can provide advice and/or relevant specifications. The STRI accept no responsibility or liability for any claims arising from work carried out pursuant to this general guide.

(IS No.15 Ref. 02/04)

SEEDING VIS-A-VIS TURFING
Choice
Renovation of thin areas on a golf course invariably involves seeding as opposed to turfing. The choice between the two comes when a bare section develops or a new surface is being prepared. Here, a number of factors are involved in selection as highlighted in the table below:-

Seeding	Turfing
1. Delay in bringing the surface into play.	A significant reduction in the time before the surface is brought into play. For example, one would expect to bring a newly turfed green (autumn) into play after approximately seven months, yet for an equivalent autumn sowing the wait would be at least 20 months.
2. Restricted sowing period within the main growing season.	A much wider time span allowed for turfing, i.e. at almost any time of the year.
3. Reduced cost.	More expensive in relation to seeding, particularly for larger areas.
4. Precise selection of grass species and cultivars desired.	Restriction to turf supplier's choice of grass species and cultivars.
5a. Sowing into a uniform chosen growing medium.	Apart from a small percentage of seedling grown turf or washed turf available, the majority is grown in a different soil medium to the soil profile the construction and this can lead to problems with management and drainage (see 5b and c below).
5b. Good surface drainage rates.	A significant reduction in the infiltration rate permeability due to the turf growing medium. This is particularly pertinent to golf greens.
5c. An increased management requirement for developing a mature sward cover.	Less initial management, although with the soil layer there would be a necessity for soil exchange, i.e. hollow tining. On a new green following an autumn turfing, a spring hollow tining would be recommended (if feasible) before the green is brought into play. Hollow tining would also be repeated in the autumn and possibly during spring and autumn of the following year.

On a more specific level, prevailing resource availability and the political situation within a Golf Club (timing) also plays a part in determining the preference for turfing, seeding or a combination of the two, yet generalisations can be made.

Greens and Immediate Surrounds

For new green constructions the overwhelming consideration is often the pressure to bring the green into play in the shortest possible time, which necessitates the turfing option. Where sufficient time has been allocated for the project, seed is often the preference for cost, cultivar choice and soil compatibility.

Drought, wear and disease scarring are just a few of the possible causes behind the formation of thin and bare areas on exiting greens and for small and large bare sections plugging and/or turfing is the only feasible choice. The aim here is to establish a grass

265

cover which will survive wear, and whilst seeding will fill in to some extent in a number of situations, the sward cover will not be mature or dense enough to withstand further stress due to weather and wear from foot traffic and the effects of mowing, verticutting and so on.

Within the body of a green, patch from the perimeter to achieve as good a match as possible and then renovate the perimeter area from an alternative good quality source. Any thin areas can be oversown and for the best chance of success, seeding (and turfing) should be scheduled for the early autumn. Any seeded, plugged or turfed sections at the edge of the putting surface should be brought into the collar or apron height of cut by recontouring green mowing. It should be stressed at this stage that whilst we do not want any thin and bare areas on putting surfaces, when they do occur it provides an excellent opportunity to introduce fine grasses, especially as it is invariably annual meadow-grass that has died out. It is still surprising to see how many annual meadow-grass or Yorkshire fog or perennial ryegrass plugs we see during a year!

Green Surrounds and Traffic Routes

Moving into general surrounds, here there is more leeway for seeding with increased spreading of wear and a higher height of cut with less verticutting and so on. An autumn sowing is still the best time to achieve the desired results, although if the weather conditions are slightly out of the main growing season, then the process of germination and establishment of seed sown can be improved through the pegging down of one of a number of proprietary protective grow covers now available on the market. For heavily worn traffic routes, the renovation programme must involve an aspect of turfing to have any chance of surviving wear again the following main competition season; seeding is a waste of time, money and effort.

Tees and Fairways

The policy of an ongoing progressive divoting programme is essential for maintaining good levels and restoring a uniform, dense, healthy grass cover as soon as tee markers are moved – these are the two main requirements for tee management. If there is the facility to rest the main tees over the winter period, then a general autumn hollow tining, top dressing and overseeding will prove invaluable in speeding up this aspect of the management programme, although where a time limit is imposed there is always the option of turfing. The larger the area to be considered the more the cost factor comes into play, so for fairways seeding is invariably the choice unless a section of fairway needs to be returfed for political reasons (fast restoration) or as part of a relevelling scheme for instance. The option for semi-rough or rough is almost exclusively for seeding.

Conclusion

The major considerations for the Greenkeeper in determining the choice of either seeding, turfing or a combination of the two relies on a number of factors, namely cost, urgency for bringing the surface into play, timing of work to be completed, soil compatibility and grass choice. Short and long term presentation, wearability and surface playing quality depend on it.

(CGC 1 : 73)

ESTABLISHMENT OF NEW AREAS FROM SEED

Seeding is a relatively cheap way of establishing new turf areas. However, the ultimate success of the turf as a playing surface will depend on important decisions taken with regard to major level adjustment, pipe drainage and if necessary improvement to the drainage qualities of the topsoil. All the above operations are fairly expensive nowadays and the way in which they are carried out and their timing can affect establishment and ultimately the quality of the surface produced. Naturally, these decisions will be based on available finance and the standard of playing surface required.

The big advantage of seeding is that no heavy soils are being introduced (as could happen with turfing), especially on sandy golf green constructions.

Timing

August or September is the optimum time for sowing seed in this country, particularly for the finer turf areas. At this period the soil is still warm and the early autumn usually provides adequate natural rainfall so that the young seedlings do not suffer from drought with reasonable growing weather after germination for them to establish before hard frost occurs. In the autumn there is also markedly less competition from developing weed seedlings.

Equally, if not more important, sowing at this time of year allows those preliminary operations requiring heavy equipment and traffic over the site such as earth moving, pipe drainage and soil amelioration to be carried out during the drier months of May and June which helps to keep damage to soil structure that occurs with these operations to a minimum.

Soil Type

For golf a sandy, free draining soil is required which is often produced by adding a quantity of suitable sand to the existing soil in amounts determined by laboratory tests. Off-site preparation of the soil mix is the preferred method and must be completed thoroughly so as to produce a very uniform mixture of the constituents. After spreading the soil mix on the green, ensure there are no hard, panned layers by adequate cultivation through the full depth of soil, though make sure any underlying drainage carpet materials are not disturbed.

Sterilisation/Fallowing

Fallowing can be useful in reducing competition from weeds and even weedgrasses like annual meadow-grass. However, time is necessary to allow the weeds to develop when they can be killed off by cultivations in dry weather or alternatively spraying with appropriate non-persistent weedkiller based on paraquat or glyphosate. Even a short fallowing period is better than none at all but if the aim is to achieve a seed bed free of annual meadow-grass, soil sterilising would be a better option.

Soil sterilising using methyl bromide is fairly quick and can be very effective, although it is costly and requires professional operators. Dazomet, another soil sterilising agent, may also be tried, although an adequate period (often weeks) must be allowed for the gas to escape before seeding.

Surface Levels

During seed bed preparation heeling and raking will be required a number of times to produce a fine soil tilth that is adequately and evenly firmed over the whole area though without being too compacted. During the work, surface stones should be removed.

Where surface levels are crucial, accurate level pegs should be set out on a grid pattern and the seed bed raked and firmed to correspond with the top of the pegs. Levels are less critical for tees, and on golf greens some gentle undulation is desirable to produce an interesting putting surface. Care in producing a good tilth and satisfactory levels at this stage will be more than repaid later on by the ease and speed with which levels are perfected for play through top dressing.

Lime and Fertiliser Treatment

To aid germination and rapid early development of a complete grass cover, over-acid soil conditions should be corrected by liming where necessary to achieve a pH of about 5.0. There must be adequate amounts of the main plant nutrients phosphate and potash available in the upper layers of soil. Where no serious deficiencies of these nutrients exist an application of a mini-granular or powder fertiliser that contains 6:9:6 or with similar analysis can be used at 50 g/m^2 and raked in.

Seed Mixtures

The traditional approach has been to sow 80% Chewings fescue and 20% browntop bent and this is still very satisfactory today. The fescue germinates and grows quickly to nurse along the much slower bent: with a suitable soil and correct management a good proportion of the fescue may survive though quite frequently once established the strongly competitive bent will take over. There are a number of excellent new cultivars of both these grasses available and a choice should be made from the lists in our publication "Turfgrass 1996" bearing in mind the qualities required for the particular turf area. Seed rate should be 35 g/m^2, sowing as evenly as possible, the seed then being carefully raked into the immediate surface soil – it must not be put too deep and surface levels should not be disturbed.

Disease

Occasionally damping off disease will affect young seedlings, especially under wet, cold seed bed conditions. The seedlings keel over and develop a typical reddish/bronze colour and, if noticed, affected areas can be treated with a wide spectrum fungicide such as chlorothalonil.

Early Care

When the young grass is about 25 mm long and the ground is dry, remove any remaining small stones 12 mm) and over. Follow up by a light flat rolling. When the grass reaches   40 mm in length carry out the first cut but removing no more than 12 mm of foliage. Timing of this first cut is important since early mowing will check any annual weeds that may develop and it also encourages the grass to tiller and thicken out. To avoid damage to surface levels the ground must be firm and in very wet periods, to prevent the grass growing away it may be necessary to top lightly with a Flymo type mower initially. Subsequent cuts should be with a cylinder mower, boxing off the cuttings and gradually reducing the height of cut to about 12 mm. The latter height of cut should be maintained until surface levels have been improved sufficiently by top dressing to permit closer cutting.

Top Dressing

Several applications of an appropriate type of bulky top dressing (e.g. sandy compost for greens) will be necessary in the growing season at a minimum rate of 2.0 kg/m^2. This should provide sufficient material to work in using a lute to eliminate minor surface irregularities which always occur. The treatment should be repeated a number of times until the playing surface is satisfactory.

(CGC 1 : 69)

SECTION 13
GOLF COURSE ARCHITECTURE

———— ❖❖❖ ————

Design of the Golf Course

Design and Subsequent Maintenance

*The Care of
the Golf Course*

GOLF COURSE ARCHITECTURE: SOME THOUGHTS

"A thing of beauty is a joy for ever", a line from John Keats' poem, Endymion (Book 1).

If you can say that of the Architect's work, then truly he has read the site and drawn from it all that it has to offer. He has handed down a legacy for which the next generation will be eternally grateful.

Sadly, the above is far from being the norm. Golf development in recent years has amounted to a rape of the British and Irish landscape. The reason for this might crudely be laid at the door of sheer ignorance. Two features of life as it is led today also have a bearing, and these are lack of concentration and living in the fast lane. Bring these two major ingredients (as part of your philosophy) to bear on the development of a site for golf and you have the recipe for another monument of horridness.

What is a Good Golf Course?

The formation of 9, 18 or 36 holes is born out of hours of walking a site, pondering, **concentrating**, working on and finally producing a layout which uses all the inherent characteristics of the site to the fullest advantage. Do not destroy what nature already offers. If it is offering an opportunity to create a unique golf hole, accept it thankfully.

Adjustment to existing levels may be necessary, let us say, to help with a sight-line or perhaps to open up a majestic panoramic view beyond, but such adjustment should be kept to the absolute minimum.

Always keep in mind that the site is far more important than anyone involved in its development. It has been in existence for thousands of years and if you treat it with respect, it will respond in kind – the final outcome of the Works is likely to be successful. This is so because the natural features which you have found on the site are now at the very heart of the strategic and aesthetic qualities offered by the golf course and it is these which challenge and excite the golfer. The golfer never becomes tired of such a course, frustrated perhaps, but he appreciates its fairness as well as challenge. While he or she continues to be surprised or deceived into taking the wrong club, they will return time after time in an effort to conquer.

Where is the Starting Point for This Adventure?

Time on site is invaluable in order to become as conversant as possible with its strategic and aesthetic qualities.

Having established the best position for the Clubhouse, it is useful in these days of heavy play to have two fairly long starting holes of relative ease simply to speed golfers away on their rounds. Thereafter, the holes should be formed and again fall into place as suggested by the site's natural features. The imagery of two par 3 holes, two par 5 holes and five par 4 holes on each loop of nine with a balanced yardage, etc. can lead to a very dull golf course. The desire of certain authorities in this respect is, to say the least, devoid of imagination. Imposing your will upon a **whole** site takes you down a very dangerous road indeed. You have now entered into the realm of tampering with nature and, as is widely recognised, nature always has the last laugh. The outcome could be a golf course exuding symmetry (a characteristic not to be found in nature) and therefore one with a very contrived appearance. As such, it is unlikely to stand the test of time.

While symmetry is not to be found in nature, harmony is. It is harmony which is the key to unlocking the secrets which the site offers. If the site is saying, yes, two par 3's or two par 5's in a row, then accept this concept. At the end of the day it will look natural and 'feel right' because the finished product will blend into the existing landscape in an imperceptible manner. This is fundamental to offering a course which "..... is a joy for ever".

The aim of the golf course architect amidst all of this is to offer a series of golf holes which provide a challenge to every class of golfer. Equally, as the golfer makes his or her way around the course, he or she should feel that each hole played is quite memorable in its own inimitable way. Do remember that length has very little to do with merit. Length is a detrimental aspect of many golf courses built today. Likewise, reliance on artificial hazards, i.e. sand bunkers around greens, has destroyed the real artistry of approach play.

The Part Played By Individual Hole Design

The green is the focal point of the hole and should at most holes dictate play. Green orientation, greenside bunkering (if any), putting area (and falls), surround contouring and width of entrance all have a major bearing on the difficulty of individual holes.

Visibility of the putting surface is desirable, particularly at par 3 and short par 4 holes.

Natural hazards, e.g. ponds, streams, ditches and woodland or fairway bunkers can all influence the optimum route of play to the green. The shaping of the fairways also contributes to strategy and therefore playing interest. Informal edges between fairway and semi-rough leads to a blending in of through the green to the surrounding land-scape. There are no straight lines on a golf course.

Tees need not be formed at an elevation higher than the architecture of the hole dictates.

Ultimately, easy maintenance is of prime importance, therefore when considering green and tee positions, shapes of fairways and width of landing areas, etc., traffic routes, walk-offs, proximity of trees, featuring of surround mounds, batters to fill or cut banks, areas and shapes of putting surfaces, width of green entrances, depth and shape of bunkers are among the many factors to be seriously considered by the Architect during the final preparations of his layout and individual green and tee drawings.

Strategic and Aesthetic Considerations

Successful golf architecture depends on a complementary blend of these two essential elements.

Strategic design provides different options for playing a hole in accordance with the proficiency (and ambition) of the golfer with the objective of providing an equitable and enjoyable test of golf for all.

Inextricably linked with the strategic element, there is the aesthetic appeal of the golf course. The latter is greatly enhanced by using the natural features of the site, e.g. woodland, local topography (mounds, slopes, grassy hollows), gorse or heather banks, streams and ponds, etc. Existing flora, fauna and linking habitats remain untouched and indeed the ecology of the site may even be greatly enhanced by sensible planting schemes, etc.

Conclusion

Artificiality which often arises from unnecessary earth movement and level adjustment results in the delivering up of golf holes which are devoid of interest and genuine excitement. They may never come to maturity and more often than not remain an ongoing maintenance problem for the greenkeeping staff. This is not good golf architecture, it is design, and how sad it is to see so much of it throughout the land and beyond these shores.

271

As the sincere Architect walks the site for the umpteenth time utilising all his creative processes, listening to what the site is saying to him and using what the site offers, the end product is a golf hole or series of holes of which it can be said – "Its loveliness increases; it will never pass into nothingness".

(CGC 1 : 61)

GOLF COURSES: DESIGN FOR EASE OF MAINTENANCE

In the development of a new golf course a properly conceived design will serve to minimise many of the potential problems encountered by the greenstaff when maintaining the course. This aspect of design has often been neglected, or regarded as being of low priority, by designers not familiar with, or indifferent to, the practicalities of agronomy. Moreover, many deficiencies have been inbuilt during course construction as the design is not properly translated on the ground and the original intentions of the architect become distorted due to inadequate supervision.

Course layout is interwoven with design as selection of tee and green sites can have a profound influence on subsequent management. For example, exposed greens may dry out rapidly whereas putting surfaces in valleys, cut into banks or close to water features may suffer drainage problems – unless this is mitigated by an adequate specification for construction.

Tees and greens placed in close proximity to trees can suffer shade problems: notably, weak turf growth and premature thinning over the winter, succumb more rapidly to disease, hold frost for longer and tree roots may compete for valuable water and nutrients during the summer.

Avoidance of bottlenecks or converging traffic routes within the framework of a course layout will offer greater relief to the turf and ease the pressures on the soil beneath towards the adverse effects of compaction.

Incorporation of water features in course design would serve as a potential source of irrigation water and reduce the reliance on off-course supplies during the summer months. However, these must be of adequate volume to limit the extent of "draw down" which can expose unsightly muddy banks.

On a smaller scale, good design can serve to ease the maintenance burden when rebuilding tees and greens or modifying individual holes. Whether this work is undertaken in-house or a recognised golf course architect is engaged, basic principles must be observed.

The importance of providing adequate teeing area cannot be disputed in relation to maximising distribution of wear and facilitating renovation procedures. Alternative teeing grounds, designated primarily for winter and summer play, are particularly useful against the background of increased golf through the year and greater expectations for reasonable golfing conditions during the winter months. Furthermore, a policy of siting alternative purpose-built tees in strategic locations will help to break some of the more rigid patterns of golf traffic flow and bring different landing areas into focus.

The rectangular form of tee (with emphasis on adequate width so that lateral moves can be made) continues to be pursued due to its simplicity, implicit sense of orientation and effective use of teeing surface area. Objections to this type of tee on aesthetic grounds can be countered by keeping elevation to a minimum, easing out the batter on banks so that they marry into surrounding ground (imperceptibly if possible) and rounding off all corners. Importantly, the greenstaff will appreciate these design features when carrying out routine cutting with Triplex mowers or performing other vital remedial operations where accessibility and manoeuvrability are prerequisites of mechanical treatments. Tee size should be related to the degree of damage inflicted, thus vulnerable par 3 tees are larger than par 4 or 5 teeing grounds. One large teeing area may be favoured on maintenance grounds but in broken, sharply undulating ground it can be misplaced. In these situations, dispersal of several smaller tees will cause less disturbance to the landscape, alter traffic flow patterns to advantage and cost less to construct.

The informal, randomly-shaped tee has become more fashionable with modern course architects, mainly due to its influence on landscape. This design will facilitate maintenance by Triplex mowers by avoidance of square corners, but care must be exercised so that a false sense of orientation is not created.

Putting surfaces must also be of adequate area to cope with existing and projected levels of play. Greens of less than 350 m^2 are difficult to manage due to the limited flexibility for pin positions. Heavily featured surfaces also concentrate play on the flatter sections, leading to localised turf wear. Expansion of the putting surface to accommodate the more distinctive mounds, banks and hollows would compensate (for example, a two-tier 'MacKenzie' green may have to be one third as big again as a conventional green), but other factors should be considered. Even with modern drainage layers and free-draining rootzone materials, water may still lodge within low spots unless the surface is contoured to shed water. Two or three "run-off" points are best provided, rather than simply channelling water only to the front of the green to collect on the apron. Conversely, mounds and slopes may dry out rapidly and become relatively impervious to irrigation. An increased maintenance commitment will be required to reduce these discrepancies and preserve playing surface uniformity.

Over-elaborate or idiosyncratic shaping of greens will also complicate management and any unnecessary excrescences are best avoided. As with tees, narrow greens lead to a concentration of play (and wear) down a narrow central strip.

Inextricably linked with the greens are the surrounds. The formation of subtle mounds, ridges and hollows and the placement of bunkers adds playing and visual interest but this must be tempered by the demands of efficient maintenance. Acute drop-offs, sharp precipices and angles which are inaccessible to Triplex mowing equipment are a management headache and generally increase the intensity of hand work. Surrounding banks should be eased out to certainly no more than 1 in 3 and gradients of 1 in 5, or less, are preferable. There must also be adequate scope to turn on surround areas with maintenance systems or mowing equipment, without scouring the turf and development of an adequate width of collar (minimum one Triplex mower's width) encircling the putting surface will help in this context.

Sand splash from bunkers inexorably leads to build-up on the surrounds and to reduce its impact on the margins of the putting surface there must be an adequate buffer of immediate surround or collar. Hemming in the green with a ring of protective bunkers channels golfers along narrow entry and exit routes, making it virtually impossible to sustain a viable grass cover. Contraction in the sand area or eliminating redundant bunkers would ease the situation. A policy of bunker rationalisation could also extend to the fairways where out-of-focus bunkers are surplus to requirements and only represent a drain on labour resources.

In the design of bunkers the formation of excessively steep sand faces leads to problems of under-cutting of the front lip and eventual collapse. Where stone is encountered in significant quantities, it can be pinned down by rolling turf either partially down or fully down the face. Over-elaborate bunker shapes can be difficult to cut around with Triplex mowers, therefore mowable curves should be formed throughout.

Finally, golf course design must not neglect the essentials of adequate drainage.

Slightly elevated teeing surfaces with a minor gradient in one plane (normally front to back) usually preclude the introduction of extensive drainage, but poorly-drained sites and tees designated for winter play may well demand the introduction of drainage layers – tapped by an emptying pipe drainage system. Deep excavation of bunkers in heavy soils may well create water-collecting basins (cf. links pot bunkers where sand areas are kept low to reduce wind blow), therefore adequate pipe drainage is essential. Slight elevation is preferred for fairway bunkers on poorly-drained sites to facilitate drainage as well as enhancing visibility.

An arterial system of ditches and main drains is invaluable through fairway and rough areas, but ditches may deteriorate due to erosion of excessively steep banks and restricted crossing points concentrates the effects of wear.

The vogue for American-style courses, involving mass earth movement to mould fairways to the architect's intentions, has brought with it a heavy maintenance price as well as an inflated constructional budget. The land must be treated with respect and destruction of soil structure can lead to serious drainage problems in the future. Therefore, the overriding philosophy of design must be to fully utilise the natural advantages of a site while keeping disturbance to a minimum.

(JWT : Unpublished)

PLATE 10: Powered sweepers are useful tools in the process of keeping the course tidy. On well-wooded courses they can be essential to deal with autumn leaf-fall. (Courtesy SISIS Equipment (Macclesfield) Ltd.)

SECTION 14
GOLF COURSE ECOLOGY

✤✤✤

Ecology, Conservation and Environmental Factors

Trees and Woodlands

Ponds and Water Hazards

Heather Management

Gorse Management

*The Care of
the Golf Course*

GOLF COURSE MANAGEMENT:
AN ECOLOGICAL PERSPECTIVE

Introduction

It seems that conservationists are constantly in the news, whether for opposing the destruction of the rain forests on a global scale or for defending a site of ecological importance from modification and further destruction on a local or national level. One thing is however certain, the presence of such forces are here to stay and are likely to increase.

The golf industry is unlikely to escape as European community directives become entrenched into our culture, i.e. restrictions on herbicides and particularly pesticides as they apply to earthworm control. These legal restrictions can only increase and do have perhaps quite serious implications to the golf industry. What then can be done to counteract, or at least reduce, the problems pending? We could claim to use less, but the STRI has for years been condemning preventative use, advocating the more sensible approach of minimal usage when absolutely necessary. Most golf clubs do tend to follow these guidelines, possibly due to the cost of the chemicals as much as a genuine regard for their environmental impact. Given the above, there are I feel several approaches open to individual golf clubs aimed at raising golf's environmental profile whilst not compromising the nature of the game. These centre around management and the realisation of the requirement to develop and manage the whole of the golf course as an integral feature of the landscape rather than a series of greens, fairways and tees. Almost all golf courses, including many of the public pay-and-play courses, do have ecological potential and this is often considerable. Many are already contributing positively to our recognised nature conservation strategies.

Course Evaluation

We can however only conserve the biological diversity, i.e. the habitat types and the species they support, once we have fully recognised it. This can only be achieved by an ecological assessment aimed at identifying all of the ecological, geological, geographical, topographical, aesthetic and strategic parameters that may be present. In theory many ecologists are available to undertake this work, but in practice very few have the necessary in-depth experience of the game to satisfy the architectural requirements and to fulfil the objectives of the game itself. Anyone contemplating initiating an ecological management programme must have sufficient knowledge of the game and how it fits into the concepts of penal, heroic and strategic development. Similarly, one must always bear in mind the need to balance relaxation with the challenge so as to maximise enjoyment of the game whilst retaining or indeed improving the balance between ecological interest and the aesthetics as seen both on and off the course.

An ecological assessment therefore will, given the nature of the land use, be quite complex and may indeed be made more difficult by the need to consider the many different parameters of the game Failure in the first instance to recognise these may lead to wasted resources of finance and labour and may in the longer term serve to further reduce habitat quality.

Concern and the Golf Course Resource

Public concern and criticism are being focused towards golf often for its environmental impact but, equally, often for its sociological connotations. Both can however be satisfied through ecological management.

Although, as has been demonstrated over the past few years through talks, presentations and seminars, there are numerous clubs still failing in their obligation towards environmental management, many others do ideally adopt a very positive approach with noticeable ecological gains.

With over 2500 golf courses now established through the country, golf is a major land use occupying over 1% of the total land area. Very little land (between 10 and 15% of each course) is intensively managed, leaving around 80 to 90% available as wildlife habitat in some form. Quantity alone is not sufficient to ensure that our golf courses remain valuable for wildlife. Indeed, the type of habitat represented, the size of each individual area and the way in which these areas are managed will all influence the ecological potential.

Possibly a second equally important statistic in considering the ecological status of golf courses is that golf is contributing significantly as marginal land. The many varied habitat types of a golf course can act as important wildlife corridors, helping to link other areas of habitat through the wider countryside.

What Value Ecology?

Both the above are extremely important and will certainly help to allay many of the environmental criticisms now being focused towards golf. It is however important that we look much further than the needs of today and indeed secure the needs of future generations. Nature on the golf course does have a value, although the value will differ between any individual or group (i.e. the golf course committee or the local statutory conservation body). This complex issue will eventually come down to just what value we are willing to pay for.

Through the golf industry the economic value of nature will be dependent not so much on the diversity of species or variety of habitat quality, but whether the game of golf continues unimpeded, i.e. locally from the physical problems of entangled deep rough to the wider influences of product restriction and public condemnation. To emphasise these points one can cite two examples. We at the STRI are fully aware that in Germany part of or even whole golf courses are closing, often at important times of the year, due to worm cast problems and the lack of chemical resources available to treat them. In Portugal, governmental opposition centering around environmental issues is preventing the opening of an already completed golf course, claiming the course is a potential environmental polluter.

Given these potential problems it becomes even more important to assess the value placed upon environmental management i.e. good course stewardship. It may be that the environmental value will be totally dependent upon the short term view and on whether today's needs outweigh those of future generations, i.e. those who would actually reap the benefits. But I do suspect, and trust, that the majority of people playing a responsible part in the golf industry are keen to ensure the longer term preservation of the game.

Conclusion

In summary, golf in Britain has increased dramatically over the past few years and is now a major land use. The wider public, statutory and non-statutory conservation bodies are fully aware of the losses arising through the countryside, largely as a result of human exploitation and mismanagement. At present, central government and many local government bodies are not fully active in addressing the problems relating to these losses but with closer relationships now in place throughout Europe, time is not on many golf clubs' side.

There is therefore a need to consider ecological management possibly through a full course appraisal to assess the ecological status of individual courses and to determine the most sensible programmes for their sustained future development. There are however costs which in part can be justified in aesthetic and intrinsic terms, i.e.

architectural requirements to meet the developer's objectives, but also in pure economic terms, applying management techniques for optimum effect and for both contemporary and future generations to enjoy.

(RST : Reprinted Courtesy of *Golf Club Management*)

ENHANCING THE BENEFIT OF GOLF COURSES

Introduction

It is likely that there are in the region of 2,500 golf courses in existence throughout Great Britain and Ireland, thus, given that each golf course is on average around 50 hectares (150 acres), it is likely that 125,000 hectares of land has now been secured through golf. The total amount of rough alone probably exceeds 50,000 hectares. The potential therefore exists for golf to play a vital role in our countryside's conservation. Indeed, if we consider the golf course from the playing angle, then I am in no doubt that the game would not be the same without the significant contribution, i.e. the vistas, views and landscaping, that the surrounding countryside has on the identity and character that makes each golf course different from each other.

Individual golf courses owe their intrinsic character to a number of environmental factors and not just the layout and future management, and these must be borne in mind from the onset of the development and throughout the life of the course.

The Landscape Framework

Golf is a game which demands a balance between strategic thought and enjoyment. Although the former can be artificially incorporated through green or tee positioning or bunker formation, both the strategy and enjoyment are, nevertheless, heavily dependent upon the landscape framework, which itself is a product of an assemblage of smaller components.

Factors for Consideration

1. *Vegetation (trees and shrubs in the landscape)*

The vegetation of the surrounding landscape is worth considering before undertaking any major ecological improvements. Indications as to the vegetation associations that may grow in any particular environment should be ascertained. This can ultimately save the Club from wasting considerable amounts of time and money through incorrect choice and selection. It would be wrong, for example, to attempt to plant tall shelter belts or areas of woody screening on a sandy links environment that has largely remained devoid of any tree growth. The lack of tree cover on such a site is a clear indication that the climatic and other environmental conditions are not conducive for the successful establishment of trees. Planting here would undoubtedly result in their failure. This somewhat extreme example does occur over and over again, especially on the less obvious terrains such as the heathlands, many of which have undergone massive transformations in recent years, and other sites where exposure or soil characteristics, for instance, are largely alien to the successful establishment of non-indigenous tree or shrub species.

2. *Species selection*

The vegetation of the surrounding landscape can give important clues as to the likely success of individual species. Certain species, such as lime and beech, may be confined to areas offering a markedly warmer annual temperature. Both lime and beech are considered native to Southern Britain and are only found in Scotland and

Northern England in the more sheltered areas. Alien and exotic species are best avoided as these do not only look out of character with regard to the rest of the surrounding landscape, but their growth requirements may not be conducive to the climatic conditions experienced on many golf course sites. In the case of rhododendron, its very aggressive nature is a direct consequence of its native homeland, which is the Himalayan mountainsides. Given the warmer British climate, this species is able to maximise upon its invasive nature and can in some instances, if left unchecked, take over large areas of woodland or copse to their ultimate detriment and loss of quality.

It is important that due consideration be given when selecting nursery stock. As a general rule, the harsher the environmental conditions, the smaller and more well-protected the tree should be. On many courses, large amounts of money are often wasted when fairly large numbers of standard trees are planted on very exposed hillsides, for example. These do tend to sit dormant for very long periods of time, whereas smaller forestry transplants of, say, 45–60 cm in height, suitably protected with tree guards and planted fairly closely such that each tree is protected by its neighbour, can achieve successful establishment with good growth rates. Standards are useful in smaller-scale plantings, when used individually, or when intermixed in large scale plantings to offer an immediate variation in structural height.

The utilisation and placement of trees on the golf course for screening, hole individuality, protection and strategy is of paramount importance. Other landscape features, however, should not be overlooked, such as wild flower grasslands, which will be covered in a subsequent article.

(RST : B.177)

GOLF & THE ENVIRONMENT

The golf industry over the past few years has witnessed a tremendous upsurge in interest over environmental issues. The golf boom of the early 1990s has highlighted for many the need for a greater ecological awareness in directing and guiding new developments – it has also directed many established clubs towards a realisation of their environmental responsibilities and this in turn has led to more and more clubs requesting ecological course appraisals to formulate and guide sound ecological management practices.

On a wider scale, the recently formed Ecology Unit of the European Golf Association has produced a booklet outlining an environmental strategy for golf throughout Europe which is centred around a more unified approach to environmental aspect of golf course management and development. It is hoped that gradually this work will help present golf in a more acceptable light, helping as we journey into the 21st Century to improve golf's environmental image within the public arena.

Why the apparent sudden upsurge in interest for aspects of conservation and rough management? Why is golf a prime target and candidate for increasing public criticism?

To answer questions such as these we must look back to the origins of the game and its development. If one reads the writings of the early golf course architects such as Dr Alistair MacKenzie, for example, we would find that his approach was to fit golf into the natural landscape, blending greens and tees through their gentle contouring into the given topography of the site. A quote from the book by Gordon G. Smith The World of Golf (1898) sums this up quite admirably. "A hole should always give one the impression that it owes its existence to its own intrinsic merits, to its individuality and character, and not as too often happens to the fact that it had to be there because forsooth there was no other place to put it". Such sympathetic approaches to the use of the landscape have resulted in numerous golf courses forming a semi-natural extension to the surrounding countryside. Appropriate vegetation featuring, development and management have ensured a secure refuge for a whole host of wildlife species.

It is the burden of modern day architects to have to gain inspiration from often quite featureless landscapes with a reshaping of the land required to form the desired end product. Such projects with their large-scale earth moving, land shaping techniques and inappropriate vegetation thereafter will inevitably intensify public criticism and are, in our experience at the Sports Turf Research Institute, more often than not totally unnecessary. Generally, even the most uninspiring area of arable land will offer discrete nuances such as hollows, rises, ridge and furrow, ditches and dykes, all of which can be picked out given time spent on site.

If we, as consultants, are given the responsibility of carrying golf through and into the 21st Century, then we must encourage a more sympathetic approach to landscape design and development. Indeed, present day initiatives led by the European Golf Association, The Sports Turf Research Institute and others working as golf course consultants in an ecological capacity, must provide the first step to improving the image of golf so as to ensure the security of future developments.

There is, however, a second and considerably more important reason why rough or through the green management is becoming more and more significant, particularly on courses now established throughout the country and indeed through Europe. Much of the landscape over the past 50 to 100 years or so has been dramatically altered. Modification and destruction through farming, industry, housing, forestry, etc. has taken a heavy toll on the habitats, i.e. the hedgerows, heathlands, bogs and mires, waterways and woodlands, to mention but a few, and on the species of wildlife that depend upon them. Gradual changes to our landscape over the past 3000 or 4000 years or so have created enumerate habitat types and have allowed wildlife a chance to exploit niches as and when they have become available. The modern day scenario of modification and destruction of the landscape poses a considerable threat to wild-life, primarily due to the speed of change that is occurring. Most species of wildlife are unable to tolerate such a rate of change and are therefore tending to become rare with the ultimate possibility of extinction.

Given this, conservation groups have recognised the need to conserve areas of land and nature reserves are now well-established throughout the country. These areas, however, will never be sufficiently numerous or extensive to satisfy or safeguard more than a fraction of the diversity that exists. We must therefore look to other land uses, i.e. the linear habitats such as motorway verges, railway embankments and indeed the golf course. The golf course is host to a whole series of linear habitat types which allow species of wildlife a chance to migrate and colonise other areas of countryside either on or off the course. In Europe, such ecological bridging not only runs along the length of the fairway but is also now expected to transect fairways at intervals, so allowing crossways and well as lengthways migration and movement.

Although it is often the links and maritime courses which enjoy the prestige of playing host to a great wealth of habitat and wildlife diversity, the parklands too can contribute significantly to nature conservation with often very little input. Consider "hedgerows", these features being protected on many golf courses are now nationally recognised as important for wildlife and plans are afoot to reinstate these wherever possible throughout the country. Indeed, over 43000 miles of hedgerow have been lost over the past 50 years. A typical hedge consisting of hawthorn, elder, blackthorn, oak and hazel may support in the region of 400 to 500 different species of insect and will provide a vital food source for autumn/winter immigrant birds such as the fieldfare, redwing, etc. Valuable nesting sites are also provided for summer bird visitors, possibly amounting to in the region of around 50 bird species. A number of butterflies too depend on specific shrub and tree types within hedgerow systems for their survival, examples being the brimstone, whose larvae feed on ivy, and the hairstreaks which require either oak, elm or blackthorn. It is therefore vital that only native species complementary to the traditional hedgerow are utilised in restocking and planting so as to maintain the continuity of habitat and species diversity.

A number of ancient woodlands are also represented on the parkland golf courses throughout the country and these must be maintained if their ecological significance is to be retained. Indeed, the Forestry Commission is keen to offer grant aid to landowners for the management of established woodlands for the purpose of woodland conservation. Care must, however, be taken to select the most appropriate tree and shrub types that fit the landscape and are indigenous to the "semi-natural" dominant woodland features. Water features too play an important part of many parkland golf courses and these are well known to play host to a great variety of wildlife types. One can find golf courses where even the irrigation points spread over the course are being used by great crested newts.

It is all too easy for Golf Clubs to leave areas for wildlife by offering no management at all. These areas will ultimately decline supporting generally fewer species of interest and gradually becoming unkempt and untidy. On the golf course the next stage normally pursued is to clear and reinstate a grass sward to the further loss of wildlife and an increased maintenance budget. Management therefore is vital if the ecology of an area is to be maintained or improved. This will however vary depending upon the type of habitat present, the species being encouraged and the priorities and requirements of the game of golf. Ecological management is covered in considerable depth in current publications: *A Practical Guide To Ecological Management of the Golf Course* (BIGGA & STRI 1995) and *Living Together: Golf & Nature in Partnership*, published by the EGU in 1996, to which the STRI made a substantial contribution (see Bibliography).

(RST : B.189)

LANDSCAPING THE NEW GOLF COURSE

Early golf course architects, in comparison with the architects of today, may have had a relatively easy task in choosing and developing sites for golf. At the turn of the century architects were utilising the maritime links environments, the sandy heaths and better quality parkland type habitats, the majority of which possibly displayed a varied natural topography with a substantial degree of inbuilt vegetation featuring.

Today's potential golf course sites tend to be very bland, requiring a tremendous vision and insight to be successful. Often large-scale earth moving works are employed, totally changing the character of the site to form a very artificial land form. This approach can generate criticism and opposition, particularly on heavier soil types in compromising or damaging the drainage qualities of the site and inevitably increasing the maintenance burden thereafter. Landscaping using appropriate vegetation types may, in the majority of cases, be a more acceptable approach, which if undertaken sensibly, will in the long-term offer a more natural feel to the site, so increasing the golf interest.

Ecological appraisal

The first step must be to include a full ecological appraisal of the land. This would normally be undertaken in conjunction with the initial feasibility studies. The appraisal should identify the whole ecology of the site and indeed of the surrounding landscape.

From this an appreciation of the landscaping required would be identified and the results used to further guide the landscaping works.

It may be that the site is situated within both low lying woodland and more upland gorse or heather grassland. The survey would identify the different habitats and their position would be included on the provisional golf layout. The expansion and development of these habitats over the course would need to be clearly stated and guidance should be given as to the types of work necessary. When considering tree planting the desired objectives and function should be clearly stated, e.g:

[a] trees will be planted to screen and demarcate individual holes;

[b] provide featuring and interest to individual holes;

[c] offer and increase strategy of individual holes;

[d] act as markers along fairways or as appropriate backcloths or focal points to greens;

[e] give visual and aesthetic interest.

Moreover, trees will offer ecological continuity but must not be out of balance with the other habitat types, i.e. grasslands etc. Before considering planting, the vistas on and off the course must be noted and strongly borne in mind. Periodic views of the wider countryside will give an added feeling of playing within a natural setting.

Tree and shrub selection

Trees and shrubs selected should be native to the area and indigenous to the site. This will ensure ecological continuity within the surrounding countryside and will ensure a greater survival rate and rapid establishment. A mixture of both standards and forestry transplants may be most appropriate in certain instances where an immediate mature effect is required. The larger trees, although slower growing, will offer an immediate effect. The smaller, but more rapid growing transplants may gradually overtake the standards so producing the longer-term screen or woodland feature.

When planting, one must always consider the "naturalness" – rows of intermingled trees not only appear artificial but offer very little ecological continuity. Ideally, the trees selected should be planted informally (randomly) in single-species groupings of possibly 8-32 trees. These would be at appropriate spacings depending upon the trees selected. The type of ground preparation would need to be considered at the outset. Areas of grassland adjacent to play may need to be chemically sprayed prior to treatment, to eradicate weed and competitive grass growth. This could involve a single broad-scale application or alternatively an individual treatment, spraying a 300 mm radius around each tree base. Following broad-scale treatments, further periodic chemical weed control may be necessary from time to time and should be built into the specification or works programme.

The types of trees selected should form a natural balance between the under storey, i.e. low growing shrubs, including the wood edge species, the nurse and pioneer trees such as alder, birch and Scots pine and the longer-lived, but often slow-growing, high-canopy trees such as oak, ash and beech. The trees should be indicative of the site and common within the countryside, rare species may not be appropriate due to their difficulty in establishment.

In certain environments, such as within the larger estate grounds, some ornamental tree types may be appropriate as these do offer aesthetic interest on the course, the main problems tend to arise when these are planted to form a very artificial block or distracting feature within a backdrop of more native planting.

Any tree planting should not take precedence over other more interesting habitat types. On some courses, heather or high-quality grasslands have been severely damaged by indiscriminate tree planting.

Grasslands

Turning to the grasslands, these can be used to good effect in the landscaping of a new golf course. The site may already support a good quality sward which, with appropriate management, may come to form a significant feature of the course. Scarification, in conjunction with mowing, may help to reduce any coarse tussocks to promote a more uniform sward of optimum density as determined by the intended usage, i.e. fairway, semi-rough or deep rough.

Varying the height of cut and alternating the cutting frequencies can contribute significantly to the aesthetics and strategy of the course. Given appropriate management these areas need not become untidy, impossible hazards slowing the pace of the game and severely restricting ball retrieval. The ecological benefits from a series of well-managed grassland swards can be tremendous, offering substantial additional interest to the golfer.

Other vegetation

Heather, either as heather-dominated stands or as patches within rough grassland, can also be used to good effect. Indeed, the loss of heather on a number of courses through management neglect has left several once-interesting fairways featureless with a stroke index nearer 18 than 1. Extending the areas of heather will involve producing an optimum pH for heather growth and establishment (normally 4.5) and, if an underlying seed bed is not available, then cutting and spreading heather shoots or seed/trash collected from underneath established plants. Before spreading, all grass, weed and thatch must be removed and the underlying soil/humus exposed. Heather brashings may be required and spread over the prepared areas to reduce exposure and wind-blow until seed is established. Given the complexity of this work, the selection of small areas prepared on a trial basis may be the way forward, only progressing further when the optimum methods have been established.

The sensitive use of native vegetation types when landscaping a new course can often achieve far more than would be achieved by relying on large scale earth-moving works. Similarly, appropriate vegetation types will reduce the need for sand bunkering which does, on many courses, only perpetuate artificiality and further increase the maintenance burden of the greenstaff.

(RST : B.185)

ECOLOGY AT WORK ON THE GOLF COURSE

It was extremely gratifying a year or two ago to hear that "Golf Club Hosel" Germany was to receive an environmental award. This was presented by the Local Environment Authority in conjunction with the German Golf Union. The initial ecological appraisal undertaken by STRI encouraged a response by the club to adopt a more positive approach to its rough management. Tree planting, pond clearance and appropriate grassland management have, since the initiation of the work in 1991, helped to encourage a greater wildlife diversity around the course. The roughs now give a more natural appeal with added interest to members playing the course.

The recently completed 9 hole golf course at Laceby near Goole, South Humberside, now known as the Manor Golf Club is attracting a considerable interest for its variety of wildlife. The owners have always maintained their interest in conservation and were quite surprised to find such an increase in certain species upon completion of the construction works. The owners claim that the farmland upon which the course has now been built has always supported the smaller seed-eating birds, foxes and the odd kestrel, but since its completion and the establishment of the 9 hole golf course, a marked increase in little owl numbers has been noted (possibly due to the increase in small rodents within the grasslands). Most surprisingly of all a family of badgers are now exploiting the rough grasslands and a set has been established. Regular sightings increase the interest to members.

From a purely ecological viewpoint, golf courses offer a diversity of different habitat types, ranging from wet and dry heathlands through to a range of different grasslands including chalk, downs and links environments to the woodlands (both mixed or coniferous) and moorlands. Many golf courses, by their presence, are directly conserving some of our rarest wildlife species. Moreover, the majority of courses throughout the country serve to extend the local semi-natural landscape, to form ecological corridors or highways in which species can travel between areas as required to suit their requirements, i.e. feeding or fulfilling their life cycles, etc. They allow certain species the chance to move from sites as they become unsuitable for a particular reason, permitting recolonisation either within the corridor or beyond in a suitable stable site. By linking a number of areas, the "golf" wildlife corridors will increase the overall extent of any particular habitat, providing that appropriate ongoing management can be given.

Management of the roughs

Probably the first question to address is the long-term sustainability of any management works. Any work to be undertaken must be practical and should form part of an ongoing schedule of works (policy document). The club, possibly with outside expertise, such as is available within the STRI, may need to identify the most important areas, i.e. those likely to hold the most species and which would positively benefit from the ecological management works.

When considering copse management and development, i.e. the development of woodland screens between fairways, it may be important to consider their minimum width. Where possible the screen should be between 15 and 30 m wide in order to retain sufficient trees to be of interest to certain wildlife species. The trees should be planted informally with (if possible) an outer edge or understorey of appropriate shrub types. Given the restricted movement of some insects, individual blocks may need to be of a minimum distance apart, i.e. 50 m or less, to act as stepping stones for the majority of species. Individual trees may also be useful in between blocks, helping to provide the continuity between wooded areas. The number of trees, however, on any golf course must be balanced with the need to retain vistas or views of the course and indeed the grasslands and other features present.

When considering scrub clearance or gorse management, a number of important points should be borne in mind to ensure the ecological continuity. Areas to be treated should be arbitrarily split into a number of manageable portions and one area only should be managed each year. The visual aspect may warrant that initial management works be undertaken in the centre of any one stand, leaving the edge until a reasonable re-establishment has occurred. Replanting the stand should involve the utilisation of like or similar native species as this will help to maintain the natural feature.

The grasslands occupying a large proportion of the golf course need not all be cut to a uniform height. Varying the height of cut through the given areas and determining an appropriate cutting frequency will offer a range of structurally different and diverse habitats, so maximising the overall area for a greater diversity of wildlife species.

Given a greater awareness of the types of habitat management which are necessary in golf, there is no doubt that a great many of our golf courses could act much more positively in wildlife and habitat conservation. Take Temple Golf Club as one example, Temple Golf Club commissioned an ecological report back in 1990, the STRI undertook the appraisal and realising the potential of the course, recommended a series of management operations. The local wildlife groups have since become involved in this work and a recent survey conducted through the Windsor and Maidenhead Urban Wildlife Group and the Berkshire, Buckinghamshire, Oxfordshire Naturalist Trust has revealed a number of very interesting habitats and species type. The rough grasslands occupy over 50% of the course. The semi-roughs about 25% and the greens and tees approximately 2%. The rough grasslands are now cut on a twice per year basis in spring and late summer and all grass cuttings are removed to prevent nutrient enrichment. The semi-roughs are cut more frequently varying upon growing conditions, but both these areas are extremely species rich.

The frequencies of cutting are encouraging both slow-growing species normally associated with grazing, i.e. horseshoe vetch, rockrose and wild thyme. The deeper sward supports a rich bounty of orchids including common spotted, bee orchid, pyramidal and a very large colony of the rare green winged orchid, where in one area alone over 200 plants including one pure white variant have been recorded. Other very rare and interesting species include adders-tongue fern and the white helleborine. The woodlands occupying around 22% of the course are predominantly beech, with associated areas of understorey scrub. A number of small clumps and individual trees are also to be seen around the course. The woodlands support some very interesting species including spurge laurel, wood sage, primrose, several species of violet and the wayfaring and spindle trees. Throughout summer clouds of butterflies and day-flying moths are seen over the course. It is claimed that a further attraction to members playing the course is the perfume released from the low growing herbs when trodden underfoot.

Clearly ecology is working at Temple Golf Club. It is ,however, also working on a great many more courses throughout the country and indeed throughout Europe. It is, however, a pity that much of the interest now being generated at a few clubs is not more widespread. Many golf courses do have the potential to contribute significantly to the conservation of our countryside. The management, if undertaken sensibly with guidance, possibly through a document outlining the types of work necessary in the identified areas, need not be of detriment to the game and may possibly enhance and improve it.

(RST : B.185)

GOLF COURSES, WOODLANDS AND WILDLIFE
Introduction
Broad-leaved trees and woods are a major feature of our landscape, indeed almost the whole of the British Isles following the last Ice Age some 10,000 years ago was covered with trees. Birch, a main primary coloniser, spread from the South and from the North. This tree, with its fairly rapid growth rate and relatively short life span, was largely responsible for creating and producing the underlying soil conditions which later allowed longer-lived, slower-growing species to dominate. With Britain a predominantly forested country, the wildlife that initially colonised was mainly that preferring a woodland habit. Man's growing intensification of woodland clearing, together with his rapidly expanding technology with regard to the cutting tools used, has meant that our wildlife has had to display a great deal of resilience in order to survive these rapid changes brought about within the landscape. Species lacking such an intrinsic capacity to bounce back have become extinct or, at least, very rare. Britain's wildlife is subject to pressures from many sides.

The Role of the Golf Course
The golf course is well suited to providing a relatively safe refuge from the pressures of farming and other land-use industries. Concern, however, has recently been

expressed from various quarters, including the Royal & Ancient, who have stated that golf must not be seen as a selfish user of the land. Golf is, however, in a very enviable position with respect to nature conservation and could therefore be seen as a very caring game, given appropriate sympathetic guidance. Indeed, many of the golf courses now visited by the STRI have adopted this type of ecologically based approach and are helping to maintain a balance of habitats on and around the course without disrupting the game or its enjoyment.

There are, however, limitations as to how far one can go with conservation and ecological management on the golf course, as the needs and priorities of the game must be considered. One is aware that several private consultancy services are operating on golf purely on ecological grounds with little expertise in golf course management. If conservation or ecological management and golf are to coexist, it is essential that ecologists develop an appreciation of the game and of the strategic requirements, traffic flow limitations and suitability of tree species with respect to their position on the course.

Important benefits, both ecological and aesthetic, can result as a consequence of planting trees and shrubs, though long-lasting benefit would require a greater emphasis on management than is presently given on most golf courses.

An initial assessment of the course is the key to determining the present qualities and future possibilities. By way of a very detailed and comprehensive report, an ecologist would be able to advise upon the most appropriate development programme for each individual course.

Many courses visited have had copses at intervals around the course of even-aged trees, normally either birch or pine, both of which are pioneer trees or should represent the first colonisers to arrive in more naturalistic settings. Their rapid growth and turn-over provide the basic physical conditions which encourage the establishment of the longer-lived broad-leaved trees. These plantings often provide the sole source of screening or feature and will inevitably be very short-lived. The fungus *Piptoporus betulinus* is a very aggressive parasite causing a heart rot within the wood of the birch trees. This fungus is relatively opportunistic, in that it enters the trees at any age, normally via wounds, ie. where branches have been lost. The result is a gradual deterioration of the copse until all the trees eventually die. This may, for birch, be between 30 and 80 years, depending upon the position, aspect and planting density.

The above is stressed to demonstrate just how important it is to commence a forward-thinking approach for the golf course and to consider a programme of increasing the habitat diversity of these areas.

Thinning and underplanting (enrichment) are vital tools in any woodland management. Gaps created artificially or naturally can be restocked with selected species. The gaps created after thinning should be of a diameter of at least the height of the surrounding trees. Groups of forestry transplants should be utilised, planted in the centre of the gaps. Weeding and protection are always important considerations following planting.

Creating the Woodland Edge

Many golf course woodlands come to a very sharp or abrupt end as high trees end and the semi-rough or fairway takes over. In such cases, but not in all, it may be possible to create a wood edge with broken shrub or understorey tree groupings. Not only does the wood edge provide a more gentle transition between grassland and woodland, but it has immense value ecologically; it screens the more untidy woodland floor from view, it helps reduce leaf litter and woody debris encroaching from the woodland out on to playing surfaces, and it also encourages understorey regeneration within the woodland centre. Obviously, individual site assessments are required in order to determine the merits for that site and the extent or quality of edge that can be facilitated.

(CGC 1 : 51)

TREES ON GOLF COURSES

Many golf clubs carry out extensive tree planting programmes with the object of improving appearance and providing shelter. Carefully-sited trees are also used to affect golfing characteristics. The choice of species should receive the same attention as the choice of site. Using unsuitable species will give disappointing results. In many cases the defects may not be noticeable for many years. Large forest trees such as oak, chestnut, elm, beech and sycamore do not reach any substantial size for 50 years or more and often live for several hundred years. The correct choice of species in the correct site can provide pleasure to generations of golfers yet unborn. The incorrect choice can prove a waste of time, effort and money and be a source of irritation until eventually removed. Where medium to large-scale tree planting schemes are involved it is essential to seek professional advice.

There are perhaps in the region of 1,700 tree species with innumerable varieties which could be grown somewhere in the British Isles. There are many different points to bear in mind in deciding what type of trees to plant. One of the first considerations must be the size. It is completely pointless planting large forest trees a few yards away from a green or in any other spot where space is restricted. In such situations as soon as the tree has become reasonably well established it will be necessary to either cut it down or, worse still, prune it back severely, destroying its appearance. Where space is available, however, it is well worthwhile planting forest trees. The trees listed below will all reach at least 15 metres, with good specimens perhaps reaching up to 30 metres or more.

Acacia - *Robinia pseudoacacia*

A reasonably hardy tree though it prefers open, sunny situations. It is tolerant of industrial pollution. Deciduous, the tree is of a graceful, open habit with feathery foliage and produces slightly fragrant, pea-like flowers in July. Light soils are preferable – either neutral or slightly acid in reaction. It tends to be rather shallow-rooting and grows quite quickly in the early stages.

Ash - *Fraxinus excelsior*

A very hardy tree which will withstand industrial situations and exposed positions. Again, a graceful tree of open habit with pinnate foliage. It will grow in most soils producing an extensive root system. It has a tendency to shed branches and so should not be planted in the vicinity of car parking areas.

Beech - *Fagus sylvatica*

A hardy tree and one of our most beautiful native large forest trees with smooth grey stems, graceful habit, delicate foliage in the spring and good autumn colour. The beech requires a well drained soil and though it grows naturally on chalk or over limestone, it will also tolerate acid soils. Young trees grow well in shaded situations. Several different forms are available including ones with purple foliage which are particularly attractive. Beech hedges are also very popular.

Cedar of Lebanon - *Cedrus libani*

An evergreen which grows best in the warmer parts of the country and prefers a sunny situation. It is unsuitable for areas with air pollution problems but where it can be grown it makes a magnificent specimen tree, flat topped with tiered branches and dark bluish-green needles. Though it will grow on a wide range of soils it is best in deep neutral loam. The related blue cedar (*C. atlantica glauca*) is also a good specimen tree and will grow in similar situations.

Hornbeam – *Carpinus betulus*

A hardy deciduous tree suitable for both shaded and windy sites. Sometimes mistaken for beech though the leaves are much more toothed. Tolerant of site but usually grows on clay or chalky soil.

Horse Chestnut – *Aesculus hippocastanum*

A hardy tree with large leaves. The latter can be a nuisance in the autumn, the leaves collecting on fairways and, of course, in gutters and drains of buildings. The common horse chestnut produces the 'conkers' which attract children though there are sterile forms such as '*Baumanii*' and hybrids such as *carnea plantierensis* which do not produce chestnuts. The pink flowers of the *carnea* hybrids are particularly attractive. It generally prefers a deep loam and not too exposed site.

Limes – *Tilia* sp.

Large, attractive, hardy, deciduous trees. Common species include *T. cordata, T.* X *europaea, T. petiolaris* and *T. platyphyllos*. There are some problems with these trees. Species such as *petiolaris* are narcotic to bees and X *europaea* or the common lime sometimes causes problems as it attracts aphids which then cause the leaves to exude sap and so it is generally best not planted around car parking areas. The trees are quite tolerant as to soil type but prefer a deep loam.

Acers
Norway Maple – *Acer platanoides*

This is a hardy deciduous tree which is reasonably tolerant to air pollution. It tends to be similar in appearance to the sycamore but the leaves are more noticeably toothed. Happy on most soils but best on light, well drained loam.

Silver Maple – *A. saccharinum*

Again, a hardy tree which is reasonably tolerant of wind and pollution and which also has good autumn colour. It has similar cultural requirements. Both these species along with sycamore can produce problems in the autumn because of the accumulation of large leaves.

Common Oak – *Quercus robur*

Very hardy, a broad-headed and rugged tree which is one of the longest-lived of our native species. It does well on heavy soils and is best transplanted when small but often requires protection from rabbits at this stage.

Durmast Oak – *Q. petraea*

Resembles the common oak but replaces it in wetter areas, particularly in the west of the country. It also tends to withstand exposure rather better.

Holm Oak – *Q. ilex*

One of our finest evergreen trees though it is best suited for milder areas of the country. It is suitable for coastal areas though sea winds may stunt its growth. It can also be grown as a hedge. Tolerant of acidity it will grow in a wide range of soils but does not transplant easily so container-grown stock is best. Other species of note include *Q. rubra* (red oak), *Q. coccinea* (scarlet oak) and *Q. cerris* (Turkey oak).

Plane – *Platanus* X *hispanica (acerifolia)*, also *P. orientalis*

Both are very attractive trees, the former being known as the London plane. They are particularly noted for the attractive bark which peels off in patches giving a mottled appearance to the trunk. This is particularly conspicuous in areas subject to industrial pollution as the patches show up against the remaining blackened bark. They may be grown in all types of reasonably fertile soil but will not grow to full size in chalky soils and may become chlorotic in very shallow chalk soils.

Tree of Heaven – *Ailanthus altissima*
A fast-growing tree; once established, the *Ailanthus* is particularly tolerant of atmospheric pollution. It produces very large ash-like leaves. It will grow on a wide range of soils.

Tulip Tree – *Liriodendron tulipifera*
This is a large deciduous tree which prefers a sunny position and which can be damaged by frost. It provides good autumn colour when the leaves turn yellow and is remarkable for the tulip-shaped, greenish-yellow flowers produced in July. These flowers are only seen on the mature specimens. The tulip tree prefers a deep rich loam.

Walnut – *Juglans regia*
A hardy tree but one which should not be sited in areas particularly subject to late frosts. It is fairly slow-growing but does produce a handsome tree with pinnate leaves. It can only be reasonably relied on to fruit in the milder parts of the country. It is, however, not particular as to soil type.

No list of trees can ever be complete and many good large trees have been omitted from the above. The examples given, however, can be considered for planting on golf courses, bearing in mind the points made. Large forest trees take many years to develop to maturity and so planting them is a long term project, and in tree terms this means perhaps 100 years or more. It was the foresight of our ancestors which produced the woodlands of today. The present day golf club is in a unique position to contribute to the landscape of tomorrow.

(CGC 1 : 48)

TREE PLANTING AND YOUNG TREE GROWTH

Trees not only add character and interest to our landscape, they also provide a habitat for thousands of species of plants, birds, animals and insects. Keeping this in mind, and the likelihood that, if left unhindered, the trees will be present for several decades at the very least, the initial choice of species and location when planting is of considerable importance. All too often unsuitable species are planted in unsuitable locations, usually with the best of intentions but with, at best, disappointing results, both from an aesthetic and ecological point of view. The species planted should, ideally, reflect those present or expected to be present in a native landscape. Native species have evolved with groups of birds, insects and plants which can live in close association and therefore have more ecological value compared with non-native species (known as exotics) which have been introduced to Britain and which have far fewer associated species.

Location is also of extreme importance. Foresight is required to envisage what impact the mature tree will have upon the landscape and it must also be placed realistically to fit in with the requirement of the golf course area in question. For example, it is pointless planting large forest trees close to a golf green where space is restricted and problems of leaf fall, shading and competition between tree and grass roots for water may develop. So, forward planning is all important, both in terms of species choice, related of course to size, and location.

The STRI can now offer advice on an advisory level for site appraisals, woodland management and tree planting with emphasis on the suitability of species for the golf course.

Size of Young Trees

Trees are available in various sizes for commercial planting, ranging from transplants of approximately 150-600 mm high, whips of approximately 450-900 mm to several categories of standards of 0.3-5.0 metres high. Although the larger standards appear stronger and more capable of withstanding damage and vandalism etc., they are far more costly, need to be staked and they do tend to be more prone to losses during the transplanting process. Transplants and whips on the other hand may be less advanced, but are cheaper, quicker to plant with no need for staking, and tend to grow more vigorously in the first few years following planting. Small trees, however, could easily be swamped by high vegetation such as grass, bracken, etc. unless regular weeding is undertaken.

Bare Root or Container Grown?

Trees can be acquired as bare root stock or container-grown. Container-grown trees are generally more expensive and, once planted, the roots do have a tendency to remain within the original root ball rather than extending into the surrounding soil, which could affect overall stability. Bare root stock on the other hand is usually cheaper and more likely to form a satisfactory rooting system, but may be more vulnerable to damage during transport.

Pre-Planting Care

Care of trees in the transplanting stage is of utmost importance. Tree roots are very prone to drying out and/or frost damage during transport between the nursery and the final planting site, particularly so with bare root stock. The roots must be kept moist by covering them, for example, in black polythene filled with damp peat or newspaper. Straw can also help to protect against frost. All too often trees are planted with their roots already damaged or even dead through lack of care.

When to Plant

The autumn and winter months are most suitable for planting deciduous trees. Deciduous broad-leaved species should be dormant during the transplanting operation, i.e. between autumn leaf-fall and spring when new leaves appear. Generally, mid October to early December tends to be most suitable when the soil is moist but still relatively warm following the summer. During this period the roots are provided with the opportunity to develop whilst relatively little shoot growth is taking place. In spring, there is less time available for such root development before new leaves emerge, placing demands upon the root system for water and nutrient uptake.

Evergreens should also be planted over the autumn and winter, avoiding the colder, frosty weather in December, January and February. Generally speaking, October and March tend to be most suitable. For both evergreens and deciduous species, avoid planting in frosty or waterlogged soils.

The planting period of container-grown plants is less defined and planting could, if necessary, be carried out at any time of year, although the above times are to be preferred.

How to Plant

Prior to planting, set aside time to design a planting pattern which indicates desired positions and provides adequate spacings between trees, etc. This will save valuable time and help prevent mistakes once the trees are on site.

There are a variety of planting techniques which can be adopted, depending upon size and number of young trees. Notch planting may be adequate for smaller trees such as transplants and whips which have a relatively small root system. The operation involves opening up the ground in an L, T or H pattern, providing just enough room for the roots to be slipped in before the surrounding ground is heeled down firmly.

For larger trees, container-grown plants or difficult situations, pit planting is necessary. A hole should be dug of sufficient width to accommodate the roots fully extended with several centimetres to spare each side. The soil on the bottom and sides should be loosened and, at this stage, some leaf mould or well rotted manure, etc. could be introduced, particularly in low-fertility, sandy soils. Correct depth of planting is vital. The tree should be planted to the same depth that they were grown in the nursery. Replace the soil carefully around the root ball, taking care to fill all air pockets and firm at several layers. In light, dry soils, aim to leave the backfilled material slightly lower than surrounding ground to encourage water collection. The opposite should be applied on heavy, wet soils.

Generally, trees which are higher than 1.2 metres will require staking. A suitable stake should be driven at least 300–600 mm into the bottom of the hole prior to planting with the stake remaining above-ground reaching approximately one third of the way up the tree, just below the first branch. Place the stake slightly off-centre and facing prevailing winds. The tree should then be tied a few centimetres below the top and a similar distance from the bottom of the stake using one of the variety of proprietary ties available for this purpose.

Immediately after planting, plenty of water should be applied to provide moisture and aid soil settling. If the soil is known to be infertile, then an application of fertiliser could be given to the surface or worked into the backfill. Guards may be required for protection against rabbits, etc. and to promote faster growth in the first year. Planting tubs can also give protection from the elements.

Aftercare

Following the tree planting operation, a certain level of aftercare is essential to maintain a healthy and vigorously growing tree. Young trees are susceptible to a variety of problems, including moisture stress, nutrient stress, physical damage and competition from surrounding vegetation. Newly introduced stock, particularly that planted in the spring months, or container-grown trees planted over summer, should be watered regularly throughout the first year, especially during dry weather. Competition from surrounding vegetation for moisture, nutrients, light, etc. must also be reduced as much as possible. During planting, the surface vegetation immediately surrounding the stem should be removed and kept at bay for the first couple of years. An inverted turf, chopped bark or proprietary mulch mats will help to reduce weed redeveloping and hand-weeding may be adequate to remove those which do appear. However, where a larger number of trees are involved, occasional treatments with a total herbicide will probably be more practical to keep the area weed-free. Trees do vary in their susceptibility to herbicide damage and so care must be taken to use only suitable materials. Use a herbicide approved by the Nature Conservancy Council which has been proven to be suitable in environmentally sensitive areas.

Longer Term Maintenance

The planting pattern chosen will determine to some extent the level of longer term maintenance. Whips planted at, say, 1.5 metre spacings will require thinning quite soon, perhaps five to ten years after planting and at regular intervals thereafter.

Standards should be planted at sufficient spacing to allow full development, although judicious pruning may be required to remove dead and diseased wood, as well as for shaping purposes.

The point to emphasise is that thinning and pruning should not be over-looked. All too frequently, management is simply forgotten, resulting in over-crowding and stunted growth. These operations must form an important part of long term maintenance.

Sources of Help
(1) Arboricultural Association, Ampfield House, Ampfield, Nr Romsey, Hampshire, SO51 9PA, Tel: Braishfield 01794 368717 (Contractors and Consultants throughout the country are members of the AA).
(2) Forestry Commission, 231 Corstorphine Road, Edinburgh, EH12 7AT, Tel: 031 334 0303.
(3) Any Local Authority, Parks Department or Landscape Section.
(4) The Sports Turf Research Institute, Bingley, West Yorkshire, BD16 1AU, Tel: 01274 565131.

(CGC 1 : 49)

SHELTERS FOR YOUNG TREES

Careful tree planting has always been an important aspect of maintenance of sporting areas such as golf courses to help provide shelter and to improve a site's general appearance. It is therefore essential that the growth of new trees is given every encouragement during the establishment phase following planting out. With this aim in mind, a fairly recent innovation in arboriculture has been the development of tree shelters. These not only provide protection from the elements as well as damage caused by animals, but they also encourage rapid early growth of the young trees.

Types of Shelter Used
The types of material used for tree shelters can vary but they normally comprise translucent or transparent plastic tubes of an appropriate diameter. These are anchored to the ground either by a small stake or steel rod which can be placed inside or outside the shelter. The normal height for a shelter is between 0.6 and 0.75 metres, although where protection against sheep is required then a shelter at least 1.2 metres high with a stronger supporting stake would be more suitable.

Benefits
A common problem when establishing young trees is the damage caused by various wandering animals such as rabbits, hares and sheep which can strip off large sections of bark. Tree shelters therefore provide a barrier which will discourage such damage and increase the chances of the trees' survival. These shelters can also reduce the water stress on the young trees during dry periods, thus minimising the risk of death following transplanting.

A further benefit is that most broad-leaved trees which are protected by shelters show more vigorous early growth when compared with non-sheltered trees. It has been reported that oak transplants will emerge from a 1.2 metre high shelter in two or three years compared with the five or six years taken to reach a similar height with conventional methods. On emergence from the shelter the rate of growth declines, the crown and branches develop rapidly and the tree shows little difference from others of a similar size except that it will be several years younger. Shelters also indicate the location of newly planted trees, thus enabling chemical weed control measures to be carried out around them without fear of damage.

Construction of Shelters
Sturdy nursery transplants some 200–500 mm tall with a single leading shoot can be protected using shelters. Any large side branches are best removed and the tree should be planted in the normal manner, leaving a loose, level surface so that the base of the shelter can be pushed into the ground. Any remaining weed vegetation should be

removed from the prepared surface to prevent it from developing within the shelter and smothering the tree.

It is particularly important to erect tree shelters at the time of or immediately after planting, particularly where damage from local animals is likely to occur. If a stake has been used, then the shelter should be sufficiently large to accommodate this as well as durable enough to last for at least six years. The stake should be firmly hammered into the ground close to the young tree and the shelter then placed over the tree and firmly secured to the stake by a suitable tie. The base of the shelter should be pushed well into the ground.

Weed Control

The presence of a shelter will reduce the overall need for weed control measures around the trees, although spraying may be required for one or two years. If a tree is sheltered then additional protection need not be given when spraying, although the usual precautions against drifting of the herbicide should still apply. If weeds are found to be growing inside the shelter and are restricting the growth of the tree, then the shelter should be raised and the exposed bases of the weed plants can then be pulled to the outside so that they can be subsequently included in any general control measures.

Removal of Shelter

It is normally recommended that the shelter should remain around the tree for five or six years. This will allow for the initial growth boost and protection needed by the young tree, as well as providing sufficient time for it to develop a healthy crown and strong stem capable of standing on its own. Most shelter materials last for about this period of time and in effect they can be left to disintegrate in situ although any encircling wire ties should be severed.

(CGC 1 : 50)

CLEARANCE OF SCRUB & STUMP REGROWTH CONTROL

Introduction

Scrub invasion or the natural regrowth of trees and shrubs is a major problem on many of Britain's golf courses. Although often thought of as a major problem on the heathland course, the gradual but natural increase in tree and scrub can be demonstrated on the majority of golf courses providing that ground and climatic conditions are conducive.

Possibly the main problems arising from the continued invasion of trees and shrubs on a golf course are:

(a) The often quite rapid change in course character.

(b) Deterioration in the overall playing characteristics, ie. loss of sight line from tee to green, etc.

(c) The deterioration of ecological quality over time.

Once the natural regeneration of trees has occurred and a semi-mature stand has developed, their removal can be a very difficult and often thankless task to undertake. Not only is the Club likely to receive criticism and concern from members (almost always a problem when one starts to fell larger trees), but there are the physical difficulties involving the use of pulleys and winches or uprooting, all of which are extremely demanding of time, a commodity which the Greenkeeper, even in the winter period, can ill-afford. If a policy of uprooting is undertaken, there may be an amount of surface disruption which will need reinstating and this is again both time-consuming and labour-demanding. Alternatively, cutting can leave unsightly stumps above ground level, their presence indicating to members that trees are being cut down, again possibly causing further criticism. More importantly, however, are the problems relating to ball retrieval, physical injury and possible stump regrowth, all of which may necessitate further expensive physical or chemical control methods.

Control of Scrub Invasion

The control of scrub should be an integral component of any course policy document aimed at the longer term improvement or maintenance of the course. Part of the Greenkeeper's duties throughout the winter should be to assess the through the green areas, physically removing the young regrowth as it arises. By removing the saplings in the first few years of their growth, substantial reductions in both time and labour can be effected.

Setting up a programme to suppress the natural regrowth in the first few years will undoubtedly necessitate the removal of several larger trees, particularly if sight lines or other obstructions to play are involved. As outlined above, these trees can be physically uprooted using a winch and pulley system. This operation does necessitate caution and may involve a certain amount of relevelling and reseeding or returfing work so as not to encourage weed or ailing grass species.

Alternatively, the trees can be cut and, if necessary, the stumps ground to below surface level. Many stump cutters are now available costing between £5,000 and £19,000. The hire of suitable equipment is often a sensible option.

Once well-established, many trees have the capacity to regenerate from the cut stump. These include rhododendron, sycamore, birch and willow to mention but a few. Where this is a problem, it will be necessary to chemically treat the stumps in the following manner. Drill three holes down into the stump to a depth of 80 to 100 mm using a No.10 wood bit and apply a super-saturated solution of a brushwood killer, possibly the most appropriate being those containing ammonium sulphamate or fosamine ammonium in a super-saturated solution in strict accordance with the manufacturer's recommendations.

Possibly one of the most labour-intensive tasks following the scrub clearance works is the removal and disposal of the cut trees and shrubs. These should be removed off site and either burnt or, preferably and presuming that substantial woodland or copse areas are present, they can be stockpiled within the centre of such areas, thus helping to maintain and perpetuate the woodland nutrient cycle. Alternatively, several wood chippers are now available, ranging from the smaller 5 to 15 hp machines costing between £500 and £8,000 through to the larger tractor-drawn 20 to 50 hp machines costing above £10,000. Machines can again also be hired.

Summary

Scrub invasion and its subsequent control is a problem on many golf courses throughout Britain and is now reaching the stage where if no action is taken, a major deterioration in course quality and, indeed, course character will inevitably ensue. The clearance of scrub and the regrowth control must therefore form an integral part of the overall management programme for the golf course.

(RST : B.181)

THROUGH THE GREEN WITH WILD FLOWERS

Introduction

Recent figures have shown that golf courses support a range of physically diverse grassland types ranging from acidic, fairly species-poor to the floristically very species-rich, calcareous grasslands characteristic of the Southern Downs. Grasslands may be dry or wet, all of which support their own very distinctive and diverse floras.

Recent figures have also shown that out of the total 3100 hectares of golf course land designated as Sites of Special Scientific Interest, approximately 52% or 1600 hectares of this total is represented by grasslands.

Of major importance to wildlife is the degree of structural variation within the grasslands, which is primarily brought about by the differing cutting heights employed over the whole course. These may range from the very intensively mown greens through to the carry, fairways, semi-roughs and finally the deep roughs which may possibly be cut only very infrequently or not at all. Thus, golf courses indirectly are, in many cases, supporting a substantial floristic and faunal diversity.

Management of Existing Areas

These areas, particularly the deep roughs, are subject to natural changes and without any form of upkeep or management will undergo a process of change called succession. In most cases therefore without a degree of active management, competitive grass and herb weed species will rapidly reduce the overall diversity of the sward, leaving an unintended stand of untidy grasses which will impoverish the overall aesthetic and ecological objectives.

Thought given to carefully timed mowing of the through the green areas, whilst not in itself likely to give a diverse show of flowers, will make the most of whatever flowers already exist. An eye-catching effect can be achieved with just one or two species. Leaving the mowing in a particular area for a short period during the flowering season can produce a surprising effect, without making it difficult to resume the mowing thereafter. The period of time left for flowering needs to be timed according to the needs of the species present within the sward. It may, for example, be possible to mow up until May or June and resume again during late July, this period of just two months (maximum) being sufficient to allow the existing sward to flower and set seed. It is important that the resulting debris is removed from site following cutting on each occasion so as to maintain the fairly low soil fertility.

Starting from Bare Ground

Once the vegetation has been physically or chemically removed, a full analysis of the substrate and soil chemistry is vital. This will influence the types of seed to be used in the seeding programme.

The important chemical factors are nitrogen (N), phosphate (P) and pH. High levels of N and P in the soil will increase the speed of succession and therefore the loss of species planted, so it is vital that steps be taken to reduce these levels to within acceptable limits.

Several methods are available for reducing the soil fertility. These would include sowing a nurse crop in the first year before sowing the final seeds mix, and stripping and selling the top layers of topsoil so as to retain the infertile soils below. This method is quite drastic and not recommended here.

Alternatively, it may be possible to slit various materials into the topsoil such as sand or other inert top dressing. This approach is more long term and, to be effective, would need to be carried out annually for several years (obvious costs involved).

Wild Flower Seeds Mixtures

Following the final surface preparation of cultivation, harrowing and raking to produce a uniform, firm surface, the appropriate wild flower mixture can be introduced. Several methods have been tried for introducing the seed including strip seeding, contraseeding and drilling. The different methods do have their own intrinsic advantages for individual sites.

Turning to the seed itself, it is important that a reputable source is obtained as seed does differ in quality. Once a good quality source has been found, it is essential that the seed to be chosen matches the chemical conditions (including pH) of the substrate and that the seed falls within its 'natural' geographical area. Many species stand a greater chance of success if kept within their natural area range.

Seed merchants supply ready-made mixtures for particular soil types, ie. loams, calcareous soil, etc., and these are normally quite successful providing that appropriate soil preparation has been carried out prior to seeding.

There is much to be said for choosing extra species for inclusion into a standard mix as these, if appropriate, may further increase the overall chance of survival. It is important when evaluating species mixtures to consider the following:
- Avoid rare species – these tend to have specific habitat preferences, are unlikely to survive and are costly to purchase.
- A few common species chosen to suit the site conditions are preferred to a long list of unnecessary species. Common species are less expensive and more likely to survive.

The usual practice has been to sow appropriate grasses together with wild flowers in a percentage ratio of 80% (grass sp.) : 20% (wild flower sp.) at a total rate of 30 kg per hectare. The grass component would normally involve the less vigorous types such as Chewings fescue (*Festuca rubra* ssp. *commutata*) and slender red fescue (*Festuca rubra* ssp. *litoralis*). More recently, mixtures of 90% grass and just 10% wild flowers have been shown to be very effective and successful.

The seed should be sown during the spring (March to May) or autumn (September). The latter is preferred as an adequate water supply is more likely throughout the germination and establishment period.

Before undertaking any work on the golf course involving wild flower grasslands, a preliminary appraisal of the areas involved should be initiated to determine the existing ecological value of the site and to formulate an appropriate programme of development and management works.

(RST : B.178)

HEATHER ON THE GOLF COURSE

Heather is an extremely important component of many British golf courses from the playing or strategic point of view. Heather can offer a moderate to severe hazard and on many courses totally dictates how a given hole is to be played. Consider for example a green set within a banking surround completely dominated by heather. Here, shot placement must be accurate.

Heather on the golf course is ecologically important too. Not only does it contribute to the total heathland now extremely fragmented in Britain, but also forms a very important linking system analogous to the ecological corridors provided by road verges and railway embankments, which are becoming an essential part of our countryside. These, including golf courses, offer important routes for travel and movement. Indeed, a number of the weaker flying insects are totally dependent upon such land-bridges for their movement.

Although heather on our nation's golf courses does appear totally natural, it is a man-made environment. Early tree clearances and past management (or in some cases the lack of it) have encouraged the formation of these habitats.

It is because of the above that such areas are constantly changing (via the process known as succession) back to the former woodland via scrub invasion or to coarse grassland, through grass competition and eventual exclusion of the heather sward. On the golf course where rough management is normally limited, these changes can occur very quickly.

On the heathland golf course, tree invasion from rapidly-establishing pioneer species, such as birch and pine, can totally destroy the character and appearance of the course. Once the trees become readily visible, the concern regarding their removal may increase. Similarly, the physical method required to remove the trees can be extremely damaging to the heather sward. Regular annual inspections of the roughs during relatively slack periods, i.e. when other works are limited due to prevailing weather conditions, will help to prevent invasion and spread of trees.

Grass competition is directly due to a gradual increase in nutrient levels via the recycling of leaf litter, which enables the progressive spread of a few invasive grass species. Thatch or fibre accumulation will eventually choke out the heather, creating a marked separation between the relatively infertile and acidic humus layer below and the fibrous grass sward above.

Although to some extent grass growth can be checked via selective herbicide application, in the majority of cases more intensive sod cutting or deep scarification treatments are necessary to remove the fibre, so exposing the humus to light and stimulating the germination of the heather seed-bank. Once the rough has been brought back into condition, chemical applications using a selective herbicide at the appropriate time of the year will check further grass regrowth.

The heather plant itself has an extremely interesting, but finite, life cycle passing through the juvenile phases allowing its natural vegetative regeneration. During the later stages, however, it will enter into a period of decline whereby its capacity to regenerate drops considerably. Older heather plants, without management, greatly lose the vegetative regeneration capacity and reliance must be based on a viable seed-bank at the surface and the removal of the above-ground material. This can be done via burning or mechanical means, both of which have several advantages and disadvantages. The method chosen will be dependent upon the size of area and its position with regard to play.

It is vital that individual clubs recognise the importance of the plant and its role on the golf course and through the formation of a policy document implement a continuous, but infrequent, management programme. The heather sward and its condition thereafter is so maintained.

To further illustrate the above, one aspect not usually considered is the heather beetle and the damage which this can cause on unmanaged heather stands. The beetle is a relatively nondescript insect of 4 mm or thereabouts in size. Known scientifically as *Lochmaea suturalis* the heather beetle is more common in years when the climate favours it or when its main predator, the ladybird, is common.

The damage caused by the beetle can be of sufficient intensity to kill older plants outright. Younger, managed plants do tend to recover and may survive several attacks before finally succumbing. This outlines therefore, the need for ongoing but infrequent management. The heather beetle will lay its eggs in the spring on *Sphagnum* moss; again the presence of the moss may indicate poorly managed conditions. The larvae emerge during June-July and feed on heather shoots and leaves through to early September, whereupon they drop to the ground and pupate in the litter and debris collecting at the surface.

Because of the nature of the beetle's life cycle chemical treatment offers little advantage. It is not possible to spray when the problem is first noticed due to the many beneficial insects, including bees and the ladybird, its main predator, which also may be present on the plants. At the first sign of disturbance the larvae will drop from the plants and so become covered by the canopy of heather above them, this will further reduce the effectiveness of any spray treatment.

Flailing and possibly scarification, using appropriate heavy duty machinery, may prove useful but if the resulting heather sward is quite old, possibly even degenerate, it may not tolerate the intensity of this work. The ultimate scenario could therefore result in the total loss of heather for at least part of the golf course. Its long-term reinstatement via the underlying seed-bank would then be necessary.

There is a lack of heather management on a great number of golf courses in Britain. A small commitment to the "through the greens" or rough areas on an ongoing but infrequent basis would ensure that one of our nation's greatest natural resources is conserved for wildlife, which so often goes unnoticed but whose presence we nevertheless should enjoy. The golfers' game can be substantially enriched by the strategic and aesthetic presence of heather.

(RST : B.184)

HEATHER AND GORSE ON THE GOLF COURSE – THE LIMITATIONS & PROBLEMS WITH MANAGEMENT

Introduction

Heather and gorse are a significant feature of many golf courses, particularly heathland and downland, where they add to both the visual (aesthetic) appearance of the course as well as playing an important role in the strategy of the individual holes (influencing how each shot is to be played).

Because both heather and gorse appear naturally within the open countryside, it is often the general tendency of golf clubs to neglect the management of these areas until their eventual demise and loss of quality demands a rapid and immediate response.

Clearly, the 'left to nature' approach can never be successful in such small areas as are normally encountered on the golf course. Invariably, the shrubs decline in vigour, lose their inbuilt capacity to regenerate vegetatively and ultimately become untidy, with straggly growth and an increasing weed and scrub invasion.

Both heather and gorse are shrubs with a finite life cycle of around 30 years. During this period, the shrubs will pass through an initial pioneer or seedling establishment phase, the building or juvenile phase lasting for 5 to 15 years or so. This stage in the growth of the shrub is the main phase in which active management can be carried out. Infrequent but correct management during this time will help keep the plants juvenile and retain their capacity to regenerate vegetatively. If neglected during this period, the shrubs will pass through into the mature and, finally, degenerate stages, where the intrinsic inbuilt capacity may be seriously reduced to approximately one tenth of that observed during the building phase. From this very short biological resume, it is clear therefore that if the golf course is to retain its heather and gorse features, appropriate but carefully timed management is essential. Similarly, representatives of new courses built within areas where heather and gorse form dominant components of the surrounding vegetation are now seeking information on appropriate methods of gorse and heather introduction.

Introducing gorse and heather to new golf course sites

Gorse

Gorse can now be readily purchased from commercial suppliers in various forms, i.e.

seed, root-trained or container-grown stock. Seed is certainly the cheapest and often the most successful method of establishment for larger scale plantings. The key to success with this method is in the preparation of the soil prior to sowing. If gorse is plentiful within the local countryside, a site may be locally available from which seed can be collected. This would involve the hiring of an industrial type vacuum which could be used to collect the seed from underneath existing plants. Once collected, these would be spread over the prepared areas at a rate of approximately 400 to 500 g/m^3 of fresh material. This is a very tentative estimation as it is difficult to make an accurate quantitative comparison between gorse applied as clean seed and that viable proportion of seed collected as fresh surface material. The seed should be applied during early spring (February to March) or alternatively during the autumn (September to November) when climatic conditions are most favourable.

Preparation of the surface will involve an early application of a broad spectrum herbicide to kill the surface vegetation in the intended areas, leaving the treated areas for one month or so before removing the resultant dead grass and weed through successive heavy duty scarification work. This should be continued until the underlying soil has been exposed. Thereafter, soil tests should be carried out to determine the chemical status of the soil, together with an analysis of the pH. This should be between 4.0 and 5.5 and an optimum would be at 4.5. Should the soil not conform to these figures, then an early application of flowers of sulphur may be necessary to reduce the surface pH to the desired level. Application rates for this would be dependent upon the results of chemical analyses undertaken during the initial site inspection. A surface tilth should be created prior to spreading or sowing the seed. Thereafter, it would be necessary to maintain an adequate source of irrigation throughout the establishment period.

Root-trained or container-grown plants could also be used, though these, due to the expense, are preferred in small areas. Apart from the capital outlay, a considerable labour input is required in their planting. The ground, once cleared of existing vegetation, would need to be lightly cultivated and the surface firmed by alternate heeling and raking. The pH and chemical status of the soil must be favourable. The plants would then be notch or pit planted into the soil individually at spacings of up to 1 x 1 m^2. A programme of watering following planting would need to be adopted.

Heather

The introduction of heather, like gorse, involves producing the correct soil conditions, preferably fairly infertile (important to suppress competition from coarse grass and weed species) with an optimum pH of around 4.5. All vegetation must be cleared from the surface leaving a base humus in which to initiate seeding. As pointed out earlier, no commercial seed is available for purchase and so in this case its establishment is dependent upon locally available seed sources. Seed can be obtained by one of several measures, including cut brashings (whole above-ground shoot material), capsules (top 50 mm [2 in.] of plant with seed heads) or by collecting surface material in the manner described earlier for gorse.

Provisional results from the STRI's heather trials have found that brashings cut and spread immediately (without storage) at the appropriate time of year may be most effective. Brashings certainly help to prevent erosion of the prepared surface during high winds and this is especially important on the lowland heathlands of southern Britain. Furthermore, the plants too will be protected from the climate as they grow. Moisture retention is also favoured by the surface woody material such that seedling growth can proceed into the drier summer period. Once the heather has established, steps towards its management must be provided and adhered to.

Conservation and encouragement of heather and gorse on the established course

Heather

Several methods of management are available to the greenkeeper for the conservation of heather, but much depends upon the age of the plant and the area which the heather occupies on the course (semi-rough, carry, etc.).

Burning is used to control heather in semi-natural heath and moor situations, but it does have several limitations when applied to the golf course. Apart from the obvious reasons such as smoke interrupting play, etc., it is a very exacting science which is difficult to execute. The temperature of the burn must be carefully controlled so as not to destroy the undersurface seed bank and, indeed, the whole ecology of the area. If burning, this should be carried out over small areas only and preferably on an annual rotational basis.

Mechanical methods for old and woody heather management are preferred, though are reported not to generally produce the desired effects as rapidly as would be found from burning. Trials set up on the Bingley St. Ives golf course adjacent to the STRI, however, have shown that mechanical methods can be just as effective.

Where old, mature or degenerating heather stands dominate, large heavy-duty vertical flails are preferred which are able to cut the heather to 50 mm (2 in.) and collect the resulting debris (brashings). Following this, the surface should be scarified to remove the accumulated debris, increase the light at the surface and produce a fine surface tilth. The collected brashings should then be respread over the surface to protect the seedlings as they are stimulated into germination from the underlying seed-bank. The brashings help prevent wind exposure, soil erosion and will help in the retention of moisture at the surface. This operation is easily executed, though expert advice should be sought prior to commencement to ensure that this method is the most appropriate course of action.

In many instances it has been found that relatively young heather is being lost as coarse weedgrass species invade and out-compete the relatively slow-growing shrubs. Here, appropriate courses of action, depending upon areas involved, may involve selective chemical herbicides judiciously applied to kill the grass at the most suitable time but leave the heather plants. Alternatively, heavy-duty machines could be employed to flail and then scarify the sward to reduce the accumulating fibre at the sward surface. Again, these methods should be closely supervised.

Gorse

Gorse management, like heather management, is best carried out on a rotational basis to retain a diversity and density of structure. Gorse is normally cut during the late winter on an annual or every third year basis depending upon the desired growth form and height required. The latter again will depend upon the position with respect to the golf course. Following cutting, all litter must be raked up and discarded. Failure to remove this will suppress germination of seed and may favour bracken invasion in certain instances. Older stands of gorse (more than about 15 years of age) may die as a result of cutting and so, as was pointed out earlier, infrequent but more regular attention is vital if these features are to be retained.

Summary

The conservation and establishment of heather and gorse dominated habitats on the golf course, be it within the deep rough, carry or semi-rough, is worthy of special consideration for several reasons. Not only do they influence the overall strategy of play, but in many cases these areas are part of large Sites of Special Scientific Interest (SSSI's), requiring careful and considerate management under strict regulation as directed by English Nature. Thus, before contemplating work of any nature in such areas, a full site evaluation is strongly recommended. The STRI's Conservation and Ecological Management Service is actively engaged in carrying out such appraisals and is fully committed to the priorities of the golf course.

(RST : Unpublished)

BRACKEN: FRIEND OR FOE ON THE GOLF COURSE?

Introduction

Pteridium aquilinum, or bracken as it is more commonly known, is often thought of as a total undesirable on the golf course. This, in the majority of cases, is true.

Before passing sentence on this species however, it may be worthwhile considering its ecology from the point of view of both the prosecution and the defense.

Ecology

Bracken is an opportunist able to associate with quite diverse communities. It usually achieves dominance in gaps and clearings within open woodlands. It is normally suppressed as the tree canopy develops. Once dominant, its large leaves or fronds cast a dense shade which, together with the large quantity of litter, tend to totally suppress the growth of higher plant species.

Occasionally bracken-dominated stands may be ecologically quite important, forming communities which are relatively species-rich. Here, because the bracken effectively suppresses aggressive summer flowering species of both grass and flowers, and because the fronds are late in unfolding, vernal or spring flowering communities may be preserved. In the cleared copse areas or open woodland edges, bluebell, wood sorrel and possibly even rarer species may be found. The preservation of this flora may also have very positive benefits for the associated invertebrate fauna and so on.

Bracken-dominated stands offer cover for the nests of several birds, though actual numbers recorded in bracken are much less than would be found in most other habitat types. On the heathland golf course the change in habitat type from predominantly relatively open heath grassland to bracken may result in a total loss of reptiles and snakes as the open basking areas are reduced.

The very invasive nature of bracken in Britain is normally thought to cause an alarming reduction in habitat quality, often resulting in the further fragmentation of already very small roughs, etc.

Management

Physical cutting and chemical spraying are the two most successful methods of bracken control. Both are expensive in resources or labour and have various problems associated with them. There is a need for continued or periodic retreatment to prevent its regrowth. Because bracken increases the nutrient status of its surroundings, there is often a tendency towards its replacement with fast-growing, weedy species rather than the slower growing, desirable flora.

Before any management work is undertaken in areas of bracken invasion, an ecological appraisal would be useful to fully evaluate the ecological potential of the communities present overall.

A five-year programme of eradication involving both physical and chemical control may be most successful, with chemical control methods being adopted in the first and fifth years. The careful use of asulam has proven to be very effective in bracken control. Spray drift will, however, kill underlying vegetation. This is particularly damaging in heather-dominated communities. The dicamba-based herbicides are also effective and are less aggressive to the understorey. Dalapon and dichlobenil, also approved, will kill underlying perennial grass species. Spraying should be carried out during calm, still periods in June once the fronds have fully opened.

Physical control should concentrate upon cutting or physically lifting and should be carried out through June and July when the nutrient reserves in the rhizomes are low.

Summary

Whether judge or jury, prosecutor or defence, a site evaluation to determine all the relevant facts should be a prerequisite before embarking upon an expensive programme of bracken eradication.

(CGC 1 : 56)

PONDS AND WATER FEATURES ON THE GOLF COURSE

Introduction

There is an enormous variety and range of water features on golf courses throughout Europe serving many different functions. Knowing the character, location and purpose of each water body is vital if decisions are to be made with regard to future management.

We can only conserve the biological diversity of any water feature once it has been recognised and in this respect an ecological appraisal is essential. Data collection during the appraisal should consider the nutrient status, the depth, any seasonal fluctuations, likely wind and wave action, and the position of the watercourse in relation to other habitats through the green. Often overlooked is the proximity of the water feature with regard to human influences, i.e. constant disturbance and the importance (including the aesthetic contribution) of the feature with regard to play.

From the data collected, it will be essential that a suitable strategy towards management or redevelopment is produced. This should ideally take the form of a management plan which can then become an integral component of the course policy documents now becoming commonplace throughout the golf world. Indeed, a wide-ranging document covering the more important aspects of management is vital if a sustained long-term policy is to be continued as committees change and new representatives strive to leave their mark on the future of the course. More details on the objectives and the formation of a management plan are available through the STRI.

The biology of water features

Water bodies are classed primarily on their nutrient status and in particular the level of alkalinity present. Eutrophic water features show high phosphate and high amounts of dissolved calcium carbonate levels. Seasonal (climatic) effects may encourage high levels of algae in such waters which can reduce available oxygen levels and light penetration inhibiting vegetation development whilst further suppressing and perhaps killing aquatic life. Moving down the alkalinity and nutrient scale, we have mesotrophic, oligotrophic and finally dystrophic ponds supporting the lowest levels of both dissolved calcium carbonate and phosphorus.

Water features are susceptible to nutrient build-up through their position in a geological context, their proximity to roads, through litter deposition and decomposition from surrounding vegetation, from silt and organic material entering at the inlet point (if present) and, more importantly, from chemical run-off. Fertiliser and pesticide run-off into groundwater is an obvious concern and one which is continuously voiced to fuel the mounting criticisms aimed at the sport. STRI research has shown that providing advised limits are observed, there is likely to be very little or no leaching of these chemicals into watercourses (Lawson, D.M. & Colclough, T.W. (1991). J. Sports Turf Res. Inst. 67, 143-150).

Management Considerations

Recognition of the problems and therefore prevention or at least control of the nutrient accumulation will be vital in maintaining the health and quality of the water feature.

Emergent and marginal vegetation can be used to good effect to filter nutrients that enter the watercourse, possibly from an inlet stream or drainage outlet.

Consideration could be given to the introduction of barley straw which has recently been found to inhibit the growth of algae.

In those water bodies that have become acutely enriched by high levels of nutrient and silt, the most appropriate course of action may be to dredge and pump out the sediment during the autumn and early winter period. Obviously, the timing of this work must take into account both the ground conditions and the potential effects on the wildlife present.

When considering management, one must also take into account the seasonal fluctuations of the water body. Most wildlife is likely to be found in the shallower margins; increasing depth will tend to inhibit light penetration and therefore plant growth. Depth however is important in controlling vegetation spread and will therefore help to reduce the management input. Taller emergent plant species such as bulrush and yellow iris are unlikely to spread out into water bodies greater than 2 metres depth and this can be used as a natural control method. Ducks cannot reach much below 0.35 metre and are therefore dependent upon shallow, open water.

Seasonal fluctuations will affect the amount of light penetrating the pond and will therefore affect growth and spread of the vegetation. Thus, those ponds showing a marked loss in levels are likely to require a greater management input than those experiencing minimal fluctuations. Some wildlife, particularly amphibians, prefer sites that dry considerably as this process does tend to inhibit the number of species preying upon them.

Many larger water bodies on the golf course are used for irrigation and may suffer a considerable loss of depth at certain times through the year. This in turn may lead to a loss of plant life, particularly around the margin, due to exposure and desiccation. Repeated recharging and draw-down of the water may with each cycle destroy more vegetation. To counteract this, the shape of the bank sides must be seriously considered. Gentle slopes of 1 in 6 may facilitate ball retrieval but in highly fluctuating water bodies retaining a full and healthy grass cover may be somewhat difficult. Vertical banks, on the other hand, will limit ball retrieval but may require a minimal input of management. Obviously, safety will be a major implication here. It may be possible to construct a bund zone to encourage and maintain a moderate species density through areas of the water feature, so helping to maintain a stronger vegetation cover during the dry periods.

Turning to the action of the wind on the water's surface, one sees on a number of golf course water features waves lapping over into shallow banks, resulting in a marked loss of the vegetation and thereafter a significant amount of bank side erosion. Although stone and rock can be and is often used to counteract this problem, the ecological potential of such a strategy may be limited. Areas of rock do tend to support little plant growth and will limit the faunal diversity, particularly around the margin. Geotextiles have a place here in limiting erosion whilst allowing plant growth to continue. Other alternatives aimed at reducing wave action may be to create a reef, perhaps 2 metres from the shore, of stone so allowing plant growth to establish within the more settled water behind. A shelter belt of trees may help to intercept the wind over the smaller water bodies, although this is obviously a longer term solution. Ideally, any trees planted must be set back from the shoreline so as not to impede light falling on the watercourse. This will also help to reduce the direct deposition of litter.

The location of a pond on the golf course is obviously a major factor when considering its ecological status. Ideally, at least part of the water feature should connect with an area of rough, i.e. taller herbage such as grassland, scrub or copse, this being essential if the movement and spread of wildlife is to be effective from area to area. Many species living within the pond, for example dragonflies, are dependent upon taller grasses for their development to adulthood.

Practical aspects of management

The aesthetic and ecological aspects of developing and maintaining the vegetation

Aquatic plants are vital to the water feature in many respects; they not only serve to enhance the overall natural aesthetics but are the primary food source for most of the wildlife present. Plants, as noted above, can help reduce wave action, so helping to counteract bank-side erosion.

When considering what species to plant, several factors must be borne in mind. These include the position or location of the feature with regard to play and its intended function. The location of the plants will affect the overall aesthetics, for example consider a par 3 hole standing on the tee and viewing the green. Vegetation on the near and far shore could potentially restrict ball retrieval and it is therefore essential that an appropriate landscape strategy be employed to ensure that taller species are positioned out of the direct line of fire. Smaller emergent and marginal species however may be appropriate planted in groups within these areas, possibly in a broken or irregular manner.

The most vigorous species should be avoided in areas of shallow water, remembering that these will spread outwards, being only inhibited by water depths in excess of 2 metres. Taller vegetation however may be suitable in those areas out of direct play. The plants chosen should ideally be planted in single species groups so as to give a greater competitive ability with adjacent plant species.

True aquatics should be included so as to help maintain a reasonable balance of light penetration and shade over the surface. Lilies, for example, can be weighted and planted at 0.5 metre spacings to a depth of 1 metre. The rhizomes will in time become fixed into the unconsolidated mud at the bottom of the pond. Larger emergent species such as bulrush should not be planted in the shallows where dabbling ducks or waders are known to feed.

In those ponds becoming choked with larger plant species, some clearance work will obviously be required so as to restore the open water condition. One must however always remember that many species of insect, for example, are largely dependent upon such conditions. Similarly, many birds are totally dependent upon the insects, particularly during the winter months when shelter also forms a major factor. Total eradication is therefore not recommended. Management must aim towards holding back the natural succession to accepted limits, ideally to cover an area of between a quarter and half of the total area of the shallows. Over-managing these areas will have a very undesirable effect on wildlife populations. Management therefore will need to be infrequent following a rotational programme during the late autumn and early winter period. An item in the course policy document must cover regular monitoring and clearance thereafter so as to maintain a good variety and structure around the margin.

When considering the practical aspects of cutting and lifting the vegetation, it may be worth remembering that individual species do have preferred niches extending some way out into the water body. It may therefore be appropriate to remove perhaps the leading edge in one area, cutting back thereafter in bands towards the bank-side so as to help maximise species diversity within the habitats being created. Any physical management work being carried out must be undertaken with extreme care so as not to damage or severely disrupt the base of the water feature which, in some instances, may consist of puddled clay or, in others, a liner, both of which are susceptible to damage.

Herbicides are used in conservation management and certainly do have a place in the management of water features on the golf course. Obviously, great care is required with regard to their use, label recommendations must be strictly followed. When considering herbicides, do bear in mind that physical cutting will facilitate complete removal of litter, so reducing the nutrient status of the water body. Chemical herbicide treatments will slowly kill the vegetation, resulting in a gradual decomposition and a gradual increase in nutrients released, all of which may once again encourage algal proliferation. Remember also that herbicides are not target-specific, a further reason why the utmost care must be given to their use.

(RST : B.192)

CONSERVATION ON THE GOLF COURSE

As more and more land is developed for industry, intensive agriculture or residential estates, there is a growing threat to the habitats which support our native wildlife. Those who are concerned with our environment seek to overcome this threat in two main ways.

Firstly, they conserve such habitats by limiting man's activity to varying degrees in strategic areas. This is achieved by designating certain areas as Sites of Special Scientific Interest (SSSI), Areas of Outstanding Natural Beauty, Nature Reserves and National Parks, etc. This approach can, of course, also be practised on any natural or semi-natural site even if it is not given a special title – this has been the case on many of our motorway verges.

The second approach is to turn areas previously unattractive to wildlife into more appealing areas by creating suitable habitats. This may involve such operations as constructing marshy areas, increasing the floral diversity in grasslands and the use of native species in tree planting schemes.

Golf's Responsibility

Golf courses are very important elements in the conservation picture for a number of reasons. Unlike most other sports, the game actually requires a degree of semi-natural vegetation to provide the rough and other opportunities for conservation exist in the areas between holes. Figures from 1973 suggest that the total amount of golfing rough in the UK amounts to nearly 500 km^2 which is something like half the total area of National Nature Reserves.

Golf courses are spread fairly evenly over the whole country compared to the National Parks which are concentrated in the less-populated, upland areas. Many types of landscape are represented on golf courses from coastlands and moorlands to heathlands and parklands, not to mention marshlands (some of which may occur in undesirable places!). Unlike Nature Reserves, golf courses do not tend to attract egg snatchers to the nests of rare birds or flower pickers to endangered patches of orchids. Finally, golf courses also have the advantage of being fairly permanent barriers to development while they themselves are part of the development process, providing recreational facilities for a society which seems to generate more and more leisure time. So, golf courses have an important role to play in conservation and are likely to be encouraged to face up to this responsibility even more in the future.

Getting Started

Some Clubs have already had to start thinking about these issues, having been designated SSSI's. At the last count, there were 84 golf courses so designated. Others may wish to initiate the process themselves and their first move should be to contact the Nature Conservancy Council or the local County Naturalist Trust. With the help of these groups the potential of each course can be examined and a management document drawn up to outline which species should be encouraged and how this can be brought about. Their support and advice will be vital as some aspects of the conservation work may be regarded as controversial by some club members who may for instance have a favourite cherry tree or conifer thicket on the course. Local Naturalist Trusts can also prove to be a very helpful source of voluntary labour for clearing and planting jobs.

Conflicts and Benefits

In drawing up the management document most clubs will find that it is only the management of the rough areas which are involved. However, in some cases operations such as weedkilling or worm control may be restricted or completely ruled out on the fairways. In such instances conflicts begin to arise between the objectives of producing a good golf course and conserving wildlife. Such conflicts should be few and far between however and can generally be resolved by negotiation between the club and the conservation body. In fact, there are likely to be more mutual benefits than conflicts – the conservation body gains valuable land while the Golf Club will normally receive the results of surveys showing the local flora and fauna. This can be of great value when undertaking any course alterations or tree planting schemes. Knowing which tree species are native to the area can mean a lot of money being saved by avoiding the use of species which will not survive on the course. The Club will also end up with a conservation policy which will encourage wildlife and add to the course's attractions.

The Need for Positive Management

In nature grasslands tend to become invaded with low scrub vegetation and in time, without interference from grazing animals, they become heathlands. These can then be invaded with pioneer tree species such as birch, hawthorn, ash or sycamore and eventually become woodlands. If a Club wishes to halt the development of this process at any one stage, it will be necessary to carry out some maintenance to eradicate the invading species. Habitats such as chalk grasslands are now becoming increasingly rare partly because rabbit populations suffered so much through myxomatosis – in the past their close grazing prevented any hawthorn bushes or other shrubs invading the grassland. Operations such as occasional mowing (after any desirable species have flowered and set seed) may be necessary nowadays, or chemical control of the invasive scrub may also be needed.

To maintain heathland vegetation any invading tree species must be kept out and this is commonly done by rotational burning which encourages the production of fresh heather growth while killing off the trees. However, this is not always practical on golf courses and pulling up seedling trees or chemical control (using the correct rate of a chemical such as glyphosate) is to be recommended. Regular mowing is another possibility though this will encourage regrowth from the cut tree stumps.

In conclusion, it is difficult to generalise on any particular management policies as these should all be tailored to meet each individual site's requirements following negotiations between the Club and conservation body. No Club should fall into the trap of copying the policies of the course 'down the road' as the potential of each site will be different.

(CGC 1 : 54)

SECTION 15
PESTICIDE LEGISLATION

✣✣✣

Legal Reguirements for Pesticide Usage

Pesticide Storage

Spraying

*The Care of
the Golf Course*

GOLF CLUBS AND LEGISLATION CONCERNING PESTICIDES AND OTHER HAZARDOUS SUBSTANCES

FOOD AND ENVIRONMENT PROTECTION ACT PART III : CONTROL OF PESTICIDES REGULATIONS 1986 (COPR)

Control of Substances Hazardous to Health Regulations (Coshh)

This section outlines some of the obligations placed on golf clubs by the COPR and COSHH Regulations. To obtain full details golf clubs must consult the publications listed at the end of this article and check their specific requirements and duties with their Local Authority and local office of the Health and Safety Executive Agricultural Inspectorate.

Control of Pesticides Regulations 1986

Aims: the FEPA legislation aims to protect the health of human beings, creatures and plants, to safeguard the environment and to secure safe, efficient and humane methods of controlling pests. If also seeks to make information regarding pesticides available to the public.

Pesticides: are anything used for destroying any pest, ie. the fungicides, herbicides, insecticides, earthworm and moss killers commonly used on golf greens and other parts of the course, are all pesticides. Plant growth regulators are also included. Outside the scope of the regulations are fertilisers, soil conditioners and wetting agents, as no pest control is involved.

The main restrictions under COPR can be summarised as follows:-

[a] *Approved products:*

Only products approved for use in amenity horticulture may be used, as listed in "Pesticides 1996" or any subsequent annual edition available from HMSO bookshops. Providing you obtain your pesticides from a reputable turf products supplier, and a MAFF number and a **recommendation for use on turf** can be found on the label then it is likely that the product is approved. It is advisable to only purchase pesticides from a salesman qualified under the British Agrochemical Standards Inspection Scheme (BASIS).

[b] *Greenkeeper training and certification:*

The golf club must ensure that its greenkeepers have received adequate training and are competent to use pesticides. To achieve this, appropriate training followed by an examination leading to a certificate of competence being issued is necessary. There are exemptions under the so-called "grandfather clause" for those born before 1 January 1965. A person so exempted may use pesticides if he has received adequate instruction and guidance in the safe efficient and humane use of pesticides and is competent for the duties which he is called on to perform. In the event of accident, misuse or incorrect storage of pesticides the employer will be criminally responsible for the actions or failings of the employee. "Competence" could well be interpreted as meaning capable of passing the requisite exam to obtain a certificate. Further, only a certificate holder may supervise others. Certification for all users is the direction in which things are likely to proceed in the future with more and more users being brought into the categories of mandatory certification. Training and certification is highly recommended for **all** users of pesticides. For details of pesticide training courses, contact your local horti-cultural college. Training is conducted in "modules". The foundation module (coded PA1), hand-held applicator (PA6a) and ground crop sprayer (PA2) modules are probably most suitable for golf greenkeepers. Examinations are organised by the National Proficiency Tests Council, National Agricultural Centre,

Stoneleigh, Kenilworth, Warwickshire, CV8 2LG and are detailed in their booklet "Pesticides Application".

[c] *Legally binding parts of the label:*

Every pesticide container carries instructions, many of which are **now mandatory**. For example, any instructions on maximum dose rates, maximum number of treatments, limitations on area to be treated or quantity of pesticide to be used and latest time of application must be followed strictly. Also, the label may have statements on environmental protection, e.g. avoid contamination of waterways, protective clothing (which **must** be provided by the club and **worn** by greenkeepers during spraying) and greenkeeper training. Any breach of these or other statutory conditions will constitute a criminal offence. Generally speaking, however, if the greenkeeper is trained, possesses appropriate certificates of competence and follows strictly the statements on the pesticide label, he can feel confident that he is working within the COPR.

[d] *Storage of pesticides:*

For moderate to large quantities of pesticides likely to be stored at a golf course, special lockable metal vaults are available commercially or a purpose built store may be erected. Guidance on storage is given in the next section "Storage of Pesticides".

Control of Substances Hazardous to Health Regulations

Aims: Applied from 1 January 1990, the COSHH regulations provide the framework for the control of substances at work which may be hazardous to health.

The COSHH and COPR regulations are intended to complement one another and operate together. Whilst COSHH is primarily aimed at protecting people at work, COPR covers creatures, plants and the environmental as well as human health. It must be emphasised that COSHH is concerned not only with pesticides but with all potential hazardous substances which may be present in the workplace.

(1) *Risk assessment*

It is necessary to assess the risk to health arising from working with pesticides and other hazardous substances, and to determine what precautions are needed. Risk is defined as the likelihood that it will cause harm in the circumstances of use. An assessment of risk must be made by the employer which must usually take the form of a written document. First, the hazard, i.e. its potential to cause harm, of each particular pesticide should be determined, and then the potential risk can be assessed. Proprietary pesticides currently available are all Approved by the Ministry of Agriculture, Fisheries & Food (MAFF) and a MAFF number is displayed on the product label. Consequently, in this case it is evident that the pesticide in question has satisfied MAFF from the safety viewpoint. However, some pesticides are safer than others and it is the essential point of COSHH that the employer has to decide which pesticide to use. Pesticide product labels also contain relevant statements on safety, advice on protective clothing and a standard warning sign such as "harmful" or "irritant". These are just some of the considerations to be made when assessing the hazard which a pesticide represents.

The risk assessment must be in written form. It is important that the assessment is received and if appropriate revised, whenever a new member of staff is employed, a new hazardous substance introduced to the golf club or responsibilities changed. All revisions should be dated and a copy served to **all** members of staff and to those club members responsible for ensuring compliance with the Regulations.

(2) *Reduction of exposure to hazardous substances*

Once risk has been determined, then work procedures must be examined critically to prevent or reduce exposure to hazardous substances. For example, the potential hazard posed by a pesticide may be eliminated if a non-pesticidal method of achieving the same aim is practicable. Reduced exposure to a pesticide may be achieved by the employee wearing suitable and adequate protective clothing, which is the employer's responsibility to provide and ensure it is worn by employees. Again, refer to the product label for specific guidance on protective clothing. To prevent or control exposure to hazardous substances, COSHH lists the control measures in the following order or priority. Firstly, substitute the substance with a safer alternative. Secondly, introduce technical or engineering methods of safety, for example, use a sprayer with a specially designed filler pump rather than pouring the pesticide into the spray tank manually. Finally, reduce exposure by following safe systems of work – correct storage and handling of pesticide concentrates, protective clothing etc.

(3) *Information and training*
Employees must be trained in the use of and informed about the pesticides with which they are asked to work. The COPR training courses available currently for users of pesticides would seem essential towards the requirements of COSHH. Safety and toxicological information, usually available as technical safety data sheets from the manufacturers of pesticides, must also be made available to all concerned, so the risk may be assessed before a spraying operation. In summary, employees have to be informed about the risks arising from their work and the precautions to be taken.

(4) *Recording exposure to hazardous substances*
The exposure of employees to hazardous substances must be monitored and a record kept. Standard risk assessment sheets, to be completed by the employer **before** a spraying operation, are available, together with COPR log books for monitoring pesticide usage for these purposes.

Further Reading
Pesticide Regulations
The "Code of Practice for the Amenity Use of Pesticides" giving much useful information applicable to golf clubs has been drawn up jointly by the National Turfgrass Council and the National Association of Agricultural Contractors.

The Ministry of Agriculture has issued a free explanatory leaflet UL79 Pesticides : guide to the new controls (revised 1987). A further revision is due shortly. Write to: Ministry of Agriculture, Fisheries and Food (Publications), Lion House, Alnwick, Northumberland, NE66 2PF.

The Health and Safety Executive issue the following leaflets and booklets, available from HSE Library & Information Services, Broad Lane, Sheffield, S3 7HQ. Tel: (01742) 752539.

COSHH Assessments (a step by step guide to assessment and the skills needed for it).

Introducing Assessment (a simplified guide for employers).

Hazard and Risk Explained.

Control of Substances Hazardous to Health Regulations 1988, Approved Code of Practice *Control of Substances Hazardous to Health* and Approved Code of Practice *Control of Carcinogenic Substances*, HMSO, ISBN 0 11 885468 2.

Guidance Note EH40/89 (and subsequent editions) *Occupational Exposure Limits*, HMSO, ISBN 0 11 885411 9.

NOTE This section contains no more than a summary of statutory regulations and requirements and does not set out in full the obligations and responsibilities of employers and employees. The purpose of this leaflet is to draw attention to matters requiring consideration and reference must be made to the Code of Practice and other publications mentioned above and the authorities mentioned therein.

(CGC 1 : 91)

STORAGE OF PESTICIDES

The requirements of the Food and Environmental Protection Act 1985 and the Control of Pesticides Regulations 1986 with regard to the safe storage of pesticides are set down in detail in the 'Code of Practice for the use of Approved Pesticides in Amenity Areas'. More detailed advice can be obtained from the Health and Safety Executive in the form of a guidance note entitled "Storage of Approved Pesticides: Guidance for Farmers and Other Professional Users". The Health and Safety Executive Agricultural Inspectorate are the enforcing body for this legislation, and for specific queries relating to individual sports clubs it is strongly recommended that the local HSE be contacted, their telephone number should be in your local directory.

This section summarises the information on storage of pesticides contained in the Code of Practice and HSE guidance note. It is highly recommended that the documents referred to above should be consulted for comprehensive information on the subject.

Criteria for Pesticide Storage

Depending on the quantity of pesticide involved, the necessary storage facilities can be provided by a specially made metal cabinet or by a purpose built store. Whatever storage facility is chosen, the following criteria apply:-

    (a)   the store should be suitably sited;
    (b)   of adequate storage capacity;
    (c)   soundly constructed of fire resistant materials;
    (d)   provided with suitable entrances and exits;
    (e)   capable of containing spillage and leakage;
    (f)   dry and protected from frost where necessary;
    (g)   suitably lit;
    (h)   suitably ventilated;
    (i)   marked and secure against theft and vandalism;
    (j)   equipped and organised to accommodate the intended contents.

Application of These Criteria to Metal Cabinets

If only a relatively small amount of pesticide is stored, e.g. at a private bowling club, cricket club or 9-hole golf course, then metal cabinets that are currently available should meet the storage requirements. The following companies have marketed containers of capacity from 65 litres or kilogrammes to 1300 litres or kilogrammes of total pesticide quantity:-

Cleveland Sitesafe Limited	Portasilo Limited	Rhone-Poulenc Environmental
High Farm	Huntington	Products
Old Lackenby	York	Regent House
Eston	YO3 9PR	Hubert Road
Middlesbrough	Tel: 01904 624872	Brentwood
Cleveland TS6 8DN		Essex CM14 4TZ
Tel: 01642 464986/453629		Tel: 01277 261414

These cabinets are sufficiently robust so as not to be significantly damaged by any reasonably foreseeable accidental impact and are capable of containing any leakage up to a total capacity of the contents stored. They are designed to be fire resistant and are lockable to prevent unauthorised access.

The storage container should be marked with an approved notice consisting of a yellow triangle with black edge and exclamation mark, at least 125 mm long on all three sides, the notice also being displayed on the outside of any building in which the container is housed.

The pesticide store should not be sited within a staffroom, office, human or animal food store or food processing area, a dwelling house or building adjoining and directly accessible from a dwelling house. It is also recommended that emergency eye-wash facilities, First Aid kit, list of cabinet contents and a 9 litre aqueous fire extinguisher are provided.

Application of Criteria to Buildings

If large amounts of pesticides need to be stored (over the quantities that can be stored in metal cabinets), then a purpose built store will have to be constructed. The criteria for purpose built stores are numerous and are summarised on the diagram attached.

Useful Information

The Health and Safety Executive publication is available from MAFF Publications Unit, Lion House, Willowburn Trading Estate, Alnwick, Northumberland, NE66 2PF.

'Pesticides: Guide to the New Controls (Control of Pesticides 1986)'. MAFF Leaflet UL79 (revised 1987).

(CGC 1 : 92)

PAPERWORK FOR SPRAYING

Hopefully, greenkeepers are now fully aware of their responsibilities for the safe use of pesticides under the Control of Pesticides Regulations Act 1986 (COPR). An integral part of those regulations relates to the need to maintain accurate records of spraying operations. The implementation of the Control of Substances Hazardous to Health Regulations (COSHH), which have been in force since 1st October 1989, now means that further paperwork is necessary to conform to the law. This article will briefly outline and, hopefully, reinforce the user's obligations relating to paperwork under COPR and also provides a guide to the type of information which should be recorded as part of the risk assessment under COSHH.

Requirements Under COPR

An accurate record should be kept of every spraying operation, and this includes details such as operator name, product, reason for use, rate of application, quantity used, timing, weather conditions, etc. An example of a suitable format for these records is provided in the "Pesticides Code of Practice for the Use of Approved Pesticides in Amenity Areas" booklet which is obtainable from the STRI. The Institute suggests that separate sheets are prepared for each sprayer and include details of calibrations so that application rates for different nozzle sizes, tractor speeds and boom widths are available. These record sheets should be stored in a separate area from the chemicals.

Requirements Under COSHH

This article will deal specifically with the written assessment of risk which needs to be completed in order to conform with this new legislation. Remember that these regulations apply to all substances which are hazardous to health, so it will be necessary to include materials other than pesticides such as cleaning fluids, fuel, dust (which may be generated during top dressing preparations for example). However, for the purposes of this article, I will outline a risk assessment checklist aimed at pesticide use. Only include pesticides which are considered to be hazardous, these are identified with a warning symbol or other information on the product label. The assessment should be completed at the **beginning** of the year prior to spraying, to be updated on, say, an annual basis. The employers are responsible for the implementation of this procedure, in the case of a Golf Club the Secretary would be the appropriate person. However, he has the power to delegate the responsibility to the Head Greenkeeper, who would be in a better position to assess the risks.

The risk assessment could take the following format:

Step 1: Identify the weed/pest/disease/ other problem which will require control.

Step 2: List alternative methods of control other than chemicals, i.e. management techniques.

Step 3: Identify and list all the hazardous pesticides which you are planning to use. At this stage, include information about the chemical, such as formulation, degree of hazard, e.g. are there any warning signs, any special instructions on the label? If there are any specific worries, further information should be sought from the manufacturers, who are obliged to provide safety data sheets for their products.

Step 4: Assess the area of use and risk to the general public, e.g. adjacent to housing, public footpaths may cross the area. Publicise details of spraying operations, Golf Clubs should inform the membership on the notice board for example.

Step 5: Detail the method of application, i.e. tractor-mounted sprayer or knapsack, hydraulic nozzle or CDA, operating pressure, etc.

Step 6: Assess the measures which will be taken to control exposure or contamination. Include the various stages of possible risk, i.e. transportation, storage and methods for mixing and bulking into the spray tank. Provide details of the operations, i.e. National Proficiency Test Certificate (NPTC), experience, supervision, etc., and any written instructions to them.

Step 7: Make a decision and choose the product which is the least hazardous to be applied by the safest method. At this stage, consider the protective clothing which is necessary rather than using it as an excuse to choose a product at an earlier stage. Remember that you must be able to justify a decision to choose a hazardous chemical, the question of efficacy is important but should not be the first consideration.

Step 8: Check the decision process.

Step 9: Decide on the steps necessary to comply with COSHH, i.e. ensure that exposure is prevented and the hazard no longer constitutes a risk.

Step 10: Give details of risks to contractors or non-employees in the work place.

Step 11: Monitor exposures if necessary and keep a record of results, e.g. it may be necessary to monitor dust productions from top dressing mixing.

Step 12: Monitor the health of staff.

These steps are a reduced version of the British Agrochemical Association (BAA) leaflet, which provides a more detailed explanation of all the procedures. This is available from the British Agrochemicals Association Ltd, 4 Lincoln Court, Lincoln Road, Peterborough, PE1 2RP (Tel: 01733 49225) and is called "The COSHH Assessment for Pesticides – A Plain Man's Guide for the Amenity User".

The important point is that management is seen to uphold the spirit of the law and in this respect written documentation provides evidence that risk evaluation has been completed and that employees and staff are aware of the dangers.

Further Reading

The Health and Safety Executive (HSE) produce several relevant publications available from your local HSE office. A series of leaflets are available, free of charge, which give a concise introduction to COSHH. An Approved Code of Practice is also available together with a step by step guide to assessment and the skills needed for it.

(CGC 1 : 93)

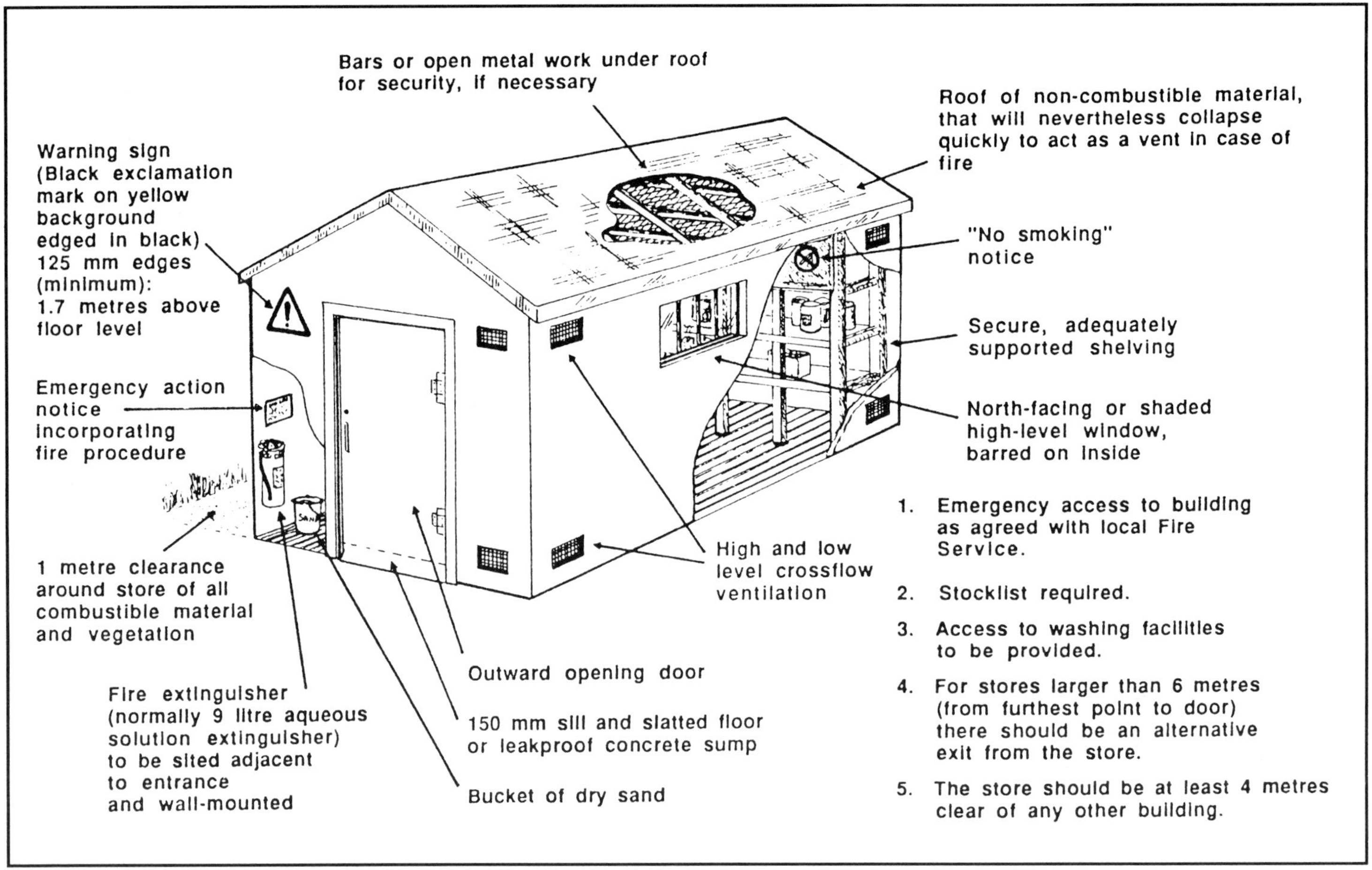

FIGURE 25: Pesticide store for golf course usage.

Warning sign (Black exclamation mark on yellow background edged in black) 125 mm edges (minimum): 1.7 metres above floor level

Emergency action notice incorporating fire procedure

1 metre clearance around store of all combustible material and vegetation

Fire extinguisher (normally 9 litre aqueous solution extinguisher) to be sited adjacent to entrance and wall-mounted

Bucket of dry sand

Outward opening door

150 mm sill and slatted floor or leakproof concrete sump

High and low level crossflow ventilation

Bars or open metal work under roof for security, if necessary

Roof of non-combustible material, that will nevertheless collapse quickly to act as a vent in case of fire

"No smoking" notice

1. Emergency access to building as agreed with local Fire Service.

2. Stocklist required.

3. Access to washing facilities to be provided.

4. For stores larger than 6 metres (from furthest point to door) there should be an alternative exit from the store.

5. The store should be at least 4 metres clear of any other building.

North-facing or shaded high-level window, barred on inside

Secure, adequately supported shelving

SECTION 16
ADMINISTRATION & FACILITIES

❖❖❖

Course Management Policies

The Chairman of Green

Communication within the Club

Shed Facilities

*The Care of
the Golf Course*

COURSE MANAGEMENT: A GUIDE TO A POLICY DOCUMENT

Changes in Green Committee on a regular basis (ie. every one to two years) do not provide the continuity required to develop a golf course on a long term basis. Invariably there are changing policies with changing Committees. For example, bunkers which have been put in one year may be taken out again within four or five years at the whim of a new Committee which is a waste of valuable time and money. To eliminate the risk of sweeping and continued changes, Clubs should formulate their own course management policy document, working to a five or ten year plan. Such a document should be obligatory for all Green Committees and Club officials to implement.

This article is set out to help Committees formulate their own document for their own situation which can then be drawn up and possibly voted on at an Annual General Meeting. Several people should be involved in compiling the document, but of particular importance are the Chairman of the Green Committee or Green Convenor, the Green Committee, the Head Greenkeeper, the Club Secretary/Manager and the Club's Agronomist.

1. Introduction

Roles and Responsibilities. Mention should be made of the "Chain of Command" of the Green Committee and greenkeeping staff, confirming the individual's roles and responsibilities within the Club.

2. Course management objectives

This section should identify the characteristics which typify the course, eg. heathland, parkland, links, etc., and the type of vegetation that should be the target for various parts of the course. Stated management objectives should include playing characteristics and structural features of putting greens, surrounds and aprons, tees, fairways, rough and semi-rough, together with areas not in immediate play but which still contribute to the course providing valuable areas for conservation, eg. woodlands, gorse, heather, ponds and watercourses.

3. Course management policy

Having established objectives, broad but detailed principles of management of the various areas should be laid down. Where professional advice is required, it should be taken from experienced qualified consultants with a proven record.

4. Resources

The optimum number of greenstaff should be identified by a project management exercise and a commitment made to training and education. A complete inventory of machinery should be made with a phased programme of replacement. Only specified materials should be applied to the course. Quality should not be sacrificed – it is often a false economy (a statement which is particularly applicable to top dressing for greens and sand for bunkers).

5. Usage

There should be a clear understanding and statement of policies relating to temporary greens and winter tees or trolley regulation, and avoidance of over-use. Furthermore, there should be properly identified periods when essential maintenance work should be carried out.

6. Professional advice

(a) *Agronomist*

The Club should have a policy of regular (at least annual) monitoring visits undertaken by an experienced professional Agronomist. The STRI can provide this service.

(b) *Architecture/construction work*

Any alterations or additions to the course should only be undertaken after consultation with a professional golf course architect. Construction work must only proceed after advice from the Architect or an Agronomist. Bunker or tee alterations or additions should form part of a staged phased construction programme. The STRI can provide this service.

(c) *Ecology/conservation management*

A proper programme of ecological/conservation management should be started after consultation with a recognised Ecologist sympathetic to the needs of the golfers. The STRI can provide this service.

7. General remarks

Once a management policy has been drawn up, implementation should be obligatory but with some scope for necessary minor adjustment agreed by all parties involved in course management. Any major changes should only happen after broad consultation with the membership.

Further reading

The Way Forward: Discussion Document of British Golf Course Management. Greenkeeping Panel, The Royal & Ancient Golf Club of St. Andrews.

(IS No.7 Ref. 02/04)

THE ROLE OF BUDGETING IN GOLF COURSE MANAGEMENT

The dictionary definition of a budget is "an estimate of income and expenditure" normally prepared on an annual basis. A reliable budget is as essential to the smooth operation of a Golf Club as it is to one's personal finances.

Preparation of such a document is one of the basic responsibilities of the Head Greenkeeper with regard to course maintenance and as such is often stipulated in his job description and contract.

The budget will detail all maintenance requirements for the year to come and should be prepared in a form that is easily understood by laymen on the Green Committee, or the owner or Manager of the course. Each request for funds under various headings should be accompanied by an explanation and reason for each item, along with an accurate estimate. If this is linked, as it should be, with a detailed course maintenance plan, which states as simply as possible the objectives and standards that are required on the course, the chances of receiving adequate funding are enhanced.

A thoroughly prepared budget can be used as a reference through the year to ensure that targets at the start of the year are being met – or otherwise. It will help in assuring that funds are spent in an orderly manner, since monthly requirements will be known. At the same time it should identify all expenses and may indicate means of cost reduction or more efficient use of labour.

Budget Preparation

Two types of budget will normally be required covering capital expenditure and normal running costs. A capital budget covers those items such as machinery and equipment which have an expected life greater than a year. The operating budget covers costs that are incurred only in the forthcoming year.

The budget will be developed systematically by passing through several stages. The starting point must be a review of the Club's objectives for the coming year covering maintenance levels, policies and any constructional projects that are planned. The establishment of target dates for the start and completion of, say, tee construction or drainage projects helps with their planning in relation to normal daily maintenance, and these must be correctly timed in respect of anticipated weather conditions, which in turn may involve adjustment of the golf calendar of events.

The second stage is to evaluate existing maintenance practices and techniques, discussing items which have cropped up during the year's work with the First Assistant, Foreman or Mechanic to determine whether there is scope for increased efficiency or improvement with any job or item of equipment.

Clearly, it is necessary to have available adequate records of routine maintenance operations and the basic needs are for:-

(1) *Labour Utilisation* – Since cost of salaries amounts to some 70% of the operating budget, careful use of this resource is vital to the proper running and efficiency of the course. Minimum records are an employee's daily log which identifies by code the job, time expended and area, collected into monthly and annual summaries.

(2) *Equipment Records* – The basic requirement is for a machine record sheet for each unit of equipment – often a simple card file works well, with details of expected life and date of disposal. The card should also show the maintenance and service repairs that are necessary, so a complete history for each unit can be built up giving an invaluable guide as to serviceability, routine maintenance and any expensive breakdown repairs. This allows realistic budgeting for routine maintenance and likely bills, as well as an overall assessment of the operational record. There should never be a need to rack one's brain trying to remember how many times and how many hours a particular machine was unserviceable, or the cost of repairs. With the facts at one's fingertips, a clear case can be made for scrapping an inefficient machine before its allotted replacement date. Alternatively, the record can show when a unit reaches the end of its reliable working life and, of course, picks out equipment which has been excellent in service – the same type can then be purchased with some degree of confidence. Committees appreciate a concise statement of the facts such as well kept records allow and good presentation will certainly smooth the path for the new acquisitions or replacement machinery.

(3) *General Running Costs* – The high cost of fuel these days emphasises the need for maintaining accurate records of fuel and lubricants. The daily log for each of the staff should tally fuel consumption for individual items. Petrol has historically always been much more expensive than diesel and it is likely that differentials will persist, so information on fuel use must figure in decisions about new purchases where there is choice of diesel or petrol engines. It goes without saying that there should be records of fertiliser, seed, sand and top dressing. If it was not common sense before, there is now a legal requirement to maintain a record of purchase and usage of pesticides. Remember that the broad term covers not only the obvious, i.e. herbicides, fungicides and insecticides, but also substances such as soil sterilants, wood preservatives and animal repellents. There should also be a record of water use on the course – for irrigation, washing down equipment, spraying, etc.

Budget Content

Having assembled the facts needed to cover the capital side of expenditure, the data necessary for normal day to day running costs can be drawn from the records mentioned above. The various categories within the budget will include:–

(a) *Capital Improvements*: value added to property such as new maintenance buildings, bridges, shelters, paths; course construction work such as new tees, bunkers, fairway drainage; landscaping work such as tree planting; irrigation systems.

(b) *Capital Expenses*: will cover new equipment and vehicles, as well as office furniture, staff lockers, etc.

(c) *Operating Expenses*:

[i] Salaries and wages – covering tax, personnel, insurance, any pension provision, expense allowances including meals, cost of phone calls, car running costs whilst on Club business. Also part-time employees, students taken on in summer.

[ii] Training and education – covering cost of apprentice training, staff attendance at seminars, publications, manuals and subscriptions.

[iii] Clothing – including both safety foot and headwear, protective clothing, both rainwear and safety spray overalls, face shields and gloves.

[iv] Materials – including top dressing, soil and sand, bunker sand, turf, seed, fertiliser, pesticides (includes herbicides, fungicides and insecticides).

[v] Fuel – separate amounts allowed for petrol, diesel, oil.

[vi] Irrigation – water costs averaged over five years if supplies are metered, annual maintenance costs. As the system ages allow for replacement pop-up heads.

[vii] Equipment repairs and maintenance – based on past costs available from records and projected for new equipment.

[viii] Hire of equipment.

[ix] Sundries – covering flags, flag pins, out of bounds and hazard markers, hole cups, tee markers, boxes and litter baskets. An item to cover theft and vandalism based on past costs.

Long Term Planning

Every Golf Club should have a planned approach to course improvement and general maintenance strategy. This should be based over at least five years, drawn up by the current Committee and made available for the general membership to examine and discuss over a period. It should be presented with appropriate amendment at the Annual General Meeting and passed by the membership as a whole. The Head Green-keeper or Course Manager then has a clear statement of where the Club is going – basic management strategy is approved – areas that need improvement are agreed, capital building or construction projects are laid out and costings can be applied to each item in a logical way.

Budget Presentation

Presentation of the operating budget to the Green Committee or Directors of the course will normally be the responsibility of the Head Greenkeeper in conjunction with the Chairman of Green. At some Clubs the capital budget may be presented by the Chairman of the Green Committee, but always after consultation with the Head Greenkeeper, or it may be a joint presentation. A copy of the proposed budget should be sent to each Committee member before the crucial meeting. In present-ation, the main items of the budget can then be summarised and backed up with appropriate supporting information. Try to keep the presentation as short and concise as possible without waffling, but you must effectively get over your proposals and justifications. Simple language is always better than trade or scientific terms, because most Committee members may be unfamiliar with jargon.

With construction projects, use visual aids – drawings, overheads, etc. to graphically illustrate your aims. Finally, always allow adequate time for discussion and questions.

(CGC 1 : 99)

SOME DUTIES OF A CHAIRMAN
OF GREEN COMMITTEE

The chairman of green or green convenor is elected by the membership to work closely with the head greenkeeper to develop and maintain the golf course on their behalf. To quote a passage from the Way Forward "........ there is often one brave soul who will battle on as chairman until he tires of the yearly abuse thrown in his direction by impatient golfers. His thankless task includes attempting to protect his green staff from the more belligerent members and fighting in general committee for sufficient funds with which to manage the course". While many clubs elect a new green chairman annually, the most successful appointees are those who are prepared to 'stick it out' a little longer. Continuity therefore is desirable; the learning curve is steep, and ideally a chairman should be elected for a minimum of three years. This will allow the development of an understanding of his role and build up a good working relationship with the head greenkeeper or course manager.

Traditionally the chairman of green has led a large green committee, though following publication of the Way Forward by the Royal and Ancient Golf Club, ideas were put forward for the 'streamlining' of the committee, especially the green committee. This was to reduce numbers to include the green chairman, club secretary and the course manager. Whether your Club have taken the decision to reform or not, the basic role of the chairman remains the same.

The term "green" and not "greens" is important as the green chairman will have responsibility for all that is green on the golf course. Alongside greens, tees and fairways therefore ecology and conservation must be encompassed within the management schedule.

The profile of a Golf Course Policy Document has been raised within the last two years and many clubs have formulated such a policy. The document should include items of agronomy, ecology, architecture and budgets with project work mapped out on a 5-10 year plan. It is the role of the green chairman to supervise and update the policy in future years to ensure course development and avoid sweeping changes of ideas which can occur with new green committees. Within the framework of a Course Policy Document a rolling programme of machinery upgrading and replacement could also be included together with proposals for the purchase of additional equipment to add to the pool of machinery to forward course development.

Without the necessary financial support it would be difficult for the course manager or head greenkeeper to realise the full potential of the course or to maintain it in first class order. In association with the course manager and club secretary the chairman of green must approve the annual budgets, but more importantly provide forecasts for the following three to five years. A monthly green account should also be produced to account for any significant variations which may arise during the year. Often quoted, successful course management revolves around the availability of the four "M's" i.e. machinery, manpower, materials and money and it is the role of the green chairman to ensure that where possible the course receives an adequate level of investment.

The chairman of green is accountable and a positive link between the green staff and the members. Good communication is essential and the chairman should make provision for reporting and commenting on the condition of the course. This can be achieved within the Club's own newsletter, which may be produced quarterly. Items for inclusion would be course disruption to be expected in the near future, especially following hollow tine aeration, Verti-draining or other specialised treatment. Ongoing course maintenance can be confirmed alongside decisions for the use of temporary greens, a trolley ban or encouraging divoting parties from the membership. Details of the forthcoming winter programme would also be of benefit to the membership and encourage them to take an interest in course development and likely course disruption.

The design of the course or course architecture may also come under review from time to time. While each and every member will have a view on how the course should be "changed" it is vital that major course alterations should only be contemplated with full consultation with a qualified golf course architect. Course maintenance may also be reviewed and the chairman of green is encouraged to attend the agronomist's advisory visit. The advisory visit provides an opportunity for the chairman of green, the course manager or head greenkeeper and other interested members of the green committee to review your course and discuss specific details with the agronomist. The chairman of green should take a healthy interest in the maintenance of the course and meet regularly with the course manager or head greenkeeper. It is important to develop an understanding of the problems facing the green staff and be able to report back to the members. As indicated earlier, the information can be passed on through newsletters, or as at many golf clubs, through a formal suggestions book.

While the club expects the course manager or head greenkeeper to keep abreast of developments within greenkeeping, the chairman of green is also encouraged to attend seminars and courses to widen his knowledge and understanding of the job in hand. The STRI runs ocasional courses specifically aimed at golf club secretaries and chairmen of green to provide an appreciation of golf course management and these are generally well-attended.

There may also be a legal onus on the green chairman who should ensure the club is fully aware of the Health and Safety requirements centred around the golf course. A pesticides store, log books, safety equipment and COSHH must all be included.

The chairman of green will also be responsible for staffing levels, job descriptions and greenkeeper training; he will also be responsible for the provision of a good working environment for the staff. If we were to provide a single word for the role of a chairman of green it would be "supportive" of the course manager or head greenkeeper, who has the responsibility of presenting the course in its best possible condition given constraints placed upon him. Ideally, he will be given the full vocal and financial backing of the club.

(ARC : B.189)

COMMUNICATIONS WITHIN THE GOLF CLUB

Introduction

Just as an inability to listen in the widest sense is a common human failing, so too is an unwillingness to listen to the other person's point of view. But without good, structured communications no organisation can operate efficiently, least of all a Golf Club. Members, officials and staff must all strive to achieve effective communications in the interests of the Club's most important asset – its course.

Communications on the Course

The effective management of golf courses hinges on the Head Greenkeeper and depends just as much on his skill as a communicator as it does on his practical abilities and technical know-how. Course maintenance requires team effort, hence the head man must be able to instruct each of his assistants as to which jobs require doing, including where, when and how. In addition, the Head Greenkeeper must make it understood that he is also a receiver of information from assistants acting as scouts; in this way he should be able to spot the first signs of trouble with the turf or machinery, so that small problems may be promptly dealt with.

This, then, is communication, namely a two-way movement of information which is received and interpreted on the same level at which it is formulated and transmitted. To prevent a breakdown in this process, explanations must be sufficiently detailed, simple and clear and put over patiently. Many people are poor listeners and can only concentrate for short periods, so the Head Greenkeeper must allow for this when helping young lads in particular. He must also be a good listener, so that as well as receiving direct messages, he should pick up hints and clues of possible sources of trouble, and follow up as necessary. There is never any harm in double-checking. Achieving the right level of communication between the Head Greenkeeper and his assistants can only improve the standard of maintenance. It should also prevent silly mistakes which reflect adversely upon the reputation of the Head Greenkeeper and his staff. If poor spread of fertiliser, slow response to breakouts of disease, scalping with mowers, poor pin positions, doing the right job but on the wrong area, etc., can be prevented, then golf courses, golfers and Head Greenkeepers will benefit.

Explanations of what assistants should do *and why* they should be doing it must benefit the younger members of the greenkeeping fraternity too. This takes time and trouble, but if interest is stimulated the standard of workmanship will improve; a foundation will also have been laid which will help to raise the future standard of greenkeeping.

Communication with the Club House

The quality of course maintenance does not fail solely through poor communication on the course and in the mess room. Many problems on golf courses seem to stem from a breakdown in communication between the Head Greenkeeper and those in the Club House too. The outcome of such a breakdown is frustration, with each side feeling that the other is not getting the message. Such situations can – and frequently do – explode to the detriment of all concerned and, not least, to the condition of the course as well.

To prevent this happening, it is essential that every Golf Club sets up a structure for communication, and accepts that this communication has to be a two-way process, as the Head Greenkeeper should be the person within the Club most technically qualified to comment upon ideas coming from the Club House and how these will affect the golf course in the long term. If, in any situation, he is in doubt, reference should be made to an independent body, such as a golf course agronomist or a golf course architect, who can comment upon the situation impartially. Seeking outside advice does not reflect ignorance – it is the intelligent who have an open mind to receiving information and to assessing its value.

In setting up a structure for communication between the green staff and Club members *one* is a key word. Whilst the Head Greenkeeper does have a duty to talk with and listen to members who, after all, are his ultimate employers, concerning factors which affect the running of the course, the Head Greenkeeper should be dealing with only one person on matters of maintenance policy. This person should be the appointed representative of the members, and whether it be the Chairman of the Green Committee, Green Convenor or Club Manager, it is important that the appointment be of sufficiently long duration to allow the development of both an appreciation of the work done on the course and a working relationship with the Head Greenkeeper. By this means each will acquire an understanding of the other's problems. Day to day running of the course is the Head Greenkeeper's responsibility but it is necessary to have someone with whom he can liaise for the development of a framework of long term policy, and through whom feedback on results should be channelled. A situation in which any Club official may issue orders to the Head Greenkeeper or his staff leads to confusion and contradiction. Similarly, it is wrong for Club members to pass comment or criticism upon the work of green staff. After all, imagine the disruption which would be created if any shareholder were allowed to walk into a factory and give direct orders to a production manager, foreman or workers!

Communication within the Club House

It is the task of the Club official having responsibility for the course to communicate with other officials and with the membership as a whole. He must be sufficiently primed on the projected maintenance programme and its cost when presenting his budget to the finance committee: about the effects of levels of play resulting from visiting societies and projected tournaments: and have answers for the grumblers! Success in golf course maintenance is achieved through long term planning over a period of years, inaugurating an integrated programme of treatments, and ensuring that jobs are done at the right time. There must be a clear, agreed programme, based on the needs of the course as a whole, rather than upon the pet theories of individuals, and adequate funding. The right time for treatments is not always the most convenient time to golfers, and compromise in such matters means give and take from *both* sides.

The collation of statistics relating to levels of play during the weeks throughout the year will provide a guide as to when treatments can be applied with least disruption, as well as to when play should be reduced for the long term good. Information from the Head Greenkeeper's diary, e.g. work done in the past, under what conditions and with what success, could modify these decisions, as could also the seeking of advice from an outside agency on the timing and effectiveness of individual operations, and where any changes might be made.

The Club representative needs to keep abreast of costs and expenditure too, so that he can ensure priority consumables are always available, repairs can be effected promptly, and machines replaced before they collapse into a pile of scrap. All this is to ensure that the best possible surfaces for golf are provided at all times of the year. Being the Club representative in charge of a golf course is not a job to be taken on lightly; it is hard work and unlikely to ensure universal popularity. Neither is it just a job involving dealings with committee people: the membership as a whole also has to be kept in touch with problems and development.

Both the Club representative and the Head Greenkeeper should be available to members to discuss course matters on a general basis, so long as it is appreciated that they are not just there to be the butt of hostilities. A Club rule that suggestions and complaints about the course must be put in writing (anonymous contributions to be rejected) and posted in a marked box for discussion at the next course care meeting can reduce the number of frivolous complaints. Such an approach tends to concentrate attention on longer term problems, rather than all those small items that someone has got steamed up about after a bad round! But as with all other matters, communication with the membership must be a two-way process too because to produce a successful golf course the backing of the majority is a prerequisite. An occasional newsletter can be a useful way of getting over long term aims and giving an update on progress. In addition, posting bulletins of work to be done during the following month can take the element of surprise out of disruptive procedures on any one day. When giving information to members, avoid the purely technical approach – try to relate more to the effect on their game, time scales and value for money, plus the fact that all work done is for their ultimate benefit even though this may not be immediately apparent.

Projecting the Greenkeeper

Finally, a point to the Head Greenkeeper. If the status of greenkeeping is to be elevated to its proper level, the Head Greenkeeper must try to project a favourable image at all times, both individually and through associations of greenkeepers. Be polite, keep up appearances, make people aware of the technicalities and difficulties but try to do this without a lot of moaning; facts and figures are far more persuasive. The golfing public holds the key to the status of greenkeeping, and it is only with direct communication or with communication through indirect channels that they will become aware that the greenkeeper is no longer just the odd job man.

(CGC 1 : 97)

PLAYER/GREENKEEPER RELATIONSHIPS

There is possibly always the foundation for something of a mutual antagonism between the man who looks after the turf and the player who wears it out. Blame for an unsatisfactory relationship can be apportioned to the greenkeeper or to the player or to both depending on circumstances.

Both Sides can be at Fault

Sometimes a greenkeeper, embittered by some injustice imagined or real, will give up all pretence of using his undoubted skill and experience to produce the quality of playing surface he prepared in the past. He can even occasionally be deliberately obstructive. In other cases it may be the player, unfairly critical or clamouring to be allowed to play on a turf which is unfit, probably due to weather conditions, who upsets a hitherto well-balanced apple cart. Ultimately a very difficult situation can arise.

In view of the conflicting interests, the wonder of it is really that, in the majority of golf clubs, such a good rapport exists between ground staff and players. An appreciation of the other side's point of view is essential and here are some ideas which may be helpful in preserving harmony.

Maintenance Work is Essential . . .

The average golfer does not know much about growing grass (though he thinks he does sometimes!). He is therefore quite innocently unaware of the necessity for the annual maintenance jobs which, although they temporarily interfere with his game, are completely necessary if a suitable playing surface is to be preserved. An obvious instance comes to mind of the regular top dressing of golf greens which is needed on all courses these days in order to keep putting surfaces true and free-draining. This dressing is bound to make the greens a little rough for a day or so and complaints from the golfers can be loud and long, and extremely irritating to a conscientious greenkeeper. The Club Secretary in fact can prevent a good deal of fuss in cases like this by pinning on the notice board in the Clubhouse a short announcement of what is to be done shortly on the course and the reason for it.

On the other hand every man working on a golf course, if he does not actually play the game for which he caters must have an extremely good knowledge of it, so that he knows exactly what is required from the turf by the players. He must be able to dovetail his work as neatly as practicable into the programme of fixtures so that any disturbance he does cause is minimal. For example, a good time to put a summer top dressing on golf greens is usually on a Monday, so that by the time the busy weekend arrives the putting surfaces are practically clean again, although Tuesday is often Ladies' day and they can object to compost on greens early in the week.

No Play when Grounds are Unfit

Suspension of play when the playing surface is unfit is a very common source of grievance. Considerable damage can be done to golf greens when they are played upon in frosty weather, particularly when surfaces are thawing out over a still-frozen under-surface. When such conditions prevail the golfers should be playing on temporary greens and the best way to reduce the number of complaints is to do sufficient work on these temporary greens during the growing season to ensure putting surfaces with a reasonable finish. Here again a notice displayed in the clubhouse outside the Secretary's office helps considerably to turn away wrath.

The Hazards of Greenkeeping!

Nobody likes to be set up as a target, but this is the unfortunate position in which a greenkeeper sometimes finds himself when, for example, mowing greens on a golf course. Determined golfers, with the bit in their teeth, will occasionally brook no interruption and it is rather sad to have to record that the 'gentler sex' in this context are often said to be the readier to loft an approach shot on to the head of a preoccupied greenkeeper. They have been known in fact not to spare advisory agronomists in the pursuance of their lawful duties! The introduction of the triple greens mower has had one indisputable advantage in that it has allowed the greenkeeper to mow a green quickly and then rapidly get out of range!

One Boss is Sufficient

Too many masters, especially when they give conflicting orders, can be a great source of irritation. There should really be only one official at any Club who has the supreme authority to give instructions to the Head Greenkeeper. Ordinary Golf Club members for instance, playing a round of golf, should have no brief to stop by the greenkeeper for a chat and a few words about filling the second bunker on the previous hole!

Good Results

Consideration and thoughtfulness by all concerned (players, members, committees, staff) in relation to sensitive aspects of ground maintenance such as those described here usually lead to good playing conditions and happy job satisfaction.

(CGC 1 : 96)

GOLF MAINTENANCE SHED FACILITIES

Skeletons in the cupboard

With members and visitors demanding higher standards out on the golf course and in the clubhouse it is vital the shed and staff facilities provide the sound base to achieve the desired aims. In recent years the majority of clubs have taken the necessary positive steps forward with strict enforcement of Health & Safety at Work as well as Control of Pesticides Legislation highlighting deficiencies and promoting rapid compliance. Nevertheless, non-approved chemicals stacked around an old pull chain toilet, spartan staff accommodation, a cramped ramshackled building surrounded by a sea of mud are situations still sometimes encountered which should pertain to a bygone era.

The cost of equipping a new 18 hole golf course would be in the order of £200,000 and it is therefore totally illogical to accelerate depreciation costs and increase the risk of theft and vandalism by poor, low grade storage areas. Staff morale will inevitably be higher if adequate facilities are provided, which in turn is reflected in increased general care and maintenance as well as prolonging the life span of machinery and promoting higher productivity.

First steps

New sheds are a large-cost item which will be designed to last a long period of time, so it is vital to plan well in advance and therefore bring together a good case for proceeding with the project at the vital committee meeting which will decide on implementation, deferment or rejection.   In evaluating needs a number of bodies will have to be contacted starting with the Local Authority in respect of planning permission to satisfy building regulations whether the sheds are to be new or a replacement.   Remember that in conservation areas the overall cost may rise due to the requirement for more expensive building materials, e.g. stone. Their Pollution Control Officer will give details on the safe storage of chemicals, the Local Fire Service will check fire precautions and safety aspects, such as clearly-signed access doors and also the storage of petrol with information on acquiring a licence. Notification of diesel requirements and provision of a special storage tank should also be discussed whilst the officer is on site. The National Rivers Authority can provide details concerning drainage and especially the requirement for separate drainage, silt, grass clipping and oil traps.

Location

Good use of available man hours is an important part of successful golf course management, and so to minimise travelling time a central site position is vital. In addition, a balance must be made between keeping the facilities away from the club-house and car park, yet not being too isolated when there is a high risk of vandalism and theft, especially in densely-populated towns and cities.

The location should preferably be flat, certainly well drained and large enough to allow turning of lorries and manoeuvring of machinery.   The essential provision of services – primarily water, sewage disposal and electricity – and a suitable road for deliveries (particularly 20-25 tonne lorries), will have a fundamental bearing on positioning. Further to this keep the sheds away from golf holes where wayward shots would be a safety problem to staff as well as causing damage to the building or machinery.

Ancillary facilities

Many golf clubs have upgraded the buildings in recent years yet left the surrounding areas untouched, often due to cost. However, the following aspects are an integral part of the overall success of the project:-

• A hard standing area for washing down machinery so it can be cleaned of grass and dirt, hence reducing damage and wear. The area is also a location for transient storage of machinery and materials.

• The provision of a car parking enclosure a discreet distance from the sheds for both staff and visitors. Increase the overall size to meet members needs if required, i.e. near an adjacent practice area.

• Storage of gravels, sands and top dressing if not included in an appropriate building. A common choice of construction consists of a concrete base, breezeblock bays with the material kept dry by sheeting or a wooden erection. Contour the concrete base to facilitate satisfactory drainage.

Landscaping

Surrounding the shed facilities with mounding and/or a tree belt is important in gaining a degree of security and safety if close proximity to golf holes cannot be avoided. They also significantly reduce the undesirable visual impact for the golfer.

The excavations obtained from the shed and access road works can be put to good use in the surround mounding foundation, yet always ensuring a minimum uniform firmed 150 mm (6 in.) of topsoil is returned to support grass growth in the future. A mix of rapid growing conifers such as Cupressus leylandii plus some longer lived Scots Pine will provide a wind break and offset the visual aspect through winter.

In these days of ecological awareness a further addition of native species such as rowan, birch, beech and oak sympathetically planted would also enhance wildlife and give all year round colour, shape and form.

Costing

Make a priority list to ensure all aspects are included in the building cost estimates as items often forgotten include site survey plans and the connection of telephone, electricity, water and sewage services. As well as the building do not forget to include internal fittings such as tables, chairs, cooking and office equipment, storage racks and shelving. From a safety angle include fire extinguishers, First Aid kits and remember the hardstanding area, storage bays, landscaping and access roads.

The building

To only accommodate existing machinery and materials is a common mistake, the course management team must have the vision to allow scope for expansion in future years. Accordingly, the essential requisite is size with a minimum depth of 11.5 m and a minimum length of 16 m – longer if the club can afford it, i.e. 20 m. Eaves and lintel heights must comfortably accommodate a tractor, cab and front loader, i.e. a minimum of 4 m. A facility to allow large lorries to tip bulky materials would demand extra height and area which in turn escalates the overall cost and is therefore often omitted.

With regard to the basic structure a popular choice is a prefabricated, concrete beam, plastic-coated, steel clad agricultural building with a concrete block wall construction to approximately 1.3 m height. A loading and unloading bay is an extremely useful asset and choose sliding or roller shutter doors for maximum security, safety and convenience.

Interior layout

To fit in all the requirements to the size of shed designated it is vital to plan floor space economically and position internal fittings to best advantage. A good move is to initially contact other course managers in the locality to gain ideas and background knowledge. Even consider looking at other professional organisations e.g. a tyre specialist or larger garage. Take into account the following.

● Keep windows to a minimum for security and where they are deemed necessary, i.e. in the staff canteen and office ensure adequate protection, e.g. wire-reinforced glass and metal grills. To help make up the short-fall translucent corrugated or flat sheets in the roof of each section will help offset the loss and supplement artificial light.

● Staffing facilities are important and should include a separate office for the course manager, a wash room with shower and toilets plus a canteen. Ensure the office is kept well away from noisy working areas. The design is normally of blockwork construction with internal walls, tiled or plastered. A lower ceiling height over the office and canteen is recommended, as it not only conserves heat but also provides the opportunity to gain valuable additional storage area above as long as adequate joists and floor grade chipboard are introduced.

● For small quantities of pesticides proprietary lockable metal bins are available which adhere to legislation requirements, yet it may well be necessary to provide a separate secure and fireproof structure with a bund to retain spillage plus a facility for washing down. The pesticide area or bin must be well labelled, a point that should apply to other pertinent items and areas within the shed area.

● Permit enough access space around equipment storage areas and where slotted racking houses spare parts, tools and so on.

● The provision of a pit is by no means essential unless the operation is big enough to incorporate a mechanic and major repair work. An alternative would be power assisted lifting gear.

- For smaller outfits at least budget for a workbench, vice, adjustable spot light, enough power outlet sockets and storage of machinery maintenance tool kits. For larger establishments it is worth having a separate workshop with more facilities in the way of light, heating, bench and storage space.

The advantage of your own mechanic and general in-house repairs will help reduce servicing costs, lost time and aggravation. Indeed, there is also the benefit of being able to carry out essential work out of dealers' and service engineers' hours.

- A compressor would also be invaluable to power tyre gauges, air jetting lines and a range of hand tools.
- Exterior doors in particular should be sited away from the prevailing wind side of the sheds and a general policy of keeping doors closed when possible not only helps with security but also keeps heat loss to a minimum, especially in the winter.

Security

In these days of increasing crime, security is becoming a major factor, in which case it is recommended that key-holders be kept to a minimum and more desirable items such as tool kits kept under lock and key. Current regulations also affect security, i.e. the pesticide and petrol store. In fact it is a good move to budget for a burglar alarm system at the outset and staff should be generally conscious of security, a successful tenet being "if the building is empty lock it". At the end of the day protection is the key to avoid theft as well as the "borrowers".

Confessional

Every site has its own special demands, but the fundamental question must be do your facilities incorporate all of the above list of requirements. There are still a number of clubs who need to own-up to the fact that a complete new facility is urgently required or upgrading in a specific area.

It is vital that modern functional maintenance sheds and facilities plus ancillary area provide the basis for the green staff to complete the full maintenance schedule on the course quickly, effectively and professionally, whilst at the same time gaining cost effective results with the resources available.

(SJO : B.189)

BIBLIOGRAPHY

✤✤✤

Books for Further Reading

Current British Periodicals

Videos

*The Care of
the Golf Course*

BIBLIOGRAPHY

BOOKS AND BOOKLETS : MODERN GREENKEEPING (1985 to Date)

Adams, W.A. & Gibbs, R.J. (1994). *Natural Turf for Sport and Amenity: Science and Practice.* CAB International, Wallingford, Oxfordshire, 404 pp.

Agnew, M.L. & Christians, N.E. (1992). *The Mathematics of Turfgrass Maintenance.* Golf Course Superintendents Assoc. of America, Lawrence, Kansas, USA, 61 pp.

Anon. (1986). *Nozzle Selection Handbook.* British Crop Protection Council, Farnham, Surrey, 40 pp.

Anon. (1989). *Disease, Insect & Weed Control in Turf* (2nd Ed.). Australian Turfgrass Research Institute, Concord West, NSW, Australia, 54 pp.

Anon. (1990). Golf course Europe. *Proc. Int. Exhib. and Conf. on the Design, Construction and Maintenance of Golf Courses and Golf Club Management.* Expoconsult, The Netherlands, 179 pp.

Anon. (1991). *Boom Sprayers Handbook.* British Crop Protection Council, Farnham, Surrey, 60 pp.

Anon. (1991). *Code of Practice for the Use of Approved Pesticides in Amenity and Industrial Areas.* National Assoc. of Agric. Contractors and National Turfgrass Council, 72 pp.

Anon. (1994). Health & Safety in Golf Course Management and Maintenance. Health & Safety Executive, Sudbury, Suffolk, 59 pp.

Arthur, J. *et al.* (1993). *All the Year Round Golf: Principles and Methods Required to Achieve This Ultimate Goal.* BIGGA, Alne, York, 172 pp.

Baker, S.W. (1990). *Sands for Sports Turf Construction and Maintenance.* Sports Turf Research Institute, Bingley, 67 pp.

Baldwin, N.A. (1990). *Turfgrass Pests and Diseases.* Sports Turf Research Institute, Bingley, 57 pp.

Clarke, B.B. & Gould, A.B. (Eds.) (1993). *Turfgrass Patch Diseases Caused by Ectotrophic Root-Infecting Fungi.* American Phytopathological Society, Minnesota, USA, 161 pp.

Cochran, A.J. (Ed.) (1990). Science and golf. *Proc. 1st World Scientific Congress of Golf.* E&FN Spon, London, 374 pp.

Cochran, A.J. & Farrally, M.R. (1994). Science and Golf II. *Proceedings of the 1994 World Scientific Congress of Golf.* E&FN Spon, London, 637 pp.

Crockford, C. (1993). *The Complete Golf Course: Turf and Design.* Wolveridge Pty Ltd., Victoria, Australia, 150 pp.

Daniel, W.H. & Freeborg, R.P. (1987). *Turf Managers' Handbook* (2nd Ed.). Harvest Pub. Co., Ohio, USA, 437 pp.

Decker, H.F. & Decker, J.M. (1988). *Lawn Care: A Handbook for Professionals.* Prentice-Hall, NJ, USA, 270 pp.

Gibeault, V.A. & Cockerham, S.T. (Eds.) (1985). *Turfgrass Water Conservation.* Co-op. Ex., University of California, CA., USA, 155 pp.

Gilbert, D. & Macrory, R. (1989). *Pesticide Related Law.* British Crop Protection Council, Farnham, Surrey, 68 pp.

Gould, C.J., Goss, R.L. & Byther, R.S. (1985). Diseases of turfgrasses. *Extension Bulletin 713.* Washington State Univ. Co-op. Extension, USA, 32 pp.

Greenkeeping Panel (1989). *The Way Forward: Discussion Document of British Golf Course Management.* Royal & Ancient Golf Club, St. Andrews, Scotland, 33 pp.

Hacker, J. & Shiels, G. (1992). *Golf Course Presentation.* Professional Sports Turf Design, Preston, Lancs, 39 pp.

Modern Greenkeeping Cont.

Hope, F. (1990). *Turf Culture: A Manual for the Groundsman* (2nd Ed.). Cassell Pubs. Ltd., London, 293 pp.

Jarrett, A.R. (1985). *Golf Course and Grounds: Irrigation and Drainage.* Prentice-Hall Inc., NJ, USA, 246 pp.

Lawson, D.M. (1991). *Fertilisers for Turf.* Sports Turf Research Inst., Bingley, 47 pp.

Park, E. (1990). *Real Golf.* Privately Pub. Mrs. N. Park, Woodsetts, Nottinghamshire, 179 pp.

Park, E. (undated). *The Management of British Golf Courses.* Pub. by Golf Monthly Magazine, London, 26 pp.

Pira, E. (1996). *Guide to Golf Course Irrigation System Design and Drainage.* Ann Arbor Press, MI, USA, 400 pp.

Robinson, R. (1990). *Turf Spraying: A Practical Guide.* Turfgrass Technology, Seaford, Victoria, Australia, 60 pp.

Shildrick, J.P. (Ed.) (1985). The mower for the job. *Workshop Report No.6.* National Turfgrass Council, Bingley, W. Yorks., 60 pp.

Shildrick, J.P. (Ed.) (1989). Turf nutrition '88. *Workshop Report No.15.* National Turfgrass Council, Bingley, W. Yorks., 79 pp.

Shildrick, J.P. (Ed.) (1990). Pesticide use after COSHH. *Workshop Report No.18.* National Turfgrass Council, Bingley, W. Yorks., 76 pp.

Shildrick, J.P. (Ed.) (1991). Safe disposal of amenity pesticides. *Workshop Report No.22.* National Turfgrass Council, Bingley, W. Yorks., 86 pp.

Shildrick, J.P. & Marshall, E.J.P. (Eds.) (1985). Growth retardants for amenity grassland. *Workshop Report No.7.* National Turfgrass Council, Bingley, W. Yorks., 77 pp.

Shurtleff, M.C., Fermanian, T.W. & Randell, R. (1987). *Controlling Turfgrass Pests.* Prentice-Hall Inc., NJ, USA, 449 pp.

Smiley, R.W., Dernoedan, P.H. & Clarke, B.B. (1992). *Compendium of Turfgrass Diseases.* American Phytopathological Soc. Press, MN, USA, 128 pp.

Smith, J.D., Jackson, N. & Woolhouse, A.R. (1989). *Fungal Diseases of Amenity Turf Grasses.* E&FN Spon, London, 401 pp.

Stewart, V.I. (1994). *Sports Turf Science, Construction and Maintenance.* E&FN Spon, London, 260 pp.

Tani, T. (1996). *Color Atlas of Turfgrass Diseases.* Ann Arbor Press, MI, USA, 140 pp.

Turgeon, A.J. (1985). *Turfgrass Management* (rev. Ed.). Prentice-Hall Inc., NJ, USA, 416 pp.

USGA (1994). *Wastewater Reuse for Golf Course Irrigation.* United States Golf Assoc., Lewis Publishers, Chelsea, MI, USA, 294 pp.

Walmsley, W.H. (Ed.) (1990). *Fungicides for Turfgrass Disease Control.* New Zealand Turf Culture Institute, Palmerston North, New Zealand, 26 pp.

Watkins, J.A. (1987). *Turf Irrigation Manual.* Telsco Industries, Texas, USA, 363 pp.

Weaver, C. & Weaver, M. (1989). *Ransomes 1789–1989 A Bicentennial Celebration.* Ransomes Sims & Jefferies PLC, Ipswich, 132 pp.

BOOKS AND BOOKLETS : GREENKEEPING PRE-1985

Anon. (1933). *Improvement of Lawns, Golf Greens and Fairways.* ICI Ltd., London, 23 pp.

Anon. (circa 1940). *Ransomes Royal Records 1789–1939.* Ransomes Sims & Jefferies Ltd, Ipswich, 79 pp.

Anon. (1971). *Turf Culture.* New Zealand Institute for Turf Culture (2nd Ed.), 362 pp.

Anon. (1979). *Turfgrass Diseases.* Sports Turf Research Institute, Bingley, 36 pp.

Beale, R. (1924). *Lawns for Sports: Their Construction and Upkeep.* Simpkin Marshall Hamilton Kent & Co. Ltd., London, 276 pp.

Greenkeeping Pre-1985 Cont.

Beale, R. (1931). *The Book of the Lawn: A Complete Guide to the Making and Maintenance of Lawns & Greens for All Purposes.* Cassell & Co. Ltd., London, 151 pp.

Beale, R. (1931). *The Practical Greenkeeper.* Carters Tested Seeds Ltd., Raynes Park, London (New Edition), 56 pp.

Beard, J.B. (1973). *Turfgrass Science and Culture.* Prentice-Hall Inc., NJ, USA, 658 pp.

Beard, J.B. (1982). *Turf Management for Golf Courses.* Macmillan Pub. Co. & USGA, NY, USA, 642 pp.

Beard, J.B. (1983). *Better Turfgrass Nutrition.* Par Ex Prof. Products, Florida, USA, 22 pp.

Cave, L.W. (1967). *Cave's Guide to Turf Culture.* Pelham Books Ltd., London, 188 pp.

Clouston, D. (1937). *The Establishment and Care of Fine Turf for Lawns and Sportsgrounds.* D. Wyllie & Son, Aberdeen, 121 pp.

Colvin, T.S. (1974). *Grounds Keeping Equipment Vol.1 Operating Tractors for Grounds Keeping & Ornamental Horticulture.* Americ. Assoc. for Vocational Instructional Materials, Georgia, USA, 95 pp.

Couch, H.B. (1962). *Diseases of turfgrasses.* Reinhold Pub. Corp., NY, USA, 289 pp.

Darwin, B. (1931). *Science and Greenkeeping.* Reprint from Country Life, 19 December 1931, 4 pp.

Dawson, R.B. (1939). *Practical Lawncraft* (1st Ed.). Crosby Lockwood & Son Ltd., London, 300 pp.

Dawson, R.B. & Evans, T.W. (1932). *Lectures on Greenkeeping 1931–32.* Scottish Golf Union (Western District), Glasgow, 60 pp.

Dickenson, L.S. (1930). *The Lawn: The Culture of Turf in Park, Golfing and Home Areas.* Orange Judd Pub. Co. Inc., NY, USA, 128 pp.

Emmons, R.D. (1984). *Turfgrass Science and Management.* Delmar Pub. Inc., NY, USA, 451 pp.

Escritt, J.R. (1978). *ABC of Turf Culture.* Kay & Ward Ltd., London, 239 pp.

Farley, G.A. (1931). *Golf Course Commonsense: A Non-technical Treatise on the Subject of Golf Course Maintenance.* Farley Libraries, Ohio, USA, 256 pp.

Faulkner, R.P. (1950). *The Science of Turf Cultivation.* The Technical Press Ltd, London, 64 pp.

Fichter, H.O. (1977). *The complete Guide to Lawn Mowers.* Menaid Press, Colorado, USA, 546 pp.

Forbes, G.D. (1994). *Stewart & Co. Seedsmen Ltd : The First 100 Years.* Stewart & Co. Seedsmen Ltd., Edinburgh, 13 pp.

Gault, W.K. (1912). *Practical Golf Greenkeeping.* The Golf Printing & Pub. Co. Ltd., London, 99 pp.

Greenfield, I. (1962). *Turf Culture.* Leonard Hill Ltd., London, 364 pp.

Hackett, N. (1928). *Soil Acidity: The Vital Importance of Top Dressing and Other Notes.* Private Pub., Bradford, W. Yorks., 37 pp.

Halford, D.G. (1982). *Old Lawn Mowers.* Shire Album No.91. Shire Pubs. Ltd., Aylesbury, Buckinghamshire, 32 pp.

Hanson, A.A. & Juska, F.V. (1969). *Turfgrass Science.* American Society of Agronomy Inc., Wisconsin, USA, 715 pp.

Hawthorn, R. (Rev.) (1977). *Dawson's Practical Lawncraft* (7th Ed.). Crosby Lockwood Staples, London, 313 pp.

Hayes, P. (1984). *Technical Terms in Turf Culture.* Sports Turf Research Institute, Bingley, 76 pp.

Greenkeeping Pre-1985 Cont.

Howard, F.L., Rowell, J.B. & Keil, H.L. (1951). *Fungus Diseases of Turf Grasses.* Agric. Exp. Stn., Univ. of Rhode Island, USA, 56 pp.

Hutchinson, H.G. (Ed.) (1906). *Golf Greens and Greenkeeping.* Country Life Ltd., London, 219 pp.

Kreitlow, K.W. & Juska, F.V. (1960). Lawn diseases: how to control them. *Home & Garden Bulletin No.61.* US Dept. Agric., Washington DC, USA, 16 pp.

Levy, E.B., Kiely, W.A. & Horton, W.M. (1951). *Construction, Renovation and Care of the Golf Course.* New Zealand Institute for Turf Culture, Palmerston North, New Zealand, 101 pp.

Lewis, I.G. (1948). *Turf: A Book About Golf Greens, Tennis Courts, Bowling Greens and Playing Pitches No less Than Lawns: Their Making and Keeping According to Modern Practice.* Faber & Faber Ltd., London, 141 pp.

Macdonald, J. (1923). *Lawns, Links and Sportsfields.* Country Life Ltd. and George Newnes Ltd., London, 78 pp.

Macself, A.J. (1924). *Grass: A New and Thoroughly Practical Book on Grass for Ornamental Lawns and All Purposes of Sports and Games.* Cecil Palmer, London, 204 pp.

Macself, A.J. (undated c.1925). *Lawns and Sports Greens.* WH&L Collingridge Ltd., London, 134 pp.

Madison, J.H. (1971). *Principles of Turfgrass Culture.* Van Nostrand Reinhold Co., NY, USA, 420 pp.

Madison, J.H. (1971). *Practical Turfgrass Management.* Van Nostrand Reinhold Co., NY, USA, 466 pp.

Murray, C.M. (1926). *Greenkeeping in South Africa.* Cape Times Ltd., South Africa, 14 pp.

Murray, C.M. (1932). *Greenkeeping in South Africa: A Treatise on Scientific Methods for the Establishment and Maintenance of Turf for Sporting Purposes & Garden Lawns.* Pub. by "South African Golf", Cape Flats, South Africa, 104 pp.

Musser, H.B. (1950). *Turf Management.* U.S.G.A. & McGraw Hill Book Co., NY, USA, 354 pp.

Palmer, A.E. (undated but circa 1935). *Garden Lawns and Greens: Their Maintenance, Improvement and Renovation.* The Country Gentleman's Assoc. Ltd., Letchworth, Herts., 40 pp.

Peterson, F. (1973). *Handbook of Lawn Mower Repair.* Emerson Books Inc., NY, USA, 253 pp.

Piper, C.V. & Oakley, R.A. (1929). *Turf for Golf Courses.* The Macmillan Co., NY, USA, 262 pp.

Sanders, T.W. (1920). *Lawns & Greens: Their Formation and Management.* WH&L Collingridge, London, 138 pp.

Smith, J.D. (1965). *Fungal Diseases of Turf Grasses.* Sports Turf Research Institute, Bingley, 97 pp.

Sprague, H.B. (1976). *Turf Management Handbook* (2nd Ed.). The Interstate Printers & Publishers Inc., Illinois, U.S.A., 255 pp.

Stinson, R.F. (Ed.) (1981). *Greenkeeping.* Teacher Education Series, Vol.22, No.6, Instructional Materials Services, Pennsylvania State University, Penn., USA, 103 pp.

Sutton, M.A.F. (Ed.) (1933). *Golf Courses: Design, Construction and Upkeep.* Simpkin Marshall Ltd., London, 152 pp.

Sutton, M.H.F. (1912). *The Book of the Links: A Symposium on Golf.* W.H. Smith & Son, London, 212 pp.

Greenkeeping Pre-1985 Cont.

Sutton, M.H.F. (undated). *The Laying Out and Upkeep of Golf Courses and Putting Greens.* Simpkin, Marshall, Hamilton, Kent & Co. Ltd., London, 46 pp.

Vargas, J.M. (1981). *Management of Turfgrass Diseases.* Burgess Pub. Co., Minnesota, USA, 204 pp.

BOOKS AND BOOKLETS : GOLF COURSE CONSTRUCTION AND DEVELOPMENT

Anon. (1964). *Making Room for Golf.* Golf Foundation Ltd., London, 52 pp.

Anon. (1978). *Golf: An Interim Strategy for Provision in the Lothian Region.* Lothian Regional Council, Edinburgh.

Anon. (1981). *Planning and Building the Golf Course.* National Golf Foundation, Florida, USA (Revised Ed.), 48 pp.

Anon. (1988). *Golf Course Development.* English Golf Union, Leicester, 18 pp.

Anon. (1989). *Aspects of Golf Development.* English Golf Union, Leicester, 40 pp.

Anon. (1991). *Guidance Notes for Public Footpaths and Bridleways on New Golf Courses.* English Golf Union, Leicester, 19 pp.

Anon. (1992). *The Positive Face of Golf Development.* BIGCA Seminar Report, British Institute of Golf Course Architects, Oxted, Surrey, 98 pp.

Anon. (1994). *Golf Courses and Associated Developments.* Planning Advice Note PAN 43, The Scottish Office Environment Dept., HMSO, 28 pp.

Anon. (1995). *Golf Course Putting Green Construction Guidelines.* English Golf Union, 15 pp.

Bengeyfield, W.H. (Ed.) (1989). *Specification for a Method of Putting Green Construction.* United States Golf Assoc., NJ, USA, 24 pp.

Bennett, R. & STRI (1996). *Golf Facility Planning.* Sports Turf Research Institute, Bingley, W. Yorks., 63 pp.

Brooking, T. *et al.* (1991). *Sport in the East : A Strategy for the Nineties : The Future for Golf.* Eastern Council for Sport and Recreation, Bedford, 39 pp.

Cook, W.L. & Holland, R. (1964). *Public Golf Courses: A Guide to Their Development and Operation.* National Recreation & Park Assoc., Washington DC, USA, 36 pp.

Davidson, A.W. & Leonard, J.E. (1975). Land for leisure. (Proceedings of Conference October 1974) Centre for Advanced Land Use Studies, Reading, Berkshire, 49 pp.

Ferguson, M.H. (1968). *Building Golf Holes for Good Turf Management.* United States Golf Assoc., NY, USA, 55 pp.

Finger, J.S. (1972). *The Business End of Building or Rebuilding a Golf Course.* Private Pub., Houston, Texas, USA, 47 pp.

Jones, R.L. & Rando, G.L. (1974). Golf course developments. *Technical Bulletin No.70.* Urban Land Inst., Washington DC, USA, 112 pp.

Muirhead, D. & Rando, G.L. (1994). *Golf Course Development & Real Estate.* Urban Land Institute, Washington, USA, 180 pp.

Nicholls, D.C. & Massey, D.W. (1969). *Study of Golf Course Provision in Britain.* Dept. of Social & Economic Res., University of Glasgow, 37 pp.

Shildrick, J.P. (Ed.) (1988). The recreational diversification of farmland. *Workshop Report No.13.* National Turfgrass Council, Bingley, W. Yorks., 94 pp.

Shildrick J.P. (Ed.) (1991). Minimum standards for golf course construction. *Workshop Report No.20.* National Turfgrass Council, Bingley, W. Yorks., 94 pp.

Stutt, J.H. (1980). *The Reclamation of Derelict Lands for Golf.* Golf Development Council, London, 12 pp.

Various Authors (1964). *Municipal Golf Courses: Their Layout, Upkeep and Economics.* Journal of Park Admin. & C.R. Books Ltd., London, 20 pp.

BOOKS AND BOOKLETS : GOLF ARCHITECTURE

Anon. (1972). *Elements of Golf Course Layout and Design.* Golf Development

Golf Architecture Cont.

Council, London, 24 pp.

Bauer, A. (1913). *Hazards: The Essential Elements in a Golf Course Without Which the Game Would be Uninteresting.* Tony Rubovits, Chicago, USA, 61 pp. Also Reprint by Grant Books, Worcestershire, 88 pp. (1993).

Colt, H.S. & Alison, C.H. (1920). *Some Essays on Golf Course Architecture.* Reprint 1990 by Grant Books, Droitwich, Worcestershire, 78 pp.

Cornish, G.S. & Whitten, R.E. (1981). *The Golf Course.* Rutledge Press: W.H. Smith Pub. Inc., NY, USA, 320 pp.

Cornish, G.S. & Whitten, R.E. (1993). *The Architects of Golf.* Harper Collins, NY, USA, 648 pp.

Doak, T. (1992). *The Anatomy of a Golf Course: The Art of Golf Architecture.* Lyons & Burford, NY, USA, 242 pp.

Dye, P. with Shaw, M. (1995). *Bury Me In A Pot Bunker.* Addison-Wesley Pub. Co., Reading, Massachusetts, USA, 241 pp.

Green, R. & Morgan, B. (1989). *Classic Golf Holes: 72 of the World's Greatest.* Willow Books, William Collins Sons & Co. Ltd., London, 160 pp.

Hawtree, F.W. (1983). *The Golf Course: Planning, Design, Construction & Maintenance.* E&FN Spon, London, 212 pp.

Hawtree, F. (1991). *Colt and Co. Golf Course Architects.* Cambuc Archive, Oxford, 214 pp.

Hotchkin, S.V. (undated). *The Principles of Golf Architecture, etc.* Reprint of articles from "Club Sportsman", London, 25 pp.

Hunter, R. (1926). *The Links.* Charles Scribner's Sons, NY, USA, 163 pp.

Hurdzan, M.J. (1996). *Golf Course Architecture : Design, Construction & Restoration.* Sleeping Bear Press, MI, USA, 406 pp.

Kato, S. (1991). *What Makes a Good Golf Course Good.* Ueno Shoten Pub. Co. Ltd., Tokyo, Japan (2nd Ed.), 255 pp.

Kirk, J. & Jacobs, T. (Eds.) (1988). *The Golf Courses of Robert Trent Jones Jr.* Bison Books Ltd., London, 191 pp.

Kroeger, R. (1995). *The Golf Courses of Old Tom Morris.* Heritage Communications, Cincinnati, Ohio, USA, 351 pp.

MacKenzie, A. (1920). *Golf Architecture: Economy in Course Construction and Greenkeeping.* Simpkin, Marshall, Hamilton, Kent & Co. Ltd., London, 135 pp.

MacKenzie, A. (1995). *The Spirit of St. Andrews.* Sleeping Bear Press, Chelsea, Michigan, USA, 268 pp.

Simpson, T. (1933). *A Broadcast Talk on Golf Architecture.* Pub. by the British Broadcasting Corp., London, 7 pp.

Sorensen, G.L. (1976). *The Architecture of Golf.* Private Pub., College Station, Texas, USA, 106 pp.

Thomas, G.C. (1927). *Golf Architecture in America: Its Strategy and Construction.* Times-Mirror Press, Los Angeles, California, USA, 342 pp.

Wethered, H.N. & Simpson, T. (1929). *The Architectural Side of Golf.* Longmans Green, London, 211 pp. (Revised Ed. 1952 entitled "Design for Golf", Sportsmans Book Club, London.)

BOOKS AND BOOKLETS : GOLF COURSE ECOLOGY & CONSERVATION

Anon. (1983). *Wildlife on the Royal Birkdale.* Interpretive Branch, Nature Conservancy Council, Shrewsbury, 6 pp.

Anon. (1988). *Heathland Restoration: A Handbook of Techniques.* Environmental Advisory Unit, University of Liverpool. Pub. by British Gas PLC, Southampton, 160 pp.

Golf Course Ecology & Conservation Cont.

Anon. (1990). *Your Course . . . . Preparing a Conservation Management Plan.* Nature Conservancy Council, Peterborough, 15 pp.

Anon. (1993). *Golf Courses – Friend or Foe of the Countryside.* British Assoc. of Nature Conservationists, Newbury, Berks., 72 pp.

Anon. (1994). *Golf's Natural Heritage.* Scottish Natural Heritate, 32 pp.

Anon. (1994). *Golf and the Environment.* United States Golf Assoc., NJ, USA, 20 pp.

Anon. (1994). *Golf Courses Benefit People and Wildlife.* United States Golf Assoc., NJ, USA, 4 pp.

Anon. (1994). *Golf & Wildlife.* United States Golf Assoc., NJ, USA, 20 pp.

Anon. (1995). *An Environmental Strategy For Golf in Europe.* European Golf Assoc. Ecology Unit, Pices Publications (Nature Conservation Bureau Ltd), Newbury, Berkshire, 42 pp.

Anon. (1996). Proceedings of "Environmental Issues for Turf" A Symposium. Australian Turfgrass Research Institute Ltd., NSW, Australia, 400 pp.

Balogh, J.C. & Walker, W.J. (Eds.) (1992). *Golf Course Management and Construction: Environmental Issues.* Lewis Publishers, Chelsea, MI, USA, 951 pp.

Brennan, A.-M. (1996). *Living Together: Golf & Nature in Partnership*, English Golf Union, 71 pp.

Bunce, R.G.H. (Ed.) (1989). Heather in England & Wales. *Research Pub. No.3.* Institute of Terrestrial Ecology, HMSO, London, 40 pp.

Gilchrist, T.D. (1983). *Trees on Golf Courses.* The Aboricultural Association, Romsey, Hampshire, 134 pp.

Harker, D., Evans, S., Evans, M. & Harker, K. (1993). *Landscape Restoration Handbook.* United States Golf Assoc., Lewis Publishers, Chelsea, MI. USA, 98 pp.

Klemme, M. (1995). *A View from the Rough.* Sleeping Bear Press, MI, USA, 136 pp.

Picksley, K. (1988). *A Strategy for Surrey Heathland.* Surrey County Council and The Nature Conservancy Council, Kingston-on-Thames, 40 pp.

Prendiville, B. (1985). *Flora and Fauna of Portmarnock (Golf Course).* Criterion Press Ltd., Dublin, Ireland, 12 pp.

Rorison, L. & Hunt, R. (1980). *Amenity Grassland: An Ecological Perspective.* Wiley & Sons, Chichester, 261 pp.

Schofield, M. & Dair, I. (Eds.) (1989). *On Course Conservation: Managing Golf's Natural Heritage.* Pub. by Nature Conservancy Council, Peterborough, 46 pp.

Shildrick, J.P. (Ed.) (1984). Creating Attractive Grasslands. *Workshop Report No.5.* National Turfgrass Council, Bingley, W. Yorks., 92 pp.

Shildrick, J.P. (Ed.) (1988). Wild flowers '87. *Workshop Report No.14.* National Turfgrass Council, Bingley, W. Yorks., 90 pp.

Stubbs, D. (1996). *An Environmental Management Programme for Golf Course: Report on Pilot Project.* European Golf Assoc. Ecology Unit, Pices Publications Ltd. (Nature Conservation Bureau Ltd.), 62 pp.

Taylor, R.S. (1995). *A Practical Guide to Ecological Management of the Golf Course.* BIGGA and STRI, Yorkshire, 103 pp.

BOOKS AND BOOKLETS : GOLF COURSES – GENERAL INTEREST

Allen, P. (1987). *Play the Best Courses: Great Golf in the British Isles.* Stanley Paul & Co. Ltd., London, 210 pp.

Allen, P. (1989). *The Sunley Book of Royal Golf.* Stanley Paul & Co. Ltd., London, 160 pp.

Anon. (1937). *Golf Round London.* Whitefriers Press Ltd, London (1st Ed.), 275 pp.

Anon. (1989). *A History of Golf Clubs in Fife.* The Fife Golfing Assoc., St. Andrews, Scotland, 164 pp.

General Interest Cont.

Anon. (1993). *Golf in Scotland.* Tiger Books International PLC, London, 84 pp.

Arlott, J. (Ed.) (1975). *Oxford Companion to Sports & Games.* Oxford University Press, London, 1143 pp.

Barrett, T. & Hobbs, M. (1995). *The Ultimate Encyclopedia of Golf.* Carlton Books (Hodder & Stoughton), London, 256 pp.

Booth, A. & Hobbs, M. (1987). *The Sackville Illustrated Dictionary of Golf.* Sackville Books Ltd., London, 192 pp.

Brasch, R. (1972). *How Did Sport Begin?* Longmans Group Ltd., London, 279 pp.

Browning, R. (1955). *A History of Golf: The Royal & Ancient Game.* Reprint 1990. A&C Black Ltd., London, 236 pp.

Campbell, M. (1991). *The Encyclopaedia of Golf: The Definitive Guide to the Game – Its Courses, Characters & Traditions.* Dorling Kindersley Ltd., London, 336 pp.

Clougher, T.R. (Ed.) (1929). *Golf Clubs of the Empire: The Golfing Annual* (3rd Ed.). The Clougher Corp. Ltd., London, 510 pp.

Cochran, A. & Stobbs, J. (1968). *The Search for the Perfect Swing.* J.B. Lippincott Co., USA, 242 pp.

Cochran, A. (Ed.) (1995). *Golf : The Scientific Way.* Aston Pub. Group, Hemel Hempstead, Herts., 281 pp.

Crowther, J. (1991). *Managing Your Golf Club.* Harper Trade Journals, London, 147 pp.

Darbyshire, L.C. (1961). *Go Golfing in Britain: A Hole by Hole Survey of 25 Famous Seaside Courses.* The Sunday Times, London, 75 pp.

Darwin, B. (1910). *Historic Golf Courses of the British Isles* (2nd Ed. 1987). Gerald Duckworth & Co. Ltd., London, 253 pp.

Darwin, B. (undated). *Green Memories.* Hodder & Stoughton, London, 333 pp.

Dickinson, P. (1951). *A Round of Golf Courses. A Selection of the Best Eighteen.* Reprint 1990. A&C Black Ltd., London, 159 pp.

Dobby, D.L. (1993). *Golf on the Kent Coast.* Fore Golf Pubs. Ltd., Harwich, Essex, 129 pp.

Dobereiner, P. (1992). *Golf Courses of the PGA European Tour.* Aurum Press Ltd., London, 304 pp.

Editors of Golf World Magazine (1987). *Golf in Scotland and Ireland: The Complete Guide to Courses, Clubs, Accommodation & Travel.* Sackville Books Ltd., London, 160 pp.

Edmund, N. (Ed.) (1991). *Following the Fairways 1991: The Distinguished Companion to the Golf Courses of Great Britain & Ireland* (4th Ed.). Kensington West Productions, London, 315 pp.

Elliott, A. & May, J.A. (1990). *Illustrated History of Golf.* Hamlyn Pub. Group Ltd., London, 256 pp.

Evans, W. (1974). *Encyclopaedia of Golf* (2nd Ed.). Robert Hale & Co., London, 319 pp.

Ferrier, B. (1990). *The World Atlas of Golf Courses.* Hamlyn Pub. Group Ltd., London, 208 pp.

Fittis, R.S. (1891). *Sports and Pastimes of Scotland.* Alexander Gardner. Reprint 1975 EP Pub. Ltd., Wakefield, W. Yorks., 212 pp.

Gibson, W.H. (1988). *Early Irish Golf: The First Courses, Clubs and Pioneers.* Oakleaf Publications, Naas, Co. Kildare, Republic of Ireland, 303 pp.

Grant, H.R.J. & Moreton, J.F. (Eds.) (1996). *Aspects of Collecting Golf Books.* Grant Books, Worcestershire, 195 pp.

General Interest Cont.

Green, R. (1987). *Golf: An Illustrated History of the Game.* Willow Books, William Collins Sons & Co. Ltd., London, 208 pp.

Green, R. & Morgan, B. (1989). *Classic Golf Holes: 72 of the World's Greatest.* Willow Books (Collins), London, 160 pp.

Hobbs, M. (1988). *The World's Great Golf Courses.* The Apple Press, London, 112 pp.

Hopkins, J. (1994). *Golf in Wales: The Centenary 1895-1995.* The Welsh Golf Union, Cwmbran, Gwent, 128 pp.

Hutchinson, H.G. (1890). *Golf. The Badmington Library of Sports & Passtimes.* 1987 Reprint. Ashford Press, Southampton, 463 pp.

Jenkins, L.C. (1993). *Golf in Hardy Country.* Dorset County Golf Union, 255 pp.

Kelly, G.M. (1971). *Golf in New Zealand: A Centennial History.* New Zealand Golf Assoc., Wellington, New Zealand, 262 pp.

Kennington, D. (1981). *The Sourcebook of Golf.* Library Assoc. Pub. Ltd., London, 255 pp.

Lawless, P. (Ed.) (1937). *The Golfer's Companion.* J.M. Dent & Sons, London, 498 pp.

Leigh-Bennett, E.P. (1930). *Some Friendly Fairways.* Southern Railway, London, 57 pp.

Lyle, S. & Ferrier, B. (1989). *The Championship Courses of Scotland.* Lennard Publishing, Oxford, 288 pp.

May, J.A. (1991). *The Complete Book of Golf: A Guide to Equipment Techniques & Courses.* (W.H. Smith) Hamlyn Pub. Group Ltd., London, 192 pp.

Menton, W.A. (1991). *The Golfing Union of Ireland 1891–1991.* Gill and Macmillan, Dublin, 399 pp.

Miller, D. (1977). *America's Greatest Golfing Resorts.* Bobbs-Merrill Co. Inc., Indianapolis/NY, USA, 239 pp.

Mitchell, B. (1989). *The Golf Courses of Jack Nicklaus.* Bison Books (Brompton Books), London, 192 pp.

Morgan, B. (1988). *A World Portrait of Golf.* Aurum Press Ltd., London, 224 pp.

Morrison, J.S.F. (Ed.) (1939). *Around Golf.* Arthur Barker Ltd., London, 246 pp.

Pennink, F. (1952). *Homes of Sport: Golf.* Garnett Ltd., London, 209 pp.

Pennink, F. (1962). *Golfer's Companion: A Guide to 128 of the Finest Courses in Great Britain and Ireland.* Cassell & Co. Ltd., London, 311 pp.

Plumridge, C. (1988). *The Illustrated Encyclopaedia of World Golf.* (W.H. Smith) Marshall Cavendish Books Ltd., 256 pp.

Pottinger, G. (1972). *Muirfield and the Honourable Company.* Scottish Academic Press, Edinburgh, 146 pp.

Price, R. (1989). *Scotland's Golf Courses.* Aberdeen University Press, Aberdeen, 235 pp.

Redmond, J. (1992). *Great Golf Courses of Ireland.* Gill & Macmillan Ltd., Dublin, 156 pp.

Salmond, J.B. (1956). *The Story of the R. & A.* Macmillan & Co. Ltd., London, 256 pp.

Saunders, V. (1989). *The Golf Handbook.* Marshall Editions Ltd., London, 223 pp.

Scott, T. (1978). *The Concise Dictionary of Golf.* Bison Books Ltd., London, 256 pp.

Shapiro, M., Dohn, W. & Berger, L. (1986). *Golf: A Turn of the Century Treasury.* Castle Book Sales Inc., NJ, USA, 467 pp.

Steel, D. (1992). *Classic Golf Links of Great Britain and Ireland.* Chapmans Pub. Ltd., London, 224 pp.

Steel, D. & Ryde, P. (Eds.) (1975). *The Shell International Encyclopaedia of Golf.* Ebury Press & Pelham Books Ltd., London, 478 pp.

Stirk, D. (1987). *Golf: The History of an Obsession.* Phaidon Press Ltd., Oxford, 160 pp.

Vardon, H. (1905). *The Complete Golfer.* Methuen & Co. Ltd., London, 283 pp.

General Interest Cont.

Various Authors (1931). *The Game of Golf.* Lonsdale Library, Vol.9, Seeley Service & Co. Ltd., Lonsdon, 251 pp.

Viney, N. & Grant, N. (1978). *An Illustrated History of Ball Games.* William Hernemann Ltd. (Book Club Associates), London, 201 pp.

Wilson, J.V. (1994). *Welcome to the Committee: Information & Guidance for a Newly-Elected Member of the Committee of a Golf Club.* Broadside Pub., Oxted, Surrey, 142 pp.

Wind, H.W. (Ed.) (1954). *The Complete Golfer.* William Heinemann Ltd., London, 398 pp.

CURRENT PERIODICALS (U.K. Only)

The Journal of the Sports Turf Research Institute.
Formerly the Journal of the Board of Greenkeeping Research. Published annually, 1929 to date. Britain's leading Scientific Journal of Turf Research. Sports Turf Research Institute, Bingley, West Yorkshire, BD16 1AU (Tel: 01274 565131).

The STRI Turfgrass Bulletin (formerly the Sports Turf Bulletin).
Articles and information for Greenkeepers, Groundsmen, Committee Members, etc. Published quarterly, January 1951 to date. Sports Turf Research Institute, Bingley, West Yorkshire, BD16 1AU (Tel: 01274 565131).

Turfgrass Seed.
Evaluations of currently available turfgrass cultivars. Published annually, 1977 to date. Sports Turf Research Institute, Bingley, West Yorkshire, BD16 1AU (Tel: 01274 565131).

Turf Management.
Monthly. Editor: Richard Garlick, Haymarket Trade & Leisure Pubs. Ltd., 60 Waldegrave Road, Teddington, Middlesex, TW11 8LG (Tel: 01483 776345).

The Golf Club Secretary.
Monthly, May 1991 to date. Briefing and Practical Advice for Golf Club Administrators. Articles on greenkeeping topics. J.V. Wilson (Editor), Broadside Publishing, Broadside, Kent Hatch Road, Limpsfield Chart, Oxted, Surrey, RH8 0SZ (Tel: 01883 730570).

Amateur Golf.
Official Journal of the English Golf Union. Eleven Issues per year. Paul Baxter (Editor), The English Golf Union, 1-3 Upper King Street, Leicester, LE1 6XF (Tel: 0116 255 3042).

Greenkeeper International.
Journal of the British & International Golf Greenkeepers Association. Monthly since January 1991. Scott MacCallum (Editor), Aldwark Manor, Aldwark, Alne, York, YO6 2NF (Tel: 01347 838581).

The Groundsman.
Official Journal of the Institute of Groundsmanship. Monthly. Christine Smith (Editor), 19-23 Church Street, The Agora, Wolverton, Milton Keynes, Bucks., MK12 5LG (Tel: 01908 312511).

Golf Club Management.
Official Journal of the Association of Golf Club Secretaries. Monthly. Steve Rankin (Editor), Harper Trade Journals, Harling House, 47-51 Great Suffolk Street, London, SE1 0BS (Tel: 0171 261 1604).

Parks, Golf Courses & Sportsgrounds.
Monthly. Alan Guthrie (Editor), Clarke & Hunter (London) Ltd., 254 London Road, Staines, Middlesex, TW18 4JQ (Tel: 01784 461326).

National Turfgrass Council News.
Bi-monthly. Peter Helm, Hunters Lodge, Doctor Browns Road, Minchinhampton, Stroud, Glos., GL6 9BT (Tel: 01453 883588).

Horticulture & Landscape Ireland.
Five issues per year. Pub. by Simon Williams Pub., 7 Prince of Wales Terrace, Balsbridge, Dublin 4, Republic of Ireland (Tel: 00 355 16682053).

VIDEO TAPES
The following videos are available from the British & International Golf Greenkeepers Association, Aldwark Manor, Aldwark, Alne, York, YO6 2TU (Tel: 01347 838581 Fax: 01347 838864).

GOLF COURSE PREPARATION : Covering Switching & Brushing, Course Preparation, Moving Tee Markers, Maintaining Bunkers, Maintaining Course Furniture, Changing Holes (BIGGA : AVS : 30 minutes).

GOLF GREEN RECONSTRUCTION (BIGGA : Profile Videos : 16 minutes).

KEEPER OF THE GREEN : A Career In Golf Course Management (BIGGA : GTC).

RAISING THE STANDARD OF MOWING MANAGEMENT (TORO Co. & Lely UK Ltd. for BIGGA : 40 minutes).

SETTING THE STANDARD IN SPRAY APPLICATION. BIGGA TURF MANAGEMENT TRAINING VIDEO NO.1 (BIGGA : MLA : 45 minutes).